Occupational Medicine

Managed Care

Guest Editor:

Jeffrey S. Harris, MD, MPH, MBA
President
J. Harris Associates, Inc.
Mill Valley, California
     and
Associate Clinical Professor
Division of Occupational Medicine
University of California
San Francisco, California

Volume 13/Number 4   October–December 1998
HANLEY & BELFUS, INC.   Philadelphia

STATE OF THE ART REVIEWS

Publisher: HANLEY & BELFUS, INC.
210 South 13th Street
Philadelphia, PA 19107
(215) 546-4995
Fax (215) 790-9330
Web site: http://www.hanleyandbelfus.com

OCCUPATIONAL MEDICINE: State of the Art Reviews is included in *Index Medicus, MEDLINE, BioSciences Information Service, Current Contents* and *ISI/BIOMED, CINAHL database*, and *Cumulative Index to Nursing & Allied Health Literature.*

OCCUPATIONAL MEDICINE: State of the Art Reviews   (ISSN 0885-114X)
October–December 1998   Volume 13, Number 4   (ISBN 1-56053-275-0)

OCCUPATIONAL MEDICINE: State of the Art Reviews is published quarterly by Hanley & Belfus, Inc., 210 South 13th Street, Philadelphia, Pennsylvania 19107. Periodical postage paid at Philadelphia, PA, and at additional mailing offices.

POSTMASTER: Send address changes to OCCUPATIONAL MEDICINE: State of the Art Reviews, Hanley & Belfus, Inc., 210 South 13th Street, Philadelphia, PA 19107.

The 1998 subscription price is $88.00 per year U.S., $98.00 outside U.S. (add $40.00 for air mail).

Occupational Medicine: State of the Art Reviews
Vol. 13, No. 4, October–December 1998

MANAGED CARE
Jeffrey S. Harris, MD, MPH, MBA, Editor

CONTENTS

CONTRIBUTORS

Victor Breen, MD, MPH
Managed Care Organization Medical Director, Kaiser Works, Portland, Oregon

Robert Z. Bruckman, MD
Milliman & Robertson, Inc., San Francisco, California

Jennifer H. Christian, MD, MPH
Vice President, Chief Medical Officer, ManagedComp, Inc., CareManagement Networks, Waltham, Massachusetts

Marcia L. Comstock, MD, MPH
Corporate Medical Director, Assistant Vice President–Health Services, Consolidated Rail Corporation, Philadelphia; Instructor, Occupational and Environmental Health Sciences Division, Jefferson Medical College, Philadelphia, Pennsylvania

Nhu Dana
Kaiser Works, Portland, Oregon

Allard E. Dembe, ScD
Assistant Professor, Occupational and Environmental Health Program, Department of Family Medicine and Community Health, University of Massachusetts Medical School, Worcester, Massachusetts

Stacey M. Eccleston
Workers' Compensation Research Institute, Cambridge, Massachusetts

Adrianne Feldstein, MD
Medical Director, CEO, Kaiser Works, Portland; Associate Professor, Department of Public Health and Preventive Medicine, Oregon Health Sciences University, Portland, Oregon

E. Liza Greenberg, RN, MPH
Director, Research and Quality Initiatives, American Accreditation Healthcare Commission/URAC, Washington, DC

David P. Gunn
The Stolas Group, Inc., Fresno, California

Jane C. Hall, RN, MPA, CCM, ABDM diplomate
Assistant Clinical Professor, University of California School of Nursing, Occupational Health Department, San Francisco; AON Consulting, Los Altos, California

Jeffrey S. Harris, MD, MPH, MBA
President, J. Harris Associates, Inc., Mill Valley; Associate Clinical Professor, Division of Occupational Medicine, University of California, San Francisco, California

John A. Igoe
Igoe Associates, San Raphael, California

Frank H. Leone, MBA, MPH
RYAN Associates, Santa Barbara, California

Ronald S. Leopold, MD, MBA, MPH
Medical Director, Regional Operations, ManagedComp, Waltham, Massachusetts

Barton Margoshes, MD
Vice President, Medical Director–Risk Services, Liberty Mutual Managed Care, Boston, Massachusetts

Laurence A. Miller, MD
Chief Medical Officer, Community Care Network, San Diego; Assistant Clinical Professor of Medicine, University of California, San Diego, California

Kathryn L. Mueller, MD, MPH
Associate Professor, Department of Surgery, University of Colorado Health Sciences Center, Denver, Colorado

Karen J. O'Hara
Senior Vice President, RYAN Associates, Santa Barbara, California

Dale Pratt
Manager, Information Systems, The Stolas Group, Inc., Fresno, California

Kathleen M. Rest, PhD
Occupational and Environmental Health Program, Department of Family Medicine and Community Health, University of Massachusetts Medical School, Worcester, Massachusetts

Linda Rudolph, MD, MPH
Medical Director, California Division of Workers' Compensation, San Francisco, California

Steven C. Schumann, MD
President and CEO, The Stolas Group, Inc., Fresno, California

Richard A. Victor, JD
Workers' Compensation Research Institute, Cambridge, Massachusetts

PUBLISHED ISSUES
(available from the publisher)

COMING IN 1999

Repetitive Stress Injuries
Edited by Martin Cherniack, MD
University of Connecticut
Farmington, Connecticut

Animal Handlers
Edited by Ricky L. Langley, MD, MPH
Kernodle Clinic
Burlington, North Carolina

Special Populations
Edited by Howard Frumkin, MD, DrPH
Emory University
Atlanta, Georgia
and Glenn Pransky, MD, MOccH
University of Massachusetts
Worcester, Massachusetts

Plastic and Rubber Industries
Edited by Richard Lewis, MD, MPH,
University of Louisville
Louisville, Kentucky

Ordering Information:
Subscriptions for full year and single issues are available from the publishers—
Hanley & Belfus, Inc., 210 South 13th Street, Philadelphia, PA 19107
Telephone (215) 546-7293; (800) 962-1892. Fax (215) 790-9330.

1998 ISSUES

Low Back Pain
Edited by Gerard A. Malanga, MD
University of Medicine and Dentistry
   of New Jersey
Newark, New Jersey

Workers' Compensation
Edited by T. L. Guidotti, MD, MPH
University of Alberta
Edmonton, Alberta, Canada
and John W. F. Cowell, MD, Msc
Workers' Compensation Board of Alberta
Edmonton, Alberta, Canada

Hand and Upper Extremity Injuries
Edited by Morton L. Kasdan, MD
University of Louisville
Louisville, Kentucky
and V. Jane Derebery, MD
Concentra Medical Center
Austin Texas

Managed Care
Edited by Jeffrey S. Harris, MD, MPH,
   MBA
J. Harris Associates, Inc.
Mill Valley, California

1997 ISSUES

The Pharmaceutical Industry
Edited by Gregg M. Stave, MD, JD, MPH
Glaxo Wellcome Inc.
Research Triangle Park, North Carolina
and Ron Joines, MD, MPH
SmithKline Beecham
Philadelphia, Pennsylvania

Human Health Effects of Pesticides
Edited by Matthew C. Keifer, MD, MPH
Harborview Medical Center
Seattle, Washington

Diagnostic Testing
Edited by Michael H. LeWitt, MD
Great Valley Health
Paoli, Pennsylvania

The Health Care Worker
Edited by Melissa A. McDiarmid, MD, MPH
University of Maryland
Baltimore, Maryland
and Ellen Kessler, MD, MPH
INOVA Fairfax Hospital
Falls Church, Virginia

1996 ISSUES

Law and the Workplace
Edited by Jack W. Snyder, MD, JD, PhD
Thomas Jefferson University Hospital
Philadelphia, Pennsylvania
and Julia E. Klees, MD, MPH
BASF Corporation
Mount Olive, New Jersey

Violence in the Workplace
Edited by Robert Harrison, MD, MPH
California Department of Health Services
Berkeley, California

Occupational Epidemiology
Edited by Ki Moon Bang, PhD, MPH
National Institute for Occupational Safety
   and Health
Morgantown, West Virginia

**Psychosocial and Corporate Issues
in Occupational Dysfunction**
Edited by Ibrahim Farid, MD, PhD
United States Postal Service
South San Francisco, California
and Carroll Brodsky, MD, PhD
University of California School of Medicine
San Francisco, California

Ordering Information:
Subscriptions for full year and single issues are available from the publishers—
Hanley & Belfus, Inc., 210 South 13th Street, Philadelphia, PA 19107
Telephone (215) 546-7293; (800) 962-1892. Fax (215) 790-9330.

PREFACE

Managed care in occupational medicine is both an old and a new phenomenon. Occupational physicians and other providers have designed and carried out programs for prevention and on-site care of illnesses and injuries at least since the days of Ramazzini in Europe and Alice Hamilton and Sidney Garfield in the United States. Comprehensive health management programs have been more common among large employers, including governments and the military. These programs generally have had defined management structures, objectives, and procedures to ensure that the mission of protecting and promoting employee health is carried out effectively with the available budget and resources. When the employee is considered as a valuable resource, and the program is aligned with related groups such as risk management and human resources, the focus expands to "human asset risk management." Such programs might more appropriately be called managed occupational health rather than managed occupational medicine, because of their comprehensive nature and scope.

The structure and scope of internal occupational health programs, with emphasis on population health, prevention, medical quality, and minimization of disability, in the past has not been made available by smaller employers or community occupational medicine practitioners, although a number of practices and occupational health management firms are now offering complete packages to employers. Providers of palliative or curative care have not focused on efficiency, effectiveness, disability management, and prevention, apparently seeing their mission as the provision of episodic care. On a macro level, the result has been rapidly rising medical costs for workers' compensation relative to group health, a good deal of unnecessary disability (and perhaps impairment, in the case of inappropriately provided procedures), and wide variance in the adjusted cost and quality of care.

Fully managed care is still uncommon in the care of ill or injured workers, due in part to regulatory constraints imposed by current state and Federal systems, inattention by employers, and administration of benefits by medically untrained property and casualty insurance adjusters. However, even at this early stage, occupational physicians and other practitioners feel they are witnessing a radical change in reimbursement for services, increased expectations of reporting to a multiplicity of entities, greater responsibility for outcomes, and diminution of authority within the workers' compensation benefit system.

For some physicians this change has led to decreased income, even loss of a practice, and a sense that they no longer play a central role in returning the injured or ill worker to health. The result has been confrontation or, conversely, apathy on the part of many providers.

However, some providers, frequently those already exposed to managed care in the group health arena, have become adept and successful within the managed care system. These practitioners welcome the presence of managed care in the workers' compensation system. They feel at home with benchmarking, new payment methodologies, refinements in technology, and other hallmarks of the evolving occupational health care system, and they are prospering. Understanding certain aspects of the new system and its potential impact on providers is key to successfully meeting the bottom-line challenge of optimally treating the injured or ill worker.

A major trend impacting workers' compensation practitioners is the move toward alternative reimbursement mechanisms. Acute care services typically have been reimbursed on a fee-for-service basis, usually adjusted to a state fee schedule or what was considered reasonable and customary. But new approaches to paying providers, including case rates, capitation, and incentives, are either in place or being discussed. While only a minuscule claimant volume is presently paid through these mechanisms, the progressive integration of the group health and workers' compensation systems suggests the increasing use of these new payment methodologies.

The relatively recent concept of aligning incentives in the workers' compensation benefit system has ramifications for the treating physicians as well as other players. The old paradigm was that of a frequently adversarial system in which provider, carrier, employer, and claimant were at odds. Conversely, the new paradigm is one in which all the participants have some sense of a common interest in resolving the case with the best possible outcome for everyone. These interests are not necessarily in conflict. For example, payment to physicians has taken the form of incentives for good outcomes. This goal matches the patient's, and most employers want the best possible treatment so that the employee can return to work.

Another major trend affecting providers is the creation and application of integrated disability management across both occupational and nonoccupational arenas. Large employers are beginning to integrate the separate administrative silos that kept workers' compensation and group health benefits isolated. They also seem to appreciate the importance of disability durations on both sides as a driver of health care costs. Most important for the readers of this issue, the cost-effective providers in one system are being identified and asked to participate in the other system.

Data aggregation, frequently referred to as "data warehousing," is bringing change to occupational medicine. Providers need to be aware that new and relatively inexpensive information system technology today allows greater scrutiny on the part of payers and managed care companies of all workers' compensation and benefit system participants.

Demand management is another important element in a partnership for better occupational health. It was initially implemented in group health to modify demand for higher cost or ineffective medical services through health care information and channeling to lower cost, and at times more effective, services. With slight modifications, demand management has value in occupational settings as well. A form of demand management already exists in the occupational arena, using a system that allows or requires early notice of injuries or illness, combined with information and channeling.

This issue of *Occupational Medicine: State of the Art Reviews* attempts to advance efficient and effective managed occupational health by describing the current state of the art. The authors and editor hope it will provide a road map for continued improvement in the quality of care, work life, and productivity, and a guide to the practicing physician as he or she navigates and hopefully thrives in the changing and improving world of occupational medicine.

Jeffrey S. Harris, MD, MPH, MBA
GUEST EDITOR

With contributions from Laurence A. Miller, MD

JEFFREY S. HARRIS, MD, MPH, MBA

MANAGED OCCUPATIONAL HEALTH

From Harris Associates
Mill Valley, California

Reprint requests to:
Jeffrey S. Harris, MD, MPH, MBA
J. Harris Associates, Inc.
386 Richardson Way
Mill Valley, CA 94941

Occupational medicine is perceived as one of the last frontiers for managed care, particularly in terms of disability management and acute and chronic medical care for ill or injured workers under the workers' compensation system. The American College of Occupational and Environmental Medicine (ACOEM) surveyed its members about their involvement in managed care in 1996.[35] About 8% of more than 600 physicians responding to the survey who did not work directly for employers obtained more than half of their income from managed care arrangements versus almost half of all group practices that treat general health complaints. Another 23% and 31% said they received 1–10% and 25% of total revenues from managed care, respectively. However, there are many occupational health or workers' compensation networks with contracts with thousands of providers regionally or nationally. Almost no respondents reported working for managed care organizations or being compensated on a case rate or capitated basis.

The survey results may reflect a definitional understanding of the term *managed care*, or the fact that the respondents were unaware of managed care contracts involving their organizations. The respondents may not have considered price controls as part of managed care, but the author has heard many comments about the economic impact of fee schedules and discount arrangements. Also, many respondents worked in corporate settings that do not provide acute care in conventional networks.

Occupational medicine texts have been silent on principles of management in general and managed care in particular. They typically discuss the role of the practitioner from the standpoint of disease detection and treatment but not the management of cases or population health.[47,50,61,68] Some manuals address technical or administrative issues.[14] However, the references to these topics are few.[18,28,29]

The label *managed care* is usually applied to prepaid or discounted care. However, corporate health programs are managed and provide managed prevention or care. Safety measures, industrial hygiene, medical surveillance, and onsite care are cost-effective only when they are well managed. Progressive corporate medical directors have expanded employer-sponsored health programs to prevent and manage most of the major health risks and problems affecting employees and dependents.[10,17] Interestingly, care financed by workers' compensation seems indeed to be one of the last frontiers, from the internal and external perspective. Many employers with other internally managed occupational health functions have not fully managed workers' compensation, which has historically been balkanized among risk management, medical, finance, and other functions throughout a company. Similarly, in another key area, disability management is only now being recognized as an area of great opportunity for occupational medicine in cooperation with human resources and line management.

Externally, state workers' compensation statutes and regulations have only begun permitting conventional managed care techniques (see the chapter by Eccleston and Victor). Most managed care–enabling legislation is relatively weak, burdensome, or restrictive.

The failure of states to enable managed care in workers' compensation or disability management may be due to the public opinion of managed care in group health programs. Managed care has a negative connotation among employees and providers of care. What the popular conception of managed care ignores is that unmanaged care costs more and engenders a wide range of quality.[46] Chassin has shown clearly that the assumption that quality is automatic in American medical care is incorrect.[9] Further, whether managed care's reputation is deserved depends on the definition and execution of care management.[27] This chapter explores the elements and techniques of managed care, managed health, and good management in general to present ways that the health of employees and dependents can be protected or improved more cost-effectively.

The general negative perception of managed care may stem at least in part from a misunderstanding about the definition, techniques, and benefits of management in general and managed care in particular. This chapter defines and discusses general management to frame the context for the discussion. It outlines conceptual frameworks for health management, and presents managed occupational health and practical approaches that would benefit employers and employees in the management of health and disability risks, health care, disability, and rehabilitation. Key success factors for programs in these areas are listed.

HEALTH MANAGEMENT

Manage is defined variously as "to control the movement or behavior of," "to have charge of, direct," or to "succeed in accomplishing."[58] The underlying concepts are an organized structure and process (basic concepts in medical quality[15] and public health[48]). The implication of the last definition is that organization, planning, and control will lead to relatively efficient accomplishment of goals. The science of management has evolved as it became clear that one action influences another, that many events are part of larger processes, and that planning, coordination, sequencing, and resource allocation could lead to better outcomes and greater efficiency.[13]

Management has at times become an oxymoron or a pointless activity in itself, but managed systems generally perform better than unmanaged ones. Management at its most basic level involves assigning responsibility for key activities and holding those parties accountable for accomplishing them. Management tools can be equally beneficial when applied to health programs at the worksite, to provider organizations, and to provider networks with contractual arrangements to provide services (see Laurence Miller's chapter). Good management generally improves the quality of care, employer satisfaction, employee satisfaction, market share, and the bottom line.

Any management activity starts with a vision of the final product or state of affairs.[38] The vision leads to a mission for the organization. In health care, the vision usually involves employee health status as well as a desired state for the organization itself. Goals make the mission concrete, and strategies and tactics are developed to reach the goals. Objectives quantify activities that operationalize strategies and tactics, and they usually assign responsibility and accountability. A basic tool of planning is budgeting. Teams are assigned to agreed on goals and objectives within an affordable budget, and executives hold managers and their teams accountable for meeting them on time and on budget.

Over the last half century, hierarchical management control has evolved to cooperative development of vision and mission and to team accomplishment of mutually agreeable objectives in many corporate and nonprofit organizations.[49] This evolution is occurring in health care as well as in other sectors. An alternative definition of *manage* is "to carry on business," or to "contrive to get along." To the extent that functional teams of managers, professionals, and line workers are highly effective in managing and improving production and service, this definition is consistent with modern management theory and practice.

Quality has become an organizing principle that has improved organizational performance significantly, whether performance is measured by cost of production, customer acceptance, market share, or profit. Quality is particularly important in health care, but it goes significantly beyond old concepts of quality assurance. Quality in general industry is defined variously as "an absence of defects or adverse events," "conformance to specifications," and "delighting the customer."[24] The former definitions are used in quality assurance and quality control. The latter is a generic outcome of quality improvement. One of the major contributions of quality improvement is the concept of manufacturing or service (including health care) as a continuous process that one can map and make consistent to improve efficiency and effectiveness. Conceptually, there is an analogy to the continuum of health and care from wellness to illness.[22]

An Historical Perspective

Management efforts in health care have followed the same general precepts but were typically responses to epidemics, inpatient quality problems, and economic conditions rather than proactive attempts to improve efficiency or profitability. The most successful early efforts were preventive responses to epidemics and endemic diseases through organized programs of sanitation, immunization, and nutrition.[48] Organization and management had showed its value but remained confined to public health. It took some time to extend management techniques to direct care of illness and injury.

With the development of apparently organized surgical services, the next wave of medical management involved attempts to decrease obstetric and surgical complications and mortality.[62] Interestingly, while standardized aseptic operating techniques and procedures succeeded in dramatically reducing infection and mortality rates, the obvious lesson about the benefits of evidence-based standardization was not applied to the core surgical procedures until relatively recently. Physicians have been resistant to organization and management of the basic processes of care (not support functions) and planning and budgeting.

Health care resources are not infinite. Funds that are used for medical care cannot be used elsewhere in the economy.[1,54] The same forces that led to health care inflation brought medical care to the attention of financial and health care delivery entrepreneurs who were interested in profits and efficiency. Some of them have aggressively applied planning, budgeting, negotiation, and controls to produce insurance, health plans, or medical services more cost-effectively, largely by changing support services or reimbursement frameworks rather than the underlying process of care.[67] Some such efforts have taken place in not-for-profit settings, usually in response to a change in the reimbursement system rather than as a proactive measure to provide more prevention or care for the same or less money.

As a result of the emergence of new forms of medical care finance and organization, the rate of increase in the cost of inpatient care and cost per case has dropped in the last ten years in many parts of the country. The inflation in health care costs has declined from high double digits to less than 5% per year. In addition, complications such as hospital-acquired infections and surgical errors have been reduced. While many dislike health maintenance organizations, their impact on cost, quality, and the shape of medical care in the United States is clear. The challenge is to understand the drivers of these changes and to make them less antagonistic.[35]

There are still significant challenges to be met to reduce the total burden of illness (TBI) for employers and employees,[64] including reintroducing and reinforcing prevention as a cost-effective means of managing health and to raising the level of management progressively from specific diseases to whole individuals to defined populations. Whole-person approaches are more effective for many pervasive and often vague entities such as back pain.[31]

The Evolution of Health Care Management

The definitions of *manage* in a general sense seem to parallel the evolution of medical care and disability management. Approaches to care management have changed from micromanagement of disease care, to program management, to achievement of efficient and effective care in a cooperative manner, to financial incentives and risk transfer to providers.

A major transition in approaches to health management has come from restrictions placed on providers to incentives for providers and patients. These opposing paradigms are sometimes referred to as "reins or fences."[63] Reins imply inspection and micromanagement techniques, and fences provide limits but allow providers and patients to make choices within budgetary and organizational limits.

When appropriately assigning accountability and responsibility for health and health care, one must clearly understand who can control or manage access, prevention, demand for services, prices, service volume, and quality. Only then can one decide which incentives or restrictions would be reasonable and not create perverse incentives. For example, physicians and hospital administrators in an uninformed market control both the price and volume of services. Employers and payors can manage price by signing contracts with providers or groups of providers. However, with pure price management, increases in volume of services have often followed the institution of discount payment arrangements.[26] This raises aggregate price and the potential for complications and side effects.

Employees or patients themselves can manage demand, which drives volume at least in part through lifestyle choices, self-care, and informed decision-making. These choices are most effective when practitioners or others provide clear and comprehensive information on the alternatives, risks, and benefits for prevention and care.[19,57] When properly informed consumers make decisions, control of volume and appropriateness follows.

In a comprehensive approach, the involvement of the entire health care team, as well as patients, in prevention and health management has improved cost-effectiveness and outcomes. In theory, similar teams could be used at the worksite to improve health-related productivity. This is a complex issue, because management practices affect both health and productivity, not necessarily in a linear way.[41]

Health and Health Care as a Continuous Process

An overarching way to view and organize the management of health is by understanding the point along the continuum from wellness to illness at which one makes interventions to improve health. This view encompasses three levels of prevention. Primary prevention reduces risks for illness or injury. It must be targeted carefully at the quantified risks of a specific population, such as an employee group, to be most cost-effective. Secondary prevention stops exacerbation or aggravation of an ongoing illness or injury. Finally, tertiary prevention involves rehabilitation of someone who has been ill. All are important in a comprehensive program.

Health Care Management Techniques

Attempts at management in health care have taken several directions, some economic and some concerned with public or consumer health.

Network management companies, payors such as insurance companies, or providers themselves have developed organized delivery systems.[46] Organized delivery systems, either provider networks or staff model organizations, typically manage medical care. The delivery system contracts with employers or third party payors. These arrangements may require use of the specified delivery system or may make it financially preferable for patients to stay within the delivery system. Efforts to manage illness and injury care have focused first on the price of care or services through discounts or per diem rates and then on service volume. Interestingly, providers in group model managed care organizations or in physician groups may be paid on a salaried basis, in which care they have no financial incentive to provide better service or manage care efficiently.

Provider networks have managed the volume and appropriateness of services through utilization review, case management, case rates, capitation, and exclusive provider arrangements. Utilization review is a form of inspection and match to specifications, typically guideline criteria (see Robert Bruckman's chapter). Case management, if done properly, is a form of coordination and management of access to care and also may include management of absence from work (see Jane Hall's chapter). Paying a fixed cost per case or per "covered life" (capitation) shifts the risk for the cost of care to the provider. All of these efforts might improve quality if professionalism balances budgetary goals or if quality management programs are incorporated. If one accepts Donabedian's definition of medical quality as efficiency and effectiveness, improved quality will accomplish economic as well as health-related goals.

The key endpoint of management of health care and health is to reduce the burden of illness and injury at the lowest effective cost.

THE SCOPE OF OCCUPATIONAL HEALTH MANAGEMENT

Occupational health can include acute care, rehabilitation, prevention, or all three. Many areas of occupational health can be managed, including hazardous exposures, care and rehabilitation, presence at work and disability, productivity, and aggregate costs. Managed occupational health has historically included a much broader spectrum of activities than treatment after injury or illness.

Small employers and acute care providers tend to view occupational health as acute care for workers' compensation cases, whereas corporate occupational health professionals generally take a broader view.[29] They also generally have wider accountability, but there is great variation in scope of responsibility. One's perspective on occupational health shapes interventions and degrees of management of injuries; the physical, managerial, and cultural work environment; personal health; and the health of populations. It also can dictate whether the concern is with service delivery or the entire health care system financed by an employer.

Prevention

Occupational health and safety programs have been concerned with detection of hazards and prevention of their effects for some time. The frequency of illness and injury can be reduced by an organized program of prevention of exposures to kinetic and potential energy and to chemical and biologic substances (see the chapter by Dembe, et al.). Because employer-based preventive efforts must be organized and procedure-driven to be effective, they are intrinsically managed. Such programs must be organized, supported by top management, and involve workers in design and decision-making within regulatory requirements. Proactive management of the workplace has dramatically reduced the toll of occupational illnesses and injuries in this century.

Prevention is generally more cost-effective than care or cure. Preventive efforts can address exposures to physical, chemical, and biologic hazards. While well recognized, these hazards are only part of the cause of ill health and loss of productivity. Management of the human-work interface is increasingly important as the economy shifts to a postindustrial mode. Aspects of task design such as monotony, control, rewards, and absence from work have been well documented to affect health.[21] In addition, management practices have significant effects on worker health and productivity. Personal health has an impact on productivity as well as benefit costs. In a comprehensively managed program, all areas of prevention would be addressed.

Insurers and, more recently, managed care organizations have provided some preventive services. In these cases coordination and agreement with the employer is needed and could be improved. While many providers in managed care organizations would prefer prevention to after-the-fact care, especially in risk-sharing arrangements, they have questioned the reasonableness of accountability for surveillance and prevention when they have little control over the work environment. Clearly this is an opportunity for better management.

Managed Care and Managed Disability

In the narrow sense, occupational medicine is the care of workers who become ill or injured as the result of exposures or trauma at work. Managed occupational health care and disability makes sense for four related reasons:

- Employers are generally responsible for the costs of illness, injury, and reduced productivity,
- The TBI is significantly greater than necessary in many cases,
- The health care system for workers' compensation is disorganized and inefficient, and
- Management techniques can help address these problems.

There is currently no organized system for the care or prevention of work-related illness or injury. Disability is also largely unmanaged. Economic incentives are not aligned: the dominant fee-for-service system rewards volume rather than efficiency or prevention. There is wide variation in diagnostic accuracy and the modes of treatment applied for similar conditions in occupational medicine.[23]

There are some unique problems with designing a management system for work-related health complaints. It is important to determine who has accountability and responsibility for each issue. Workers' compensation was designed as a no-fault system. As such, it is not clear who has the incentive to reduce injury frequency or severity. Employers foot the bill, but there are legal strictures on the direction or management of care. In about half the states, the worker legally controls the decision to seek care. In the rest, employers are often passive or minimally involved. In both cases, they could take charge through persuasion or by legal authority. Employers also have a key role in returning workers to modified duty; without their involvement and cooperation, attempts by providers to reduce lost time cannot succeed.

Employers are responsible for providing a safe workplace under state and federal legislation and under the doctrine of gross negligence. Employers do finance medical and disability benefits but typically delegate management to managed care plans to avoid the negative publicity from adverse coverage decisions.

Techniques similar to those used in general health have been applied to occupational medicine. The unique nature of responsibility and control (or lack thereof) has altered their effectiveness or required different approaches to the management of price, volume, and quality of care. In addition, disability can be an outcome of medical care or an independent variable that must be managed using separate techniques (see Bart Margoshes' chapter).

Price

Initial efforts at management of occupational medicine focused on reducing the unit price of services. Simply reducing fees to those mandated by state fee schedules through retrospective bill review has reduced workers' compensation costs by 10–30%. This overbilling did not foster trust or endear providers to payors. Another means of charge management is to reduce charges to the statistical usual, customary, and reasonable profile in the geographic area. One problem with state fee schedules is that they generally do not cover hospital care. While inpatient care is often involved in some workers' compensation cases, cost-shifting from other payors with discount arrangements can make it quite costly, often at levels several times higher than charges to other payors.

In the past decade, a number of payors and independent organizations have constructed networks based on discounts from fee schedules or prevailing charge levels. Average savings are about 7% after access fees for the networks. To compensate for the relatively low fee schedules, providers have increased the volume of services.[25] Discount networks can have a significant impact on hospital costs by contracting for case rates or per diem rates.

Volume and Appropriateness

Providers, network managers, utilization reviewers, and case managers have attempted to control the volume and appropriateness of occupational health services by comparison to implicit or explicit criteria such as critical paths, review criteria, and practice guidelines (see Robert Bruckman's chapter). Utilization review has been the most common vehicle for external medical management. In workers' compensation, it has typically been done by organizations external to the care process. Use of evidence-based criteria should reduce unnecessary variation in care as well as cost of inappropriate testing and treatment.[30] Empirical evidence shows that this has occurred in the group health environment.[66]

However, this form of management is superimposed on providers, engendering resentment and avoiding accountability. Perhaps a more efficient approach would be self-management by providers using evidence-based guidelines[30] and real-time information feedback on variance.[12]

In another approach to volume management, organized delivery systems have contracted with providers to deliver all services to a defined population for a fixed rate per case (case rate) or per year (capitation). The theory behind this approach is that it transfers risk to providers and forces them to find efficient and effective ways to deliver care.[51]

Case rates and capitation in occupational health are uncommon for at least three reasons:

1. Current data used to calculate insurance prices do not usually include the number of covered employees (the denominator in these calculations).

2. There is concern that fixed reimbursement will result in withholding of needed services and damage to worker health, but such has not proven to be the case in group health.[55a]

3. It remains unclear whether occupational health providers outside comprehensive employer-based programs have enough ability to affect the work environment to hold them accountable for prevention.

Quality

Quality in medical care has traditionally been defined as that which will improve the health of the patient.[48] However, this definition has limited applicability in a managed environment because it does not include the utility of the preventive maneuvers, tests, or treatment to the employee or patient, and it does not consider cost-effectiveness. Donabedian's definition of quality as efficiency and effectiveness is more insightful because it implies managing the processes of prevention and care and selection of the more efficient or effective means of producing the desired result.

Occupational health and safety professionals, risk managers, and network managers have commonly attempted to manage quality through programs of retrospective analysis of defects know as quality assurance. The studies are post hoc and focus on relatively severe and unusual negative events such as serious injuries, mortality, high costs, emergency admissions, or returns to the operating room. Quality assurance targets individuals in an attempt to find outliers and affix blame. Because it does not examine the process by which the mistakes were made, it cannot prevent problems or modify the process so that errors and inefficiencies are less likely to occur.

Quality control is a step beyond quality assurance. It involves inspection of products and services and has been used extensively in industry. Quality control is used extensively in the manufacture of medical drugs, equipment, and devices, but its application has been limited in the actual process of care. As with quality assurance, quality control does not address the causes of poor quality, satisfaction, or functional outcome.

Quality improvement (QI), the step beyond quality control, has great promise for improving organized care. QI involves the analysis of data to prospectively identify areas of opportunity and to improve the processes of prevention or care that produced the results in question.[53] QI embodies many of the principles of proactive management that are key success factors for effective management of health. Some elements include involvement of those who perform the processes of prevention and care, managing by metrics, setting specific targets for improvement, and creating a cycle of improvement. QI has produced improvements in satisfaction and some dramatic reductions in costs, surgical rates, and complications. However, most published examples have occurred in nonoccupational settings.[3,5,20]

Provider Self-Management

The most efficient and arguably the most effective way to manage occupational medical care would be by placing both responsibility and accountability with the providers of care. Methods that have been used to share the risk and the reward for efficient and effective care include case rates, conditional incentives such as risk corridors, and capitation.

Self-management of the process and outcomes of care generally is more effective in organized, provider-based delivery systems that can support an information and policy-driven infrastructure.[51] Structural elements needed to ensure the delivery of high-quality (cost-effective) care include guidelines, objective standards of care, a mechanism for peer review, active and positive clinical leadership, and a mechanism for clinical process management and improvement. Management and organizational requirements are described below (see Key Success Factors). One unanswered question, again, is whether providers should be accountable for lost time.

Disability Management

Disability is a neglected and recently rediscovered area of focus. It is related to, but not necessarily driven by, medical care. Typically issues include the appropriate management of chronic pain and management of chronic illness. Disability is often synonymous with absence from usual work, and studies show absence and the filing of claims for lost income to be driven more by supervisory and human resource practices than by impairment.[32,33] Impairment itself is an anatomic or physiologic change[2] that may or may not result in disability.

Disability is related to medical care in several ways. Suboptimal care increases the possibility of disability. Overt or unintentional messages from physicians about reduced ability to function, or at least about the need for further (unnecessary) therapy, can create expectations of disability. Conversely, encouragement to resume activity can reduce expectations of disability.

In addition to medical concerns, historical, economic, social, legal, and other variables, including the presence or absence of modified work, contribute to delayed return to work.[33] Use of structured processes for matching impairment and essential job functions can optimize return to work.

Effective disability management involves identifying risks for delayed recovery and administrative barriers and proactively managing them. Whether physicians are the most cost-effective managers of disability is debatable. If they are not, close coordination among physicians, human resource professionals, and case managers is crucial to efficient management of absence from work and prevention of recurrent absence. The focus should be on functionality rather than pain abatement (see Barton Margoshes' chapter).

Broader Views of Occupational Health Management

What has been lacking in many cases is an overall plan to manage the health of the employed population and a means to manage care that is not provided by onsite professionals. What also has been missing is attention to the effects of personal health risks, social support, and the work organization on the health of workers and their families. The TBI, which is borne by both the employer and employee, can be reduced through comprehensive approaches to managed occupational health.

Corporate health management includes all factors that affect health and productivity of an employed population.[60] Many aspects of work life other than physical, chemical, and biologic hazards affect the health of workers, their absence from work, and health care costs. Occupational medicine is unique in that many complaints and health problems are associated with the organization of work, person-job fit, the physical work environment, the regulatory and economic environment, and personal genetics and risks.[33,41,56] To be effective, therefore, management of occupational health care should reflect an integrated behavioral, administrative, managerial, and biomedical approach[37] that will improve health and productivity cost-effectively. Managing only the biomedical aspects of care for nontraumatic complaints will most likely have little effect on the frequency of work-related complaints, disability, and productivity. In fact, inappropriate and inefficient testing and treatment will likely result.

Personal health management is a recent area of emphasis for occupational health professionals.[10] In many worksites, expenditures for nonoccupational health problems significantly exceed those for work-related complaints. Since workers spend more waking time at work than elsewhere, the worksite is an ideal source of access to care, disease management,[22] disease prevention, and health promotion.[59] It is also a source of social support for behavior change and a good focus for integrated disability management. Demand management, through wise use materials and informed consent discussions, can be an important part of such programs to assure quality care.

Population health management is a broader view of personal health management that assumes accountability for the health of the employed population and dependents. It can have disease management, demand management, preventive, and promotive components.[60] It should be based on data from health insurance, workers' compensation, and disability programs to provide a view of the TBI. It emphasizes the role of social support and the family context of health and disease.

DELIVERY SYSTEMS FOR MANAGED OCCUPATIONAL HEALTH

Employers make decisions about whether to produce or buy occupational health services. One key question to start the decision-making process is whether one is discussing acute care for workers injured on the job, a more proactive system that emphasizes prevention, or management of all programs and costs related to nonoccupational and occupational health. Acute care services tend to be more separable from the intrinsic interactions at the worksite than disability management or preventive services. In any case, developing a clear system for timely exchange of information, both internally and externally, is essential.

Internal delivery systems are more practical for larger employers, because they can more effectively use full-time occupational health professionals. Such systems could include safety and health promotion, medical surveillance, onsite care, and a means for integrated health management. Data management is also an intrinsic part of such efforts. There is sometimes less question about the use of sensitive data within the organization, although the converse may be true if there is sensitivity about the confidentiality of medical or disability information.

Vended programs can be effective if they adhere to the practices outlined below and are fully integrated with any necessary internal resources. Questions about their accountability for frequency will be raised. Vended programs commonly include health promotion, medical surveillance, employee assistance, and illness and injury management. Outsourced safety programs are uncommon. Disability management is an evolving area.

Key success factors for integrated, comprehensive management of occupational health include organized delivery systems, incentives and rewards, well-defined external relationships, information systems, measurement and feedback systems, and performance improvement systems. Each is described below.

Organized Delivery Systems

The core of managed occupational health is a system that interrelates the various providers and services efficiently and effectively. *System* in this context is more complex and abstract than the physical means to deliver hands-on care to ill or injured workers. It includes the organization's vision and mission, policies, procedures, communication systems, incentives, rewards, personnel, equipment, facilities, and means of establishing and communicating roles and responsibilities, defining financial arrangements and budgets, and organizing and delivering services.

Policies define the organization's position on health and the structure needed to achieve it. Ideally, the position should be preventive, cooperative, and comprehensive. Structure may be hierarchical, cooperative, or a combination of the two. There is a delicate balance between command and cooperation, particularly among highly intelligent, trained health and management professionals.[8,11]

Policies also may define professional roles. For example, in payor and case management organizations, roles must be clearly defined to focus appropriate and legally permissible professional competencies on medical and disability management to obtain the best results. Skills and training must be commensurate with the demands of the job. If not, the product and the workers suffer.[44] Practice guidelines, particularly those that are evidence-based, are a form of policy on best practices.

Procedures define the process by which the organization reaches its desired outcomes. When they map or define the best practices in an organization, as well as define control mechanisms, procedures can act as an organizational memory and form the baseline for process or quality improvement. Procedures can be dictated from the top down, designed by industrial engineers or agreed on by the teams that do the work as part of a continuous improvement process. Critical pathways or care maps are clinical forms of procedure. Contracts for service may include terms such as *policies* and *procedures* for interorganizational relationships or networks.

Incentives and Rewards

Incentives must be in place for providers to manage health proactively and provide cost-effective care and for managers to provide a safe and healthy workplace. The motivation could be a competitive threat from a more customer-responsive delivery system, or the delivery system might be trying to increase market share by better meeting customer requirements. At the least, positive incentives for physician change toward efficiency, effectiveness, and consistency should be in place.

Employers and employees should have incentives to manage and work in health-supporting ways, ranging from containment of hazards, to clear communications, to positive supervision, to proactive involvement programs. Incentives might also exist for return to work, healthy lifestyles, wise use of the health care system, and process improvement. The best outcomes and fewest conflicts occur when employers, providers, payors, and workers have aligned health, employment, and financial incentives.

Proper task design and adequate opportunity for promotion are important incentives. Task aspects associated with poorer health include monotony, lack of control, and inadequate decision-making ability.[43] Lack of task enjoyment is the factor most correlated with the probability of filing a workers' compensation claim.[4]

Well-Defined External Relationships

Providers of occupational medical care are part of a wider system that affects health, productivity, and the ability to prevent and resolve health-related issues. Key players include safety and workers' compensation regulators, referral specialists and facilities, ancillary providers, employers, and employees.

At the employer site, supervisors, managers, and top executives have an effect on the organizational climate, the attitude toward safety, and individual employee relationships. Employers must be involved to ensure optimal disability management. There must be a transition from arbitrary payment decisions, retroactive or delayed management, and micromanagement for a successful partnership to develop and thrive.

Suppliers are key parts of the often virtual network that should provide a continuum of care. Suppliers can range from vendors of wellness programs, health education and safety materials, and organizational development facilitators to physical therapists, hospitals, and referral specialists. Policies, procedures, or contracts can define roles and responsibilities. Proactive arrangements must be in place for referral and two-way communication. The form, content, and timeliness of records and other communications should be agreed upon in advance.

Maintaining relationships with professional organizations is important to afford access to other professionals, practice guidelines, educational programs, and knowledge of the state of the art of various programs. Maintaining reasonably amicable relationships with competitors is important so that the organization can benchmark itself against others in the industry. The purpose is to understand best practices or results and to set targets for improvement. Benchmarking generally benefits all participants if they are willing to engage in continuous improvement.[6]

Information Systems

Managed care organizations, payors, and employers need meaningful information on relative resource use, absence from work, comparative costs, and outcomes to succeed in a competitive or resource-restricted environment.[36] Such information, as distinguished from data, will support management by metrics and quality improvement. Both are difficult at best without timely, readily accessible information and comparative measures.

Health care and payor organizations have traditionally underinvested in information systems. While 5–15% of gross revenues are devoted to information systems in the financial or manufacturing sectors, the figure is 1–2% in health care and insurance. Interestingly, payors may lose significant market to financial institutions as a result.[9a]

The information systems that do exist tend to process and track financial data. There are a few large data repositories for medical surveillance, but clinical records mostly remain on paper and are incomplete, and reasonably sophisticated analytic capabilities are lacking.[9a] To succeed, managed occupational health organizations and health care organizations need effective information systems for medical surveillance, risk appraisal, scheduling, supply chain management, detailed clinical data, disability management, outcomes assessment, and financial management.

Newer systems store data in relational databases, using "client-server" or distributed architecture.[34] Making data collection easier and providing immediate feedback may reduce the traditional resistance to the use of computers among health professionals. Patients and support staff can input some data. The use of electronic records should not increase the time required of personnel or create redundancies of input.

Higher-level data, such as diagnostic and treatment codes collected primarily for billing purposes, are insufficiently detailed to understand why tests, treatment, and processes of care are efficient or effective. Therefore, the electronic medical record, for individuals or groups, should be a key part, if not the backbone, of health care information systems. Data must be captured at the detailed level of mechanism of injury, symptoms, signs, and test results. A suggested data set is shown in Table 1.

TABLE 1. Suggested Standard Occupational Medical Data Set

Baseline Data	Initial Data about Potential Occupational Health Problem and Environment	Risk Factors	Interval Data	Provider Information
Employee demographics	Presenting complaint	Employee-job fit	New signs, symptoms	Name
Employer demographics	Mechanism of injury or exposures	Management practices	New information about mechanism	Specialty
Past and concurrent history	Symptoms	Psychosocial and legal issues	Changes in medical condition	Fee arrangements
Allergies	Signs	Personal risk factors and behaviors	Functional status	Track record/profile
Contraindications for imaging	Functional status		Recovery trajectory	Location
Previous disabilities and rehabilitation efforts	Laboratory results	Job-related illnesses or injuries	Changes in work situation	Vendor identification number
	Imaging results	Previous surgeries		Network membership
	Essential functions of the job	Comorbidities (especially with regard to wound healing)		Universal provider identification number (UPIN)

Harris JS, Miller LA: Sources and uses of occupational medicine data. In Harris JS, Loeppke RR (eds): Integrated Health Management: The Key Role of Occupational Medicine in Managed Care, Disability Management and Integrated Delivery Systems. Beverly Farms, MA, OEM Health Information, 1998; with permission.

The time at which each piece of data occurs and the course of illness and re-covery also are important. Tests and treatments may be appropriate at one time and inappropriate, inefficient, or even dangerous at another.[30]

If possible, information should be shared with all parties in the organized system, including employers, payors, providers, and workers. Such sharing supports informed decision-making, improves coordination of care, and can improve efficien-cies and relationships. Not all data may be accessible to all parties, but views can be created to accomplish the objectives of each.

Measurement and Feedback Systems

Almost everyone works more effectively when they know where the organiza-tion is going, why, and how progress is to be measured.[55] Ideally, executives, man-agers, and workers create a vision of the organization that will fulfill its mission. Goals then reflect the general direction of the organization, and objectives quantify steps toward the goals.

To manage the processes of care, disability management, and prevention, the managers of the organization must set targets for process and outcomes. Target-set-ting works best when the workers (physicians), other health professionals, and sup-port personnel in health care organizations are empowered participants in the discussion. Those who do the process know it best, can set achievable goals, and have an investment in reaching them. In prevention and health care, employees and patients must be involved in managing their own health risks and care to obtain the best results.[45,57]

Measurement and management of a variety of processes and outcomes should guide the organization.[36] Most measures of managed care quantify resource use or cost (see the chapters by Greenberg and Leopold and by Rudolph), but there is in-creasing evidence on correlating outcomes for the patient and others in the system with the process of care (see Kathryn Mueller's chapter). Resource use is a measure of process efficiency. Cost per case or per episode is one outcome of the process of care. It lacks underlying clinical detail that would make it clear that needed but effi-cient care was provided. As such, resource use should be correlated with process measures, either normative or benchmark standards of care, and with other out-comes, including time loss, patient satisfaction, health status, and functional ability. The object is to optimize some mix of outcomes that corresponds to the most effi-cient resource use.[42]

Time lost from work can be a measure of process if the term describes time pre-scribed by the treating physician. It also could be an outcome of the complex matrix of care, expectations, attitudes, available modified work, litigation, and other factors that influence return to work (see the chapter by Feldstein, et al.).

Performance standards are a new type of measurement exemplified by the Health and Employer Data and Information Set initiative now managed by the National Council on Quality Assurance (see chapters by Rudolph, Greenberg, and Mueller). Performance measures are typically subsets of "domains" such as access, prevention, disability, acute care, administrative management, and finan-cial management.

Performance measures can be combined into a report card or "balanced scorecard"[7] for customers, managers, and workers. In internal use, the scorecard is sometimes referred to as a "dashboard" of key performance indicators. Some have even incorporated dashboards into electronic data systems used in patient care or case management. In managed occupational medicine, domains should include

TABLE 2. Occupational Medicine Quality Indicators

Utilization	Quality	Screening/Sentinel Tracking	Sentinel Disease Rates	Access and Satisfaction	Network/Clinic Management	Finance/Outcome
Ambulatory care: Visits per case Tests per case PT modalities or visits per case Imaging per case Chiropractic per case *Hospitalization:* Bed-days per case *Pharmacotherapy:* Opioid use NSAID use Antibiotic use *Rates of procedures by diagnostic group:* Laminectomy Fusion Carpal tunnel release Shoulder repair Open Arthroscopic Knee repair Open Arthroscopic	*Possible work-related immunization rates:* Tetanus Rubella Hepatitis *Worker education:* Respiratory protection Reproductive hazards Chemical hazards Hearing protection Bloodborne pathogens Sexually trans. disease Manual lifting Ergonomics Self care *Protective equipment utilization rate:* Hearing protection Respiratory protection Radiation shielding Blood/fluid barriers *Appropriateness of procedures:* Laminectomy Carpal tunnel release Shoulder arthroscopy Knee arthroscopy *Medical misadventures:* Surgical complications Infection rates Failed backs Failed CTS release *Functional status:* Work status ADL ability Social function Overall function	*Possible work-related immunity/conversion rates:* Rubella Varicella HBV HIV Tuberculosis Coccidiomycosis Histoplasmosis Zoonoses *Biological monitoring:* Lead Cadmium Asbestos X-ray or gamma Pulmonary function Audiometry CV capacity *Soft tissue discomfort:* Neck Shoulder Hand/wrist Low back Knee Ankle/foot	*Overall rates:* Frequency of complaints, illness or injury Severity of complaints, illness or injury *Incidence:* Trauma Lacerations Eye injuries Fractures Burns Poisoning Knee derangement Sprain/strain Rotator cuff tear Occupational illness Dermatitis Extrinsic asthma Zoonoses HBV Stress-related (ergonomic) complaints Disc herniation Carpal tunnel syndrome Tendonitis	*Employee satisfaction:* Accessibility Timeliness of care Care and concern of physician Care and concern of case manager Areas of perceived excellence Unpleasant surprises Outcome *Employer satisfaction:* Timeliness of care Outcome Communication *Provider satisfaction*	*Credentialing:* Board certification Malpractice history *Clinic operation:* Geographic access Time to see MD *Quality improvement:* Policies and procedures Quality management structure Provider profiling Practice guidelines Incentives/penalties *Case management:* Ambulatory mgt. Utilization mgt. Disability mgt. *Prevention action plans with client employers:* Policies Procedures Management practices Hazard assessment Physical Chemical Biological Emergency planning Training Response system/ provider interfaces Reporting/analysis Return to work/modified duty program Prevention action plan Regulatory compliance Sentinel reporting	*Outcomes:* Cost per case Temp. disab. cost Medical cost Cost and rate of permanent disability Cost and rate of litigation Future medical cost Balance sheet and cash flow for delivery system or site Cash on hand Financial arrangement v. cost structure in aggregate Ability to make a reasonable return on managed care contracts Speed of case closure *Work-related disability:* Days absent from work Restricted/modified duty days Lost day rate

prevention, rates of procedures for commonly overtreated problems such as low back pain, access, disability, financial stability and procedures, and organizational issues (Table 2).

Performance Improvement Systems

Improving performance and outcomes over time is critical to the efficiency of organizations. Improved efficiency and effectiveness may be required for survival in a competitive marketplace as well. Improvement is not free initially, but it should be a net positive over time. Investment is usually needed in standards and guideline development or selection, process analysis, data collection, information systems, and feedback, discussion, and coaching. Much of the cost is in staff time.

There are three general approaches to bottom line improvement: cost reduction, nonparticipatory reengineering, and QI. Cost reduction generally involves across-the-board percentage cuts in budgets. Reengineering of processes without involving those who perform the processes may produce reasonable short-term results, but it also may fail, because intimate knowledge of the process and potential improvements is lacking. In addition, the stress level among disenfranchised employees may increase. Managers sometimes try reengineering because they fear resistance or concealment of information by workers.

Th third option, QI, also is known as continuous quality improvement and total quality management. Given the extent of improvement needed in costs and quality and the clear requirement that professionals and managers be given equally important roles in improving performance, the QI framework is the only approach to high-quality occupational managed health that is sustainable.

CONCLUSION

Managed care is both new and old in occupational health. Structured, managed programs to protect workers from hazards and detect subclinical effects before they cause permanent or overt damage have been in place for decades. Better managers of these programs, and those for onsite care, have used the techniques of management to identify mission, goals, and objectives and accomplish objectives within a budget.

However, the system providing care to ill or injured workers financed by workers' compensation is much more fragmented and subject to a variety of barriers and constraints. The administrative methods used to manage cost, volume, and quality in group health are just now being adopted for workers' compensation, even as group health payors are shifting risk for the costs and outcomes of care to providers, often at their request. Regulations still pose significant barriers to managed care in any form, and the plethora of legal actions in a supposedly no-fault system has led to a degree of (often iatrogenic) defensive medicine unparalled in group health. Perhaps most importantly from a management perspective, the aligned incentives and communication links needed for appropriate access, efficiency, and effectiveness are often missing, particularly for smaller employers and many payors, who have not seen their role as managers of a delivery system.

Cost management is now generally in use for workers' compensation. Most states have adopted techniques to manage the cost of care, such as fee schedules and usual and customary fee screens over the last 20–30 years. Hospitals seem to have escaped; many still bill for charges for workers' compensation. Interestingly, medical bill review to enforce these limits is not yet widespread, as it has been in group health for years. A few states permit utilization and case management (see the chapter by

Eccleston and Victor) and only one mandates use of managed care organizations. Many utilization and case management efforts are blunted by fear of plaintiffs' attorneys and attempts by insurance adjusters to maintain control of a process they are not equipped to manage. Even as these techniques are haltingly adopted, progressive provider organizations are preparing or attempting to build communication links or integrated systems and to assume risk for care and disability management.

Return to work and disability management are still uncommon. The whole area of the effects of the work climate, job design, and managerial style on health and productivity remains a fringe one despite decades of social psychology and medical and organizational stress research.

REFERENCES

1. Aaron HJ, Schwartz WB: The Painful Prescription: Rationing Hospital Care. Washington, DC, The Brookings Institution, 1984.
2. American Medical Association: Guides to the Evaluation of Permanent Impairment, 4th ed. Chicago, American Medical Association, 1993.
3. Berwick DM, Godfrey AB, Roessner J: Curing Health Care: New Strategies for Quality Improvement. San Francisco, Jossey-Bass, 1990.
4. Bigos SJ, Battie MC, Fisher LD: A prospective study of work perceptions and psychosocial factors affecting the report of back injury. Spine 16:1–6, 1991.
5. Blumenthal D, Scheck AC: Improving Clinical Practice: Total Quality Management and The Physician. San Francisco, Jossey-Bass, 1995.
6. Camp RC: Benchmarking: The Search for Industry Best Practices that Lead to Superior Performance. Milwaukee, American Society for Quality Control, Quality Press, 1989.
7. Castaneda-Mendez K, Mangan K, Lavery AM: The role and application of the balanced scorecard in healthcare quality management. J Healthcare Qual 20(1):10–13, 1997.
8. Charns MP, Smith-Tewksbury LJ: Collaborative Management in Health Care: Implementing the Integrative Organization. San Francisco, Jossey-Bass, 1993.
9. Chassin M: Assessing strategies for quality improvement. Health Aff 16:151–161, 1997.
9a. Craft GR: The Coming Battle Among Risk-Bearing Financial Service Companies: What It Means for Technology Companies Serving the Industry. San Francisco, Robertson, Stephens & Co., 1997.
10. Dalton BA, Harris JS: A comprehensive approach to employee health management. J Occup Med 33:338–347, 1991.
11. Davidson SM, McCollom M, Heineke J: The Physician-Manager Alliance: Building the Healthy Health Care Organization. San Francisco, Jossey-Bass, 1996.
12. Davis DA, Taylor-Vaisey A: Translating guidelines into practice: A review of theoretic concepts, practical experience and research evidence in the adoption of clinical practice guidelines. Can Med Assoc J 157:408–416, 1997.
13. Dessler G: Organizational Theory: Integrating Structure and Behavior. 2nd ed. Englewood Cliffs, NJ, Prentice-Hall, 1986.
14. DiBennedetto D, McCunney RS, Harris JS: The OEM Occupational Health and Safety Manual. 2nd ed. Boston, OEM Health Information Press, 1996.
15. Donabedian A: The Definition of Quality and Approaches to Its Assessment. Ann Arbor, MI, Health Administration Press, 1980.
16. Donabedian A: Quality and cost: Choices and responsibilities. In Harris JS, Belk HD, Wood LW (eds): Managing Employee Health Care Costs: Assuring Quality and Value. Beverly Farms, MA, OEM Health Information, 1992, pp 13–18.
17. Fass P, Carr R, Larkin G, et al: Corporate medical departments and managed care. In Harris JS, Loeppke RR (eds): Integrated Health Management: The Key Role of Occupational Medicine in Managed Care, Disability Management and Integrated Delivery Systems. Beverly Farms, MA, OEM Press, 1998.
18. Galvin R: Health care management. In McCunney RS, et al (eds): A Practical Approach to Environmental and Occupational Medicine. 2nd ed. Boston, Little, Brown, 1994.
19. Gardner HH, Sneiderman CA: Ensuring value by supporting consumer decision-making. In Harris JS, Belk HD, Wood LW (eds): Managing Employee Health Care Costs: Assuring Quality and Value. Beverly Farms, MA, OEM Health Information, 1992, pp 73–76.
20. Gaucher EJ, Coffey RJ: Total Quality in Health Care: From Theory to Practice. San Francisco, Jossey-Bass, 1993.

21. Harris JS, Dewey MJ: Organizational stress. In O'Donnell MP, Ainsworth TA (eds): Health Promotion in the Workplace. New York, Wiley, 1984.

22. Harris JS: What employers can do about health care costs: Managing health and productivity. In McLennan K, Meyer JA: Cost and Care: Current Issues in Health Policy. Boulder, Westview Press, 1989.

23. Harris JS, Iskowe DI, Goldstein SR, et al: Workers' compensation: Business as usual may mean going out of business. NCCI Digest 4(3):25–43, 1989.

24. Harris JS: The bridge from quality assurance to quality improvement. J Occup Med 32:1175–1176, 1990.

25. Harris JS: Why doctors do what they do: Determinants of physician decision-making. J Occup Med 32:1207–1220, 1990.

26. Harris JS, Custer WS: Health care economic factors and the effects of benefits plan design changes. J Occup Med 33:279–286, 1991.

27. Harris JS: Is health care cost management working? Occup Environ Med 5:105–108, 1991.

28. Harris JS: Workers compensation. In McCunney RS, et al (eds): A Practical Approach to Environmental and Occupational Medicine. 2nd ed. Boston, Little, Brown, 1994.

29. Harris JS: The economics of occupational medicine. In McCunney RS, et al (eds): A Practical Approach to Environmental and Occupational Medicine. 2nd ed. Boston, Little, Brown, 1994.

30. Harris JS: Clinical practice guidelines: Development, use and evaluation. J Occup Environ Med 39:23–34, 1997.

31. Harris JS (ed): Occupational Medicine Practice Guidelines: Evaluation and Management of Common Health Problems and Functional Recovery in Workers. Beverly Farms, MA, OEM Health Information, 1997.

32. Harris JS: Cornerstones of disability management. In Harris JS (ed): Evaluation and Management of Common Health Problems in Functional Recovery in Workers: The ACOEM Occupational Medicine Practice Guidelines. Beverly Farms, MA, OEM Health Information, 1997, pp 51–55.

33. Harris JS: Case management: Prevention and management of delayed functional recovery. In Harris JS (ed): Evaluation and Management of Common Health Problems and Functional Recovery in Workers: The ACOEM Occupational Medicine Practice Guidelines. Beverly Farms, MA, OEM Health Information, 1997, pp 61–69.

34. Harris JS, Guillen K: Information systems for health care delivery: Business process models, goals, and design. In Harris JS, Loeppke RR (eds): Integrated Health Management: The Key Role of Occupational Medicine in Managed Care, Disability Management and Integrated Delivery Systems. Beverly Farms, MA, OEM Health Information, 1998.

35. Harris JS, Loeppke RR: Trends and opportunities in managed care, integrated health management, and integrated delivery systems. In Harris JS, Loeppke RR (eds): Integrated Health Management: The Key Role of Occupational Medicine in Managed Care, Disability Management and Integrated Delivery Systems. Beverly Farms, MA, OEM Health Information, 1998.

36. Harris JS, Miller LA: Sources and uses of occupational medicine data. In Harris JS, Loeppke RR (eds): Integrated Health Management: The Key Role of Occupational Medicine in Managed Care, Disability Management and Integrated Delivery Systems. Beverly Farms, MA, OEM Health Information, 1998.

37. Harris JS: An integrative approach to occupational health. In Press, 1998.

38. Hax AC, Majluf NS: Strategic Management: An Integrative Perspective. Englewood Cliffs, NJ, Prentice-Hall, 1984.

39. Reference deleted.

40. Institute of Medicine: America's Health in Transition: Protecting and Improving Quality. Washington, DC, National Academy Press, 1994.

41. Kahn RL: Work and Health. New York, Wiley, 1986.

42. Kane RL (ed): Understanding Health Care Outcomes Research. Gaithersburg, MD, Aspen Publications, 1997.

43. Karasek RA, Theorell T: Healthy Work. New York, Basic Books, 1990.

44. Katz D, Kahn RL: The Social Psychology of Organizations. New York, John Wiley and Sons, 1978.

45. Kay MZ, Murphy W, Harris JS: How to zap your workers' compensation costs. Finan Exec Jan-Feb:44–48, 1994.

46. Kongstevedt PR: The Managed Care Handbook. 3rd ed. Gaithersburg, MD, Aspen Publications, 1997.

47. LaDou J (ed): Occupational and Environmental Medicine. 2nd ed. Stamford, CT, Appleton & Lange, 1997.

48. Last JM, Wallace RB (eds): Section 6 of Public Health and Preventive Medicine. 13th ed. Norwalk, CT, Appleton & Lange, 1992.

49. Lawler EE III: High Involvement Management. San Francisco, Jossey-Bass, 1986.

50. Levy BS, Wegman DH: Occupational Health: Recognizing and Preventing Work-Related Disease. 3rd ed. Boston, Little, Brown, 1995.
51. Loeppke RR: Care management and capitation. In Harris JS Loeppke RR (eds): Integrated Health Management: The Key Role of Occupational Medicine in Managed Care, Disability Management and Integrated Delivery Systems. Beverly Farms, MA, OEM Health Information, 1998.
52. Reference deleted.
53. Makens PK, McEachern JE: Applications of industrial quality improvement in health care. In Harris JS, Belk HD, Wood LW (eds): Managing Employee Health Care Costs: Assuring Quality and Value. Beverly Farms, MA, OEM Health Information, 1992, pp 23–28.
54. McCue JD: The Medical Cost-Containment Crisis: Fears, Opinions, and Facts. Ann Arbor, MI, Health Administration Press, 1989.
55. Milkovich GT, Glueck WF: Personnel: Human Resources Management. 4th ed. Plano, TX, Business Publications, 1985.
55a. Miller RH, Luft HS: Managed care plan performance since 1980: A literature analysis. JAMA 271:1512–1519, 1994.
56. Moon SD, Sauter SL (eds): Beyond Biomechanics: Psychosocial Aspects of Musculoskeletal Disorders in Office Work. Bristol, PA, Taylor and Francis, 1996.
57. Mulley AG Jr: Supporting the patient's role in decision making. In Harris JS, Belk HD, Wood LW (eds): Managing Employee Health Care Costs: Assuring Quality and Value. Beverly Farms, MA, OEM Health Information, 1992.
58. New World Dictionary.
59. O'Donnell MP, Harris JS (eds): Health Promotion in the Work Place. 2nd ed. Albany, NY, Delmar, 1994.
60. Peterson KP, Loeppke RL: Population health management. In Harris JS, Loeppke RR (eds): Integrated Health Management: The Key Role of Occupational Medicine in Managed Care, Disability Management and Integrated Delivery Systems. Beverly Farms, MA, OEM Press, 1998.
61. Rom WN (ed): Occupational and Environmental Medicine. 2nd ed. Boston, Little, Brown, 1992.
62. Starr P: The Social Transformation of American Medicine. New York, Basic Books, 1982.
63. Sullivan T: Outcomes research: Payer and provider applications. In Harris JS, Loeppke RR (eds): Integrated Health Management: The Key Role of Occupational Medicine in Managed Care, Disability Management and Integrated Delivery Systems. Beverly Farms, MA, OEM Health Information, 1998.
64. U.S. Department of Health and Human Services: Healthy People 2000: National Health Promotion and Disease Prevention Objectives. Washington, DC, US Government Printing Office, DHHS Publication No, (PHS) 91-50213.
65. Wickizer TM, Wheeler JRC, Feldstein PJ: Does utilization review reduce health care costs? Med Care 27:632–647, 1989.
66. Winslow R: Health care inflation revives in Minneapolis despite cost-cutting: Failure of efforts to change actual medical practices get much of the blame. Wall Street Journal May 19, 1998, p A1.
67. Zenz C, Dickerson OB, Horvath EP Jr (eds): Occupational Medicine. 3rd ed. St. Louis, Mosby, 1994.

MARCIA L. COMSTOCK, MD, MPH

EMPLOYER-PROVIDER PARTNERSHIPS IN ADVANCED MANAGED CARE:

Human Assets Risk Management

From the Consolidated Rail
    Corporation
Philadelphia, Pennsylvania

Reprint requests to:
Marcia L. Comstock, MD, MPH
1157 Lafayette Road
Wayne, PA 19087-2110

As managed care has penetrated the health care industry, the focus of health care delivery has slowly shifted from addressing unique needs of individual patients to a broader "system" approach emphasizing population health management through an integrated service continuum of care. Exciting new opportunities are created in advanced managed care markets for occupational health providers to develop partnerships to improve overall health and productivity of the workforce. The preventive medicine specialist's perspective, by inclination and training, is grounded in epidemiology and risk stratification as an approach to resource allocation decisions. Thus, such individuals should have an intuitive appreciation of population health management. Occupational physicians also are well suited to manage conflicts of interest that may arise in managed care systems, given their extensive experience balancing legal and ethical duties to employee-patients and employers.[11]

The evolution in health care delivery and financing has a parallel in the maturation of the specialty of occupational and environmental medicine (OEM). The role of the employer has provided a common influence. Corporate America is the main commercial purchaser of health care services for its employees, who are the primary customers of OEM. Direct and indirect health care costs for the United States workforce may exceed $1.2 trillion, including occupational illness and injury, nonoccupational medical problems paid for by employers, and health and safety costs such as wellness and regulatory compliance.[1] As the realization has grown that a competitive America needs a healthy workforce, so has the recognition of the strategic value of OEM.[8,18]

This chapter presents a framework within which occupational health professionals in corporations, the provider community, and managed care organizations can reevaluate their roles. Through assessment of an employer's specific health and productivity risks, the value of a spectrum of prevention and OEM services can be demonstrated focusing on the competitive needs of the business. Such an approach should be useful in marketing services.

First, the evolution of the employer's role in the provision of health benefits and health services is reviewed, focusing on the influence of managed care and changes in risk financing. Next, a methodology to assess risks to "human assets" similar to risk management models used by corporations for financial and physical assets is presented. From the analysis, key health care cost and productivity drivers for specific corporate customers can be defined at a macro level, needs from providers delineated, and relevant outcome measures determined. Data from the analysis might provide a foundation for development of actuarial risk adjustments for capitated occupational health services. Finally, examples of "risk control" initiatives relevant to both strategic and tactical OEM practice are described to address loss related to human assets.

In addition to identifying new opportunities for positioning OEM in the continuum of health care services, this chapter should help clarify the perspective of employer-purchasers with regard to the health care system. Corporate health and human resources professionals endeavoring to position their role as integral to the business also can use the model as a means to relate the value of "human capital" with a new slant.

EVOLUTION OF THE EMPLOYER'S ROLE IN HEALTH BENEFITS AND SERVICES

Health Benefits and Financing

Through changes in employee health benefit plans, employers have undertaken strategies that have altered the health care delivery system and, through incentives, have changed employee behavior. Faced with mounting costs, by the late 1970s and early 1980s employers sought ways to shift the pattern of financing employee health benefits and the way provider services were paid. Pre-tax corporate spending for health care by the 1,600 largest U.S. corporations was 29–62% between 1980 and 1990.[25] The negative impact of rising costs on corporate profitability represented an opportunity for managed care to penetrate the marketplace.

For 23 years, large employers focused on self-insurance and the federal Employee Retirement Income Security Act (ERISA) preemption when crafting health benefit plans. A complex law passed in 1974, ERISA blocked states from directly regulating employer self-funded benefits and created a major incentive for large employers to self-insure. Self-insurance helped control costs, permitted flexibility, and avoided state benefit mandates. Recent questions regarding interpretation of the ERISA preemption as it pertains to managed care organizations, however, have increased the risk of potential liability for health plan decisions with negative outcomes. In addition, the fully insured products typical of managed care create conflicts with self-insurance. As a result, there has been a slight decrease in the proportion of employees in fully or partially self-funded plans.

Managed care has reorganized many incentives for employers, insurers, patients, and providers as the relevance of money in medical decisions has grown. Although managed care kept medical inflation under control for a few years, results were significantly related to a one-time savings from employees switching out of indemnity plans to managed care. By 1997, costs were again on the rise. Early managed care techniques of cost-shifting and limiting access were not effective in later stages of managed care. Rather, a more systematic approach to managing health risks is needed.[2,13,14] As relationships between employers and managed care groups become more sophisticated and the line between products becomes less distinct, the opportunity for employers to pay a lower premium and assume some of the risk becomes greater.

In more advanced managed care markets, direct contracting is being explored by some employers as a strategy to control costs, but there is no consensus on its longevity. In advanced managed care markets, self-insured employers or employer coalitions buy health care services directly from physicians, provider-sponsored networks, or integrated delivery systems, reducing the need for middleparties. From the employer's perspective, there is more potential for such arrangements to be able to demonstrate value in terms of cost, access, quality, and accountability.[9]

Unfortunately, the inherent conflict between the good of the plan and the good of the patient that exists in managed care organizations is heightened in a provider services organization. Further, if nonmedical services are offered, such as benefit design, utilization review, or second opinion, the provider services organization takes on the risk of those services. Such arrangements may link employers to under-regulated and underfunded entities with little risk-bearing experience, increasing their liability. From the perspective of large, multistate employers, the arrangements are also time-consuming and a hassle unless an administrative entity is retained.[3,5]

As purchasers, employers are increasingly concerned about their fiduciary responsibilities and recognize the need to move away from a purely cost-based benefit strategy. Inexpensive but inappropriate care can result in greater liability and increased costs in the long run. Much energy is being expended today on a drive toward the definition and measurement of value in health care purchasing.[9]

Regardless of what changes occur in health care delivery systems, employers are likely to remain the ultimate payer in the commercial market for the foreseeable future. To prosper in this market, providers and health systems will structure products to meet the unique needs of various employers. Success will no longer result from increasing volume and lowering cost. Rather, winners will be those who offer the most value to the customer.[14]

The Role of the Corporate Medical Department

Corporate medicine began in plant settings as industrial medicine, generally comprising urgent care services and the provision of a policing function on behalf of supervision. Over time, however, OEM has been through many iterations prior to today's ideal model of integrated corporate health and productivity management delivered by highly qualified health professionals as full strategic business partners.[17]

In the 1980s, many large employers with geographically concentrated populations supported comprehensive onsite occupational health services as well as a focus on monitoring community providers through disability management and care coordination. Such services saved employee time off the job, could enhance quality, and were highly valued. Frequently, too few primary care providers were willing to take the time to holistically manage the patient. Because these large employers generally were self-insured, a strong argument for corporate-provided primary care as a cost-effective strategy could also be made if the right cultural environment and demographics existed.

As the prevalence of managed care and capitation grew, employers began focusing on negotiating the lowest possible premium. With no direct risk, there is less incentive to provide preventive services or in-house care unless the culture supports it for employee relations reasons or it is focused on controlling absenteeism and enhancing productivity.

The role of in-house medical departments in benefit design and health care cost management has evolved with maturation of managed care and the trend away from self-insurance to capitation and ultimately to risk-sharing. Although downsizing, outsourcing, and elimination of in-house occupational services has been common for several years, this trend could reverse as new strategic roles are defined for corporate medical professionals and their potential value in corporate health management is recognized.[8]

The View from Business

As the 21st century approaches, global competition, rapidly increasing speed of technologic change, and stringent health and safety regulations represent examples of critical business challenges. For employers, remaining competitive requires the flexibility to adapt to changing customer demands, innovative approaches to new products and services, and creatively managing a workforce with diverse needs. For employees, the future means even less security, divided loyalties, constant pressure to balance home and work life, and the need for continual learning, with renewal of old and development of new skills.

Corporations have evolved from hierarchical organizations to flattened business structures that today focus on core business competencies. Tactics such as outsourcing, strategic alliances, joint ventures, and contract employees are commonly employed to provide noncore business elements. This has significant implications if health is not defined as a core competency. An opportunity exists, however, to redefine health in the context of productivity, which is a core of any business enterprise.

Paramount to the success of business in the 1990s and beyond is the attraction, assimilation, training, maintenance, and retention of the most effective employee for each job. The caliber of the workforce may well define success more than a company's products and services. As the scarcity of skilled workers becomes more acute, it will be necessary for employers to differentiate themselves as employers of choice by offering a competitive variety of traditional and nontraditional benefits to appeal to varying needs. Given the increasing demands on employees to increase productivity and maximize performance, companies will be well-advised to ensure that the right mix of cost-effective services are provided to help ensure that deterrents to productivity and performance are minimized.

Similarly, businesses are facing increasing scrutiny from regulatory bodies and an increasingly litigious environment, particularly in the areas of employment practices and occupational health and safety. They can ill afford to ignore the need for stringent attention to compliance issues.

In some companies, responsibility for health-related programs and services is under the umbrella of environmental health and safety. In others, it is aligned with the benefit function as part of human resources. This later positioning makes intuitive sense, because health programs clearly provide specific benefits to employees. However, reframing health and safety initiatives in the context of risk reduction provides the opportunity to demonstrate their business value using methodologies familiar to corporate leaders and decision-makers.

Traditionally, risk management in industry has focused on the protection and preservation of physical and financial assets, encompassing some combination of loss control, security, insurance, and claims and litigation management. Although programs related to safety may be included in the risk management organization, it is rare that human assets are assessed and managed using the models and methodology that companies apply to physical and financial assets. Yet, much business loss can be traced, directly or indirectly, to human failure. For example, 80% of accidents investigated by the National Transportation Safety Board are traced directly to human error.

HUMAN ASSET RISK MANAGEMENT

A total "human assets risk management" model must address individual, organizational, environmental, and cultural aspects of the workplace. This analysis provides a framework for definition of key health and productivity drivers, a prerequisite for demonstrating the value of OEM services to corporate purchasers. The importance of tailoring programs and services to the unique needs of each corporate customer cannot be overemphasized. Effective customization requires in-depth knowledge of the business, its culture, and its employees. This understanding sets the stage for a mutually beneficial relationship—uncommon today—between in-house human resources and health and safety professionals and the external health care community. Providers must understand what is important to the purchaser and proactively strive to meet defined needs. They must become familiar with business strategy and the language of business. Outcomes must be related through measures meaningful to corporate decision-makers.

Occupational and environmental health professionals can distinguish themselves by helping quantify the risk that accrues to businesses that fail to attend to the preservation and protection of people. What would a risk management model look like if applied to human assets? There are three broad areas where potential risks may be identified, assessed, and controlled, as described below.

Risks to employee relations result in failure to attract the right employees and retain the best and brightest present employees—in short, failure to be the "employer of choice." A culture that supports open communication, attractive health benefits, flexible work arrangements, child and elder care programs, effective policies on threats and intimidation, employee assistance programs, personal wellness, and health promotion initiatives provides significant competitive advantage.

While some of these programs are not traditionally thought of in the context of health and safety, they legitimately belong in a spectrum of services that supports a healthy work environment. In some cases, the internal human resources group will be accountable, but OEM services should include consultation and assistance with development and implementation of such programs. Elements of the employee relations program must be interwoven in the continuum of health and productivity risk management.

Risks to productivity and performance translate directly or indirectly into increased costs and have the potential for the most significant economic loss. The most common proxy for productivity, absenteeism, is an inadequate indicator at best. Not only is absenteeism tracked poorly in many companies, policies clearly affect reported absence.[1] Further, such a measure fails to account for the significant percentage of workers on any given day who are present but functioning at reduced efficiency and effectiveness.

Targeted high-risk and occupational health promotion, integrated disability case management with effective return to work programs, employee assistance services, attention to work scheduling practices and their impact on fatigue and alertness, and substance abuse screening and treatment are some examples of initiatives that address these productivity risks.

Risks related to legal and regulatory compliance represent a third area. Failure in these areas may result in fines, lawsuits, product liability or bad public image, and accidents and injuries. Attention must be given to hiring and return to work practices, in light of the Americans with Disabilities Act (ADA), the Family Medical Leave Act, Department of Transportation requirements regarding fitness standards, drug and alcohol testing, and Occupational Health and Safety Administration (OSHA) requirements for industrial hygiene and medical surveillance pertinent to the business.

Business Life Cycle

The customer assessment should begin with consideration of the nature of the business, the corporation's current status and market position in that business and in the business life cycle, and the culture of the company and management philosophy. These variables set the context for risk identification, evaluation, and control.

Evaluation of the customer's business with regard to its position in the business life cycle is helpful in establishing receptivity to various approaches to human asset risk management. It also will suggest whether there is likely to be an innate prejudice for in-house or vendored services. Such decisions are as much a matter of philosophy as cost.

It is not likely that an emerging or growing business will push to outsource services. Between growth and maturity, when successful businesses reinvent themselves and look for innovative products and services to help maintain their leadership position, companies are generally open to creative approaches to enhanced human asset management. On the other hand, cost-cutting, downsizing, and outsourcing are often a reaction to decline. Such businesses are likely to insist on strategies with short-term results. An environmental scan is useful in identifying marketplace forces and drivers causing change in the business and the likely speed of those changes.

The concept of a business life cycle is as applicable to the business of managing the corporation's human assets as it is to the business itself. Human resources and health services professionals are key to human asset risk management. To be maximally effective, these groups need a relevant and business-oriented identity to capture the attention of senior management.

Similar to the evolution in corporate occupational medicine, the human resources function is also undergoing reevaluation and renewal. Integration of internal and external health services providers with broad-based human resources expertise focused on a risk continuum provides necessary resources and strategies to maximize potential of company's human assets. A human assets risk management model will help in-house service providers demonstrate added value or shift their focus to new areas where such value can be measured.

Core Values and Philosophy

After consideration of the customer's position in the business life cycle, it is next necessary to develop an appreciation for the business culture. For example, the operational value disciplines model can be used to discern basic philosophy.[25]

Treacy and Wiersema point out that in today's world no business can succeed by attempting to meet all needs of different customers. Rather, the business must establish a unique dimension of value to deliver to its chosen market.

The model defines three different value disciplines that can drive a business. While market leaders must maintain threshold standards in all three value disciplines, they generally excel at one dimension. A company's value discipline has significant implications for the types of programs and services the company will support to address each of the global risk areas that are identified.

Operationally excellent companies are low-cost, efficient producers that focus on best total cost, consistency, and reliability. They are results-oriented and expect service providers to be the same. Execution is key and clear measures important. These companies will not tolerate waste, will reward efficiency, and need stable, predictable, cost-conscious employees. In this environment, well-proven, standardized, streamlined programs are most likely to gain support.

Customer intimacy companies shape products and services to individual customers or segmented markets. They often are smaller companies or service organizations that offer the "best total solution." These companies need satisfied employees and will generally treat them as they want customers to be treated. A variety of customized, tailored, frequently decentralized programs and services may be supported. Such companies cultivate long-term relationships and may be particularly interested in risk-sharing partnerships.

Product leadership companies produce premium-priced, innovative products and services. They value risk-taking and creativity. Their culture encourages entrepreneurial initiatives and individual accomplishment. Their employees need a comfortable, flexible work environment without much bureaucracy. Service providers need to be capable of rapidly adapting programs to changing needs.

RISK IDENTIFICATION AND ASSESSMENT

Qualitative Tasks

The next task involves identification and assessment of specific business risks. Certainly, visiting representative worksites to assess the physical environment is recommended, as is interviewing a variety of stakeholders.

What do key decision-makers such as senior and finance managers view as critical risks to the business in terms of the core areas of employee relations, productivity and performance, and compliance? These opinions should be validated later through the data and organizational scan. Consider that opinions may be somewhat biased by availability of information as well as corporate measures. There may be a tendency to emphasize less serious risks whose impact is directly or immediately obvious over more significant risks whose impact is delayed or indirect. For example, a financial executive may be convinced that workers' compensation is a main cost driver and not appreciate the importance of personal disability absences that cost several times as much.

What do key customers have to say about the value of the programs and services being provided? What do customers want that is not being provided, and why is it important to them? What do the customers perceive as the uniquely valuable aspects of each program? As health care is becoming a commodity, the service component is often viewed as more important than the technical component.[14] Elements of "patient-centered care" may be cited as key by some customers. Components include respect for the patient's values and preferences, coordination, integration, continuity of care, education and communication, and physical and emotional comfort.[22] Others may focus on convenience, onsite availability, credibility of the service provider, technical expertise, or perceived quality.

Quantitative Tasks

How can the risk be assessed? First, general information on employee demographics such as age and gender distribution, educational level, and workforce characteristics related to population dispersion, plant size, and unionization should be obtained. Data analysis should begin with collection of quantitative and qualitative information, relative to the three risk areas (Table 1). While in-depth analysis requires integrated systems that may not exist, adequate information should be available to identify critical issues and develop preliminary risk-control strategies. It is also important to segregate data, for example by location; the most important risks, and thus costs, may differ by worksite depending on the health status of the workers, their psychological disposition, and the work environment, including safety practices and management.

Measures and Outcomes

Identifying the right process and outcome measures is critical because they will drive continuous improvement and help with resource allocation decisions. Outcomes can be defined in a variety of ways, such as through measurements of disease status, health status, patient satisfaction, and economic impact. For the employer, improvement in the first three areas should translate into positive economic impact.

For each data set reviewed, consider the metrics being used to measure results. Would other outcome measures be more powerful in demonstrating the degree of effectiveness of current initiatives or produce better alignment with overall corporate goals and objectives?

Employers continue to see cost as the default metric when measuring value in health care purchasing. However, more large employers are looking at quality indicators and outcome measures, such as the Health Employer Data and Information Set, accreditation status, and the Foundation for Accountability standards when making managed care purchasing decisions.[9] In the future, functional outcomes such as workforce productivity or a uniform measure of health outcome such as

TABLE 1. Risk Assessment Review

Employee Relations	Productivity/Performance	Compliance
Human resource policies	Industry productivity measures	Equal Employment Opportunity
Health benefit plans and	Policies related to absenteeism	Commission and Americans
enrollment	Overall absenteeism (lost work	with Disabilities Act claims
Compensation systems	days/100 employees)	Drug and alcohol testing data
Employee surveys (attitudes,	Workers' compensation data	Occupational Safety and Health
morale)	Medical and indemnity costs	Administration fines
Recruitment/training costs	by diagnosis	Injury frequency rates and trends
Annual turnover	Average lost work days by	Industrial hygiene sampling data
Grievances, claims, lawsuits	diagnosis	Medical surveillance data
	Nonoccupational disability data	Quality/timeliness of regulatory
	Distribution by disease	exams
	category	
	Highest cost claims	
	Mental health treatment costs	
	Health risk appraisal data	

Health-Adjusted Life Expectancy may be used as a management tool for purchasing population health.[16]

There are no widely recognized accreditation policies or outcome measures in the United States for OEM services, but this problem is being actively addressed by the American College of Occupational and Environmental Medicine (ACOEM). Occupational health professionals have long argued the need to consider all economic and humanistic costs associated with illness and injury, including indirect costs related to lost work time and decreased productivity. Although such costs are difficult to compute with accuracy, some have suggested that indirect costs are greater by orders of magnitude.[18]

RISK CONTROL

The described evaluation of culture and philosophy, business cycle, internal resources, and critical risk data will provide significant insight into the best overall risk-control strategy and will begin to answer questions relevant to specific programs and delivery models. One must focus on opportunities to improve processes, leverage resources, enhance alignment with the core business, and eliminate fragmentation or redundancy to ensure maximally effective human asset risk management. Once the assessment is complete, it is important to meet with the customer to review the results. Clarify needs, ensure mutual agreement on goals, define priorities, and delineate outcomes to be measured for each risk-control initiative. Employers with minimal internal expertise may well expect assistance with anticipating future needs. This is also a chance to show customers risks they may have failed to identify and to reorder priorities, if appropriate.

Population-Based Total Health Management

As a core strategy in advanced managed care, population health management provides the framework within which we can consider the continuum of OEM and related services for risk control.

The concept of population-based total health management is broad and may be interpreted differently in various contexts. Generally accepted elements include health promotion and disease prevention, occupational health services, primary care, and management of chronic disease to reduce morbidity and disability. But this framework goes beyond the sum of individual health. It requires consideration of social or community determinants of disease such as public health, education, the environment, and resource allocation issues.[15]

Thus, population health management incorporates systems historically separate, focused on "cure" and "health." Through integration of cost and health risk management, a population health framework seeks to optimize both economic and clinical outcomes.[23] Tactics include stratifying subpopulations based on risk, targeting interventions to identified needs in each segmented group, organizing delivery resources for seamless service and maximum efficiency, and limiting variation through the use of protocols. A critical enabler is a robust information system's infrastructure.

Effective use of OEM for risk control requires focus on primary, secondary, and tertiary prevention, effective teamwork among providers, ongoing communication with employer representatives, customized services, and continuity of care. In the context of population-based total health management, employers want effective, efficient, continuous management of occupational and nonoccupational problems from wherever the system is accessed. Investment in long-term partnerships contributes to a positive perception regarding quality. Developing risk-sharing direct contracts for disability and workers' compensation management, medical monitoring, and required periodic and fitness for duty assessments could do much to enhance the incentives on both sides for positive outcomes.

Risk Control: Employee Relations

While risk control strategies are described under one of the identified core areas for simplicity, most strategies affect more than one area. Responsibility for many initiatives related to risk control with regard to employee relations should be shared between occupational health and human resources professionals.

FAMILY-FRIENDLY POLICIES

The inextricable link between an employee's home life and work productivity makes attending to work–family issues good business. Effective collaboration between health services and human resources can occur around the design and implementation of policies to support employees coping with family issues. Today, more baby boomers are concerned about care for aging parents than child care. Parental care referral services as well as employer day care facilities are becoming more common. Companies will increasingly need to provide flexible work schedules and adequate time off to address family matters or pay the price of tremendous absenteeism and productivity loss.

THREAT AND VIOLENCE PREVENTION

Occupational health professionals should play a key role in spearheading workplace violence prevention policies and programs. Each year nearly a million individuals become victims of violent crimes while working. In 1994, the Department of Justice calculated that these crimes resulted in 1.7 million lost days of work a year and $55 million in lost wages.

Comprehensive threat and violence prevention efforts can go a long way toward creating a competitive advantage to attract and retain high-quality employees and in mitigating potential liability. Such programs should encompass careful prehire background screening, formal zero tolerance policies for threats and acts of intimidation or violence, and training for all supervisors in conflict resolution. In addition, the development and communication of a systematic approach to the evaluation and management of threats and potential violence, using a cross-functional assessment team, is necessary to ensure consistency of process, particularly in a dispersed workforce.

EMPLOYEE ASSISTANCE PROGRAMS

Employee assistance programs (EAPs) are commonly employed to demonstrate commitment to employee well being and mitigate risk from impaired employees. Although detection and treatment of substance abuse in the workplace remains a significant and challenging goal, today's EAPs are likely to be broadly focused on complex personal and workplace stressors and their management. Some feel that stress may be the most toxic exposure in the workplace today, leading to increased absenteeism, medical costs, and decreased performance.[17] According to a 5-year study conducted by the American Management Association and CIGNA Corp., as employers downsize, more employees are filing all types of medical claims, and stress claims and other self-reported disabilities have increased the most.

Clinical depression is an often unrecognized cause of decreased productivity, absenteeism, and safety risk. One estimate of the cost of depression to American corporations is $43 billion, $12 million of which is a result of absenteeism. It is important to identify employees with subtle signs of impairment and to facilitate referral for appropriate treatment, because early intervention reduces disability.[4] Misdiagnosis and inappropriate treatment are extremely common. EAP professionals and primary care providers need to be attentive to complaints such as fatigue, insomnia, and lack of appetite, which may mask depression.

Crisis management and critical incident support for employees who are involved in or witness severe trauma or violence is also an important EAP function. Prompt assessment and referral decreases the risk of disability and may help the organization maintain productivity by quickly resuming normal operations.

Risk Control: Productivity and Performance

HEALTH PROMOTION AND WELLNESS

Health promotion and disease prevention are not programs but rather a strategy to drive health service delivery. According to the Centers for Disease Control and Prevention, more than 50% of all medical problems are due to acquired and correctable risk factors, but only 4% of the health care budget is spent on prevention. Addressing high-risk lifestyle factors is the best form of primary prevention. The U.S. Public Services Task Force believes that educating people and encouraging them to adopt healthier lifestyles has more potential to improve health than commonly employed secondary preventive measures such as screening for early disease.

Investments in health promotion, while making intuitive sense, are not proven from a cost-benefit perspective. In the short term, wellness strategies have the greatest impact on morale. While there is considerable knowledge about the impact of risk factors on morbidity and mortality, little data exist on the relationship between specific risk factors, health care costs, and corporate return on investment. New studies by the Health Enhancement Research Organization and others are trying to show that prevention saves money for the bottom line and increases productivity.

Early health promotion and disease prevention initiatives began as worksite-based initiatives, because vendors were not providing the full array of recommended clinical preventive services. Worksite-based health promotion is more successful than community-based promotion because participation rates are higher and long-term tracking and follow-up is easier. Social support, peer pressure, and better communication also contribute to good results.

Today general health promotion has been replaced by more focused interventions addressing issues relevant to all. Employees should be educated to take an active role in health care decision-making, up to and including end-of-life decision-making. Self-care, demand management, medical consumerism, and targeted high-risk lifestyle and chronic disease management can reap benefits quickly. Some companies initiate personal health promotion programs and then leverage the trust built with employees and their increased awareness to involve them in occupational health promotion and injury prevention efforts. Ensuring that confidential, personal health information cannot be misused is a critical prerequisite to trust, especially in a heavily unionized environment.

Cost-effective health promotion and injury prevention strategies today are coordinated with health plans and providers, and more employers are demanding that prevention services be included in the purchased continuum of care. The key is the right form of risk assessment and stratification, perhaps at the worksite, followed by delivery of a customized intervention program by an appropriate team of providers such as nurses, case managers, exercise physiologists, and nutritionists.

Managed care organizations and provider groups who are assuming more risk have begun to recognize the importance of these programs in supporting population health and managing costs. Long-term partnerships provide incentive for the necessary investment. Employers unwilling to consider multiyear contracts will not be able to achieve such a partnership.[9]

DEMAND MANAGEMENT

Demand management is helping managed care balance cost and quality. An integral part of supply-side management, demand management addresses both need and demand for services, ensuring the appropriate level of care to reduce unnecessary and expensive use of health care resources. Such services encourage prevention and self-care. Information on treatment options and chronic disease management plans are also offered to patients at the time they access and need services. Demand management systems can play an important role in providing health care providers and payers with the ability to predict which patients will be future high-cost health care users, and early detection of such patients is critical in ensuring the best care.[20]

SCREENING

Almost all physicians support the testing of apparently healthy populations to detect risk factors for disease or identify medical problems at an early, generally more treatable stage. However, the data on cost-effectiveness of many such programs are less convincing. As a result, there is much controversy over the provision of such screening programs by health plans, and employers worry whether they are effectively using health plan dollars.

In population health management, as in public health, cost-benefit and cost-effectiveness analyses are key. Lack of consensus over populations to be tested, the best screening test, and frequency of testing of various age groups for common diseases such as prostate and colon cancer and heart disease make decisions difficult at best. In addition, information on costs of implementing screening or cost-effectiveness of follow-up treatments is rarely available.

Targeted screening with accurate tests for diseases for which good treatment is available and early intervention clearly affects outcome helps ensure cost-effectiveness of such secondary prevention efforts. Limiting screening by age and at least one other risk factor for the disease in question helps increase the specificity of testing by decreasing the number of false positives that subject healthy people to fear, inconvenience, risk, and expense.

ABSENCE MANAGEMENT

Traditionally, lost-time management has been recognized as a key driver of success for an occupational health program. The costs to business from lost productivity and from indemnity and medical expenses represent a major and controllable liability. Absenteeism relates as much to psychological disposition and work environment, demands, control, reward systems, and culture as it does to morbidity.

Corporations typically have focused much of their energy on workers' compensation. Yet, in most industries the financial drain on the balance sheet from personal disability is considerably greater. According to the U.S. Census Bureau, disability costs continue to rise at 8% per year, and total U.S. disability costs will exceed $340 billion by the year 2000.[24] There are a number of drivers of this trend. Employees are more prone to illness and injury as a result of the overall aging of the population. Increased personal and job-related stressors, as noted earlier, represent psychological hazards that contribute to increased mental disability. In recent years, new legal and regulatory mandates related to employment and health and safety also have proven costly.

Development and implementation of integrated and aggressive case management for workers' compensation, group health, and disability programs, using appropriate disability duration guidelines and treatment protocols, can shrink the loss. Education, aligned incentives, and stakeholder accountability are key. Employers, providers, and employees all have key roles to play in managing issues related to lost work time.

Employees and supervisors must understand how programs work and their responsibility to cooperate. Many employers are coordinating absence management by creating a single point of entry into the benefit system. A toll-free 24-hour phone line enhances ease of use, decreases administrative costs, and permits earlier assessment of functional ability and recovery. Centralized case management, accurate functional job analyses, and an aggressive return to work program for both occupational and nonoccupational illness and injury is critical to the success of lost time management as well as compliance with the ADA.

A major problem in addressing indirect costs for lost work time and disability relates to the lack of linkage between the provider and the workplace, exacerbated by the failure of managed care to reward providers for restoration of productivity. Providers tend to manage occupational and nonoccupational illness and injury differently even though the same protocols and guidelines are appropriate and timely return to work is beneficial in both. Employees on short-term disability can benefit from the same transitional work programs that help mitigate against a disability mentality with workers' compensation.

In evaluating occupational and nonoccupational illness and injury, providers must clearly understand the distinction between impairment and disability. In addition to clarifying diagnosis and assessing physical and cognitive impairment, the personal physician must understand the work setting, including expectations, specific job duties, and opportunities for task modification, to assess disability. Most clinicians not trained in disability management tend to view a clinical encounter as a discrete episode of care rather than as part of the spectrum of recovery that should include a focus on early work activity as therapeutic.

Many studies have validated the importance of the patient-provider interaction in expectation setting and attitudes regarding disability and recovery. Personal physicians frequently fail to appreciate the impact of lost work time on psychological well being and productivity, which are issues of concern for patients and their employers.

In treating occupational injuries, providers need to understand the injury benefit system and appreciate the role that incentives play in outcomes. Treatment for work-related injuries is more costly and less effective than for the same problem under group health insurance. The disparity is greatest for conditions that tend to be subjective and involve more discretionary treatment, such as low back strain.[10] It is also known that as the prevalence of litigation increases, the return to work rate drops significantly.

Ongoing communication between the treating provider and the employer's medical representative is crucial to successful management of lost work time and functional restoration. It provides the opportunity to identify relevant nonmedical factors affecting recovery and ensures linkage with resources to address them, such as mental health services or internal management processes. It also facilitates cooperation in the return to work process.

Since the gradual institution of managed care for workers' compensation using guidelines for common injuries published by ACOEM and many states, costs have declined with improvement in quality and outcomes. Innovative health systems and providers in the workers' compensation or disability management market will recognize the opportunity to partner with and target employers' needs. As employers become more sophisticated purchasers, they appreciate that inadequate products may offer savings per visit but increase overall costs and litigation rates.

DISEASE MANAGEMENT

High-quality and cost-effective management of health care requires matching the right level, site, and timing of care with specific patient needs. Chronic disease management can be an extremely effective approach to tertiary prevention, resulting in better overall care and more efficient use of resources. For disease management to be successful, an integrated delivery system, a comprehensive disease-specific knowledge base, data systems capable of analyzing practice patterns, and continuous quality improvement methods are essential components.[7] Physician roles need to be redefined, and teamwork must be a reality. An infrastructure that can identify and manage populations and subpopulations is also needed.

Disease management focuses on early intervention to prevent and control disease using standardized care and prevention techniques, once the hallmark of public health. The intent is to identify at-risk populations prospectively and ensure continuity of care. Programs seek to minimize acute episodes, maximize information available to providers, and improve the ability of patients to participate in their own care. Success is critically dependent on implementation. Bringing care to the worksite and aggressive case management can have more impact than the latest drugs.[6,12]

The most appropriate diseases for such programs are high-prevalence, high-cost conditions that demonstrate a combination of chronicity, complexity, and seriousness of complications. Good treatment must be available that affects outcomes. Illnesses associated with a wide variation in practice patterns or low patient compliance are particularly amenable to disease management protocols if developed with rigorous evidence-based standards. Attention to behavioral health needs is critical because of the high likelihood of psychological implications of chronic disease.

Large employers represent an enormous potential source of revenue for any disease management service. The greatest competitive advantage in attracting their business comes from a thorough understanding of needs and a willingness to tailor any program to their requirements. Customization requires knowledge of culture, organizational structure, and employee demographics and dispersion. As employers tend to concentrate on short-term results, the initial focus should be on diseases for which benefits can be demonstrated fairly quickly with a decrease in emergency room and provider visits.

However, several concerns about disease management programs have been raised. For example, single disease solutions are not useful for most patients with comorbidities. Outcome assessment is challenging because it requires tracking clinical and functional data over time from a number of nonintegrated sources. Some physicians feel that continuity of care may be hindered. Changes in treatment settings may make comparisons difficult. When disease management costs are assessed from an economic standpoint, the program's expense must reflect all costs from identification of the target group, through recruitment and delivery.[6,7]

Risk Control: Compliance

Creativity is not at the heart of risk-control initiatives related to compliance. Rather, conformance with requirements and proper documentation are key. While fitness for duty and placement determinations are as relevant to productivity as compliance, addressing these services here highlights the need to attend to federal regulations and laws such as the ADA.

FITNESS FOR DUTY AND THE ADA

Preplacement and fitness for duty exams must focus on maximizing human potential, both from the perspective of legal mandates and productivity concerns. Ensuring that workers are physically and psychologically capable of safely performing job tasks under the required conditions, whether in conformance with regulations, company policy, or good health and safety practice, must be attended to with appropriate care. Corporate management in an operational setting, particularly if genuine safety issues exist, may be as concerned with the thoroughness of the process used in decision-making and the method of communication as with the result.

Providers must be certain they not only understand any applicable regulatory requirements but also have current job descriptions that define functional requirements and the specific work environment. Employers who are required to abide by federal regulations of the Department of Transportation regarding commercial drivers and locomotive engineers would be well advised to contract for services with providers who are well versed in the regulations. The Federal Aviation Administration already requires certification of examiners for pilots. While most examiners would certainly consider the potential implications of insulin-dependent diabetes or seizure disorders in certain work environments, they may fail to inquire about more subtle medical problems that could interfere with the safe performance of certain job tasks. For example, employees working irregular, extended, or unpredictable shifts must be evaluated for symptoms of sleep apnea and other sleep disorders that impair alertness. Examinees in any safety-sensitive position should be questioned regarding use of over-the-counter medications such as sedating antihistamines.[18]

Although the provider delineates functional limitations, the employer makes the decision regarding employability. Such determinations are based on several factors other than the extent of impairment. Since passage of the ADA, it is incumbent upon the employer to attempt reasonable accommodation, but the ability to do so may be hampered by business realities such as collective bargaining agreements.

MEDICAL SURVEILLANCE

External providers who perform services for employers required to conform with OSHA regulations should review the company's entire program. It is important to interface with individuals responsible for the industrial hygiene function at the company and ascertain that such persons have adequate knowledge of exposure monitoring and control and have properly identified individuals for surveillance. Accurate collection and integration of industrial hygiene data with surveillance data is needed for program integrity. It is also important to ensure that training requirements are being met. By reviewing the totality of the program, the provider proactively enhances the quality of the service component.

Drug and Alcohol Testing

It is becoming more common for companies performing drug and alcohol testing to use a combination of internal and vendored resources to perform different aspects of their program. As such, external occupational health providers may be asked to oversee the specimen collection with or without performing the services of a medical review officer. Attention must be paid to compliance with the specific and stringent standards of government agencies, the use of the proper forms and procedural steps, and the flow of paperwork among the collecting agent, medical review officer, and employer. Occasionally, employees may need to be evaluated for the inability to provide a urine or breath specimen. Employers who choose to perform substance abuse testing under company policy would be well advised to follow Department of Transportation procedures, because this will enhance the likelihood that such testing will withstand legal and labor relations challenges.

In any case, care must be taken to ensure that no inappropriate release of confidential information occurs. It is imperative that providers obtain and follow all procedures as delineated by the Department of Health and Human Services.[27]

CONCLUSION

Much has been said and written about the detrimental impact of managed care on the medical profession and its patients. However, much good is derived from changes that force the health care system to be more efficient, convenient, and affordable. Enhanced focus on health rather than disease and improved coordination of care cannot help but be positive for patients. For occupational health providers, managed care can provide new avenues for promoting their unique expertise in the management of individuals, populations, and communities.[19]

Critical success factors in employer-provider partnerships to manage risks to "human assets" and enhance workforce health and productivity include alignment with specific business needs, a focus on prevention, and teamwork across disciplines to create service continuity. In human assets risk management, as in population health management, the goal is to move the risk continuum toward prevention. OEM has the ability and opportunity to lead the way by facilitating creation of integrated delivery systems for prevention, occupational health services, and acute and chronic care. Success will accrue to occupational health providers able to proactively assess risks to employee-patients for employer-purchasers and match intervention strategy to need through effective, efficient, high-quality programs and services.

REFERENCES

1. Brady W, Bass J, Moser R Jr, Anstadt G: Defining total corporate health and safety costs—Significance and impact. J Occup Environ Med 39:224–231, 1997.
2. Coile R: The five stages of managed care: Strategies for physicians in health care's market revolution. Physician Executive 23:27–31, 1997.
3. Coleman D: Will direct contractors be the cost and quality champs? Business and Health 15(3):38–42, March 1997.
4. Conti DJ, Burton WN: The economic impact of depression in a workplace. J Occup Med 36:983–988, 1994.
5. Coulter C: Integrated delivery systems and direct contracting: Three major challenges. Am J Integrated HealthCare 1(1):19–21, 1997.
6. Eichert JH, Patterson RB: Factors affecting the success of disease management. New Med 1:77–80, 1997.
7. Ellrodt G, Cook DJ, Lee J, et al: Evidence-based disease management. JAMA 278:1687–1691, 1997.
8. Emmett EA: What is the strategic value of occupational and environmental medicine. J Occup Environ Med 38:1124–1134, 1996.

9. Friend DB, Menefee JA: Positioning a healthcare organization using value purchasing information. In Miller KA, Miller EK (eds): Making Sense of Managed Care. Vol 2. San Francisco, Jossey-Bass, 1997, pp 97–127.

10. Harris JS: Development, use, and evaluation of clinical practice guidelines. J Occup Environ Med 39:23–34, 1997.

11. Hashimoto DM: The future role of managed care and capitation in workers' compensation. Am J Law Med 22:233–261, 1996.

12. Hensley S: New terrain—Physicians explore disease management as a way to improve care while cutting costs. Modern Physician 1(3):10–16, August 1997.

13. Hickey M, Gunter M: From managing access to healthcare to managing risk. New Med 1:261–267, 1997.

14. Kauer K, Berkowitz E: Strategic positioning: Part I. Sources of value under managed care. Physician Executive 23:6–12, 1997.

15. Kindig D: How do you define the health of populations? Physician Executive 23:6–11, 1997.

16. Kindig D: Managing population health. Physician Executive 23:34–39, 1997.

17. Loeppke RR: Prevention and managed care: The next generation. J Occup Environ Med 37:558–562, 1995.

18. McCunney RJ, Anstadt G, Burton WA: The competitive advantage of a healthy workforce. J Occup Environ Med 39:611–612, 1997.

19. Miller KA: Managing health: Determinants of clinical practice. In Miller KA, Miller EK (eds): Making Sense of Managed Care. Vol 2. San Francisco, Jossey-Bass, 1997, pp 184–185.

20. Moench L: Demand Management: The New Business in Patient Communication. Boca Raton, FL, CPSNET, 1997.

21. Narvell R: Personal communication. (Human Performance Investigator, National Transportation Safety Board) 1997.

22. Perry D: Patient patients no more: Aging baby boomers and healthcare. In Miller KA, Miller EK (eds): Making Sense of Managed Care. Vol 2. San Francisco, Jossey-Bass, 1997, pp 9–20.

23. Peterson G, Todd W: The evolution of disease management into population-based health management. New Med 1:82–86, 1997.

24. Service R: Downsizing and disability go together. Business and Health 15(7), January 1997.

25. Sokdov JJ: The drivers of health care. Physician Executive 23:6, 1997.

26. Spengler D: Industrial Low Back Injury: Perspectives of an Orthopedist (Gehrman Lecture). Nashville, TN, American Occupational Health Conference, October 1997.

27. Substance Abuse and Mental Health Services Administration: Medical Review Officer Manual for Federal Workplace Drug Testing Programs. Technical Report No. 97-3164. Washington, DC, Department of Health and Human Services, 1997.

28. Treacy M, Wiersema F: The Discipline of Market Leaders. Reading, MA, Addison-Wesley, 1997.

ALLARD E. DEMBE, ScD
KATHLEEN M. REST, PhD
LINDA RUDOLPH, MD, MPH

THE ROLE OF PREVENTION IN WORKERS' COMPENSATION MANAGED CARE ARRANGEMENTS

From the University of
   Massachusetts Medical School
Worcester, Massachusetts (AED,
   KMR)
   and
California Division of Workers'
   Compensation
San Francisco, California (LR)

Reprint requests to:
Allard E. Dembe, ScD
Assistant Professor
Occupational and Environmental
   Health Program
Department of Family Medicine
   and Community Health
University of Massachusetts
   Medical School
55 Lake Avenue North
Worcester, MA 01655

Prevention has always been considered to be one of the fundamental components of occupational medicine practice. Indeed, renowned occupational physicians such as Alice Hamilton, Harriet Hardy, and Irving Selikoff are perhaps best known for their impassioned efforts to persuade employers and the government to establish measures protecting workers against lead, beryllium, asbestos, and other suspected health hazards. The commitment to the primacy of prevention has stemmed from physicians' special awareness of clinical pathologies observed in groups of workers and their understanding of disease mechanisms related to conditions in the working environment.

Traditional doctrines of occupational health protection emphasize three approaches to prevention: primary, secondary, and tertiary. Primary prevention seeks to eliminate or decrease risk of injury and illness through the recognition and control of workplace hazards; secondary prevention embraces the detection of disease in early stages—for example, through surveillance and medical testing—to intervene and limit its adverse effects; and tertiary prevention includes therapy, rehabilitation, job accommodation, and other efforts aimed at minimizing disability and hastening recovery from occupational disorders.

The medical contribution to the prevention of work-related disability is part of a broader multidisciplinary struggle to achieve occupational safety and health involving employers, workers, public health officials, safety engineers, industrial hygienists, and government regulators. Most of these efforts, including exposure assessment, hazard abatement, ergonomics and job analysis, safety training, regulatory compliance, and the development of workplace safety and health programs, are focused appropriately on conditions existing in places of employment. Because the principal locus of prevention efforts is the workplace, employers are commonly considered to be chiefly responsible for preventing workplace injuries and illnesses. Indeed, the Occupational Safety and Health Act explicitly holds the employer solely accountable for compliance with federal safety regulations and standards. While acknowledging the employer's central role in prevention activities, it is widely recognized that the most effective prevention programs are those that involve workers, labor unions, insurers, safety professionals, and regulators working in concert with employers to address prevention not only at the worksite but through clinical practice, epidemiologic analysis, laboratory studies, engineering innovations, and legal and regulatory mechanisms.

Physicians, nurses, physical therapists, and other health care professionals potentially can play a critical role in this effort. Careful history taking can help identify occupational risk factors and make patients aware of the need to take specific precautions. Early detection of job-related maladies can help alert employers and public health officials to the need for investigation and control of workplace hazards, but only if medical providers effectively convey relevant information to the appropriate groups. Medical screening and surveillance may be important in identifying prevention requirements for affected individuals and populations. Analysis of medical records can help reveal trends that may help identify hazards and prioritize accident prevention activities. The provision of first-aid, emergency treatment, and referral to appropriate specialists and allied health providers can minimize work disability. Education for both employers and workers about occupational risks is an essential element in the initial prevention of workplace injuries and illnesses.

To perform these functions most effectively, the health care professional must be familiar with conditions in the patient's place of employment and the physical and sensory demands of specific jobs. Generally, this will require the medical provider to become familiar with the workplace by making onsite visits, reviewing written task analyses and job descriptions, viewing videotapes of work processes, and talking with management, supervisors, workers, and other knowledgeable individuals. Personal knowledge of work requirements is particularly important when assessing levels of work impairment, designing an appropriate rehabilitation plan, and determining the patient's readiness for return to work.

While these principles of effective medical involvement in prevention efforts have long been recognized, implementing them in daily practice is a continual challenge. Many workers receive care from clinicians who may have received little, if any, training in the fundamental aspects of occupational health or are unfamiliar with the hierarchy of approaches for preventing and controlling workplace injury and illness.[17] Other providers may not have the time or interest to become involved in prevention activities, often neglecting to perform even the most fundamental component of occupational health care—the taking of a thorough work history. To address prevention needs most effectively, health care providers must be willing to adopt an orientation that focuses on the health of populations of workers as well as the clinical needs of individual patients. This requires attention to and communication with the workplace.

A problem that has plagued efforts to incorporate prevention approaches into occupational health care is the wide variety and number of different clinicians who may provide medical services to injured (or at-risk) workers. In the traditional independent fee-for-service setting, workers had considerable discretion to select providers of their choice for treatment of work-related conditions. While this arrangement maximized patient choice and provided optimal flexibility, it also meant that the clinicians rendering care were often not familiar with occupational conditions, specific worksites, or the range of available prevention options.

Since 1990, an increasing amount of medical care for occupational conditions has migrated to managed care plans, due primarily to the dramatic rise in medical care costs in the workers' compensation system during the 1980s and early 1990s. Adapting techniques that have been successfully applied in the general (noncompensation) health care environment, these managed care plans generally incorporate intensified control measures over costs and utilization of medical services, including discounted fee schedules, bill repricing, utilization review, treatment protocols, and case management. They also typically use a preselected group of health care providers—who may or may not be directly employed by the managed care plan—to provide medical services for the plan's enrollees.

As care for occupational conditions has moved into managed care plans, different perspectives have emerged about the potential for these plans to assume a prevention orientation and to strengthen the role of medical providers in the prevention of work-related conditions. Proponents of managed care have suggested that enhanced control over the delivery of services and the standardization of training and practice patterns in managed care plans hold promise for more routinely and effectively addressing the preventive aspects of care.[10,11,13,36,48] Skeptics have expressed concern that the emphasis on restricting costs and service utilization found in many managed care plans could make it more difficult for health care providers to engage in prevention programs or gain familiarity about workplace conditions.[3,7] This is particularly true, they argue, when payment for medical services is on a prepaid per capita—capitated—basis or when the fee structure does not allow for specific revenues to be derived from prevention activities unrelated to ordinary clinical procedures.[7,34]

To help sort out these issues, it will be helpful to take a closer look at various models for incorporating prevention into managed care arrangements, drawing upon experiences in both the general health care and workers' compensation setting.

PREVENTION IN GROUP HEALTH MANAGED CARE PLANS

In the group health arena, preventive services have been a part of managed care plans for a long time, especially in older health maintenance organizations (HMOs) such as Kaiser-Permanente and Harvard Community Health Plan. Some of these preventive services focus on primary prevention, such as vaccination and prenatal care, while others fall within the realm of secondary prevention, such as mammography, routine cholesterol testing, and screening for cervical cancer. Some managed care arrangements have extended their prevention services beyond individual patients to include community-wide prevention and health promotion activities. For example, United Health Plan, a Los Angeles HMO, recently launched two community-based infant health initiatives consisting of a breast-feeding program and an educational intervention aimed at decreasing infant mortality among African Americans.[40]

To help purchasers and consumers assess the quality of care provided under managed care plans, several accreditation programs and performance measurement systems have been developed in the group health arena. The best known performance-measurement instrument for evaluating the quality of care provided by

HMOs is the Health Plan Employer Data and Information Set (HEDIS) developed under the sponsorship of the National Committee for Quality Assurance. Interestingly, of the nine indicators of quality-of-care in version 2.5 of HEDIS, seven involve preventive services: decreasing the incidence of low birth-weight infants, immunization, mammography, cervical cancer screening, cholesterol testing, prenatal care, and retina examinations for persons with diabetes.[40] Many managed care plans are developing internal information systems that automatically prompt clinicians to consider delivering preventive services under certain conditions.

There is substantial evidence documenting the efficacy and cost-effectiveness of prevention efforts in the general health care setting.[14,25,34] The most successful prevention interventions have been those aimed at behavioral and environmental factors, such as smoking cessation, reducing alcohol consumption, childhood immunizations, and control of environmental lead poisoning. In a 1989 report, the U.S. Preventive Services Task Force concluded that counseling and education services are among the most effective interventions that clinicians can use to promote health and prevent disease.[43] According to several recent research studies, managed care organizations are more likely to provide such preventive services than are traditional indemnity plans.[22,32,33]

A preventive approach that has received considerable attention lately is the use of worksite-based health promotion programs. Typically sponsored by employers and delivered at the workplace by trained professionals, these programs involve educational interventions, health screenings, referrals, and other strategies to modify the behavior of employees and their families in the areas of exercise, nutrition, stress management, substance abuse, weight control, hypertension, seatbelt use, prevention of AIDS, and smoking.[42] A growing number of worksite-based health promotion programs are being offered through employer contracts with managed care organizations.[27,38] Several investigations have found evidence suggesting that such worksite-based health promotion programs can improve health outcomes and reduce medical expenditures.[27,46] However, worksite health promotion programs generally concentrate on individual behavioral and lifestyle factors rather than on improvements in working conditions or remediation of job hazards. Such employer-sponsored programs run the risk, therefore, of diverting attention and resources from the more substantive primary prevention efforts favored in occupational safety and health programs.

Other authorities have pointed to case management as the foundation of an effective prevention effort in managed care settings. Case management is a process of coordinating a patient's total health services to ensure that optimal, high-quality care is delivered cost effectively.[2] It is usually provided by a nurse, social worker, or other health care worker on behalf of the insurer, employer, or health care organization. The case management process typically involves identifying appropriate clinicians and service providers; improving communications among providers, payors, employers, and patients; ensuring continuity of care; facilitating administrative filings, insurance claims, and payments; and educating providers, patients, and their families about important aspects of a case. Little research has been conducted on the effects of case management, but preliminary results from a few studies have suggested that this type of intervention can achieve cost savings and improve the quality of care, especially for patients with catastrophic and psychiatric conditions.[34] Based on a review of current case management practices, the Washington Business Group on Health concluded that case managers are ideally placed and trained to have a positive influence on both the primary prevention of illness and injury and secondary prevention to reduce the risk of subsequent incapacity.[45]

Although case management, health promotion programs, and other managed care techniques show promise of enhancing prevention efforts, some commentators have expressed concern that the payment and reimbursement mechanisms used in many health insurance plans can provide a disincentive for health care providers to offer preventive services.[13,26] Many traditional fee-for-service reimbursement systems, as well as the capitated and case-rate payment plans emerging in new managed care arrangements, encourage curative treatments but fail to provide commensurate remuneration for preventive care.[13] In addition, there is clear evidence that patient cost-sharing, a prominent cost-containment technique employed in many health plans, reduces the use of preventive services, especially among poorer clients.[34,44]

Other potential barriers to the optimal provision of preventive services include the significant turnover of enrollees in managed care plans and the short contract periods commonly established between purchasers (e.g., insurers or employers) and managed care provider organizations.[14] Many prevention programs, particularly wellness programs involving smoking cessation, exercise, and improved nutrition, are designed to achieve long-term health objectives. However, managed care plans striving to achieve immediate savings for purchasers might be interested only in interventions that are likely to result in cost and utilization reductions within an existing contract period.

PREVENTION IN WORKERS' COMPENSATION MANAGED CARE PLANS

Incorporating prevention services into the medical care arrangements for patients with workplace injuries and illnesses may be particularly appropriate because (1) medical care for occupationally induced conditions is generally covered under workers' compensation insurance purchased or supplied by the employer, who has primary responsibility for workplace accident prevention; (2) since workers' compensation insurance covers both medical and wage-loss (indemnity) benefits, preventive programs aimed at reducing medical costs can also potentially lead to indemnity savings; (3) for workers' compensation cases, primary care, adjunctive therapy, rehabilitation, and preventive services must be closely coordinated to achieve optimal results; and (4) there is a longstanding tradition of using loss prevention experts, safety engineers, and industrial hygienists as part of comprehensive occupational safety and health programs.

Despite these obvious advantages, workers' compensation managed care plans have been slow to adopt prevention services, and there are few examples of effective coordination between managed care delivery systems and workplace prevention efforts. One reason is the predominance of fee-for-service payment plans in workers' compensation medical care that do not provide financial incentives for clinicians to engage in prevention. Unlike the general health arena, where many preventive services are offered in clinical settings, most occupational injury and illness prevention activities take place in the workplace. In addition, many workers' compensation managed care plans have concentrated on short-term cost-containment strategies rather than long-range prevention programs that require initial outlays but may not result in immediate medical savings.

Nevertheless, there is a potential for workers' compensation managed care systems to contribute positively to comprehensive safety and health programs aimed at preventing workplace injuries and illnesses and minimizing work disability. For example, managed care organizations can retain safety professionals and industrial hygienists to provide workplace exposure assessment, suggestions for hazard abatement, and employee safety training. Many managed care plans could be easily equipped and staffed to provide medical screening and surveillance programs for local employers. Improved communications could be established between medical plan providers and workplace safety officials to help clinicians understand the potential causes of patients' illnesses and injuries and to help employers better understand injured workers' functional limitations and readiness to resume job responsibilities. At the least, managed care plans can establish protocols that standardize expectations for the doctor-patient encounter, e.g., including a thorough work history to identify areas of potential medical concern. A minimal level of specialized education and training in the principles of occupational medicine and workers' compensation could be required by managed care plans for its primary care practitioners.

Authorities have suggested that case management has a potentially important role in linking managed care services and workplace prevention.[6,20,29,30,37] Ideally, the case manager, working on behalf of the employer, insurer, or managed care organization, helps to ensure that primary preventive services are furnished, helps to design and implement effective secondary and tertiary prevention strategies to minimize work disability, performs worksite job assessment and prevention surveys, coordinates health promotion activities, and provides appropriate referrals to employee assistance programs or other required services. Case management that concentrates solely on minimizing costs and limiting the utilization of services should be avoided. To be most effective, the case manager needs to act as a patient advocate, helping injured workers navigate the health care and workers' compensation systems to obtain the best possible care. Table 1 provides examples of prevention services that can be provided or coordinated by a nurse case manager.

The Washington Business Group of Health has drawn attention to "disability case management" as a distinctive form of case management intended to minimize work absences and promote a speedy return to productive employment for all persons with disabilities irrespective of whether the patient's incapacity is the result of a

TABLE 1.   Examples of Prevention Services Offered by Occupational Nurse Case Managers

Primary Prevention	Secondary Prevention	Tertiary Prevention
Provides education and counseling about accident prevention and workers' compensation	Ensures effective medical surveillance program	Maintains communications with injured worker
Provides involvement in worksite hazard identification and control efforts	Provides early intervention on serious cases	Helps develop appropriate return to work plan
Helps design and implement postoffer medical examination and screening	Coordinates care and expedites referrals to appropriate providers	Coordinates rehabilitation services
Facilitates suitable health promotion efforts	Facilitates communications among employer, insurer, clinicians, and injured worker	Assesses options for alternate and light-duty assignments
Ensures that job demands are evaluated and documented	Identifies community resources and support systems	Helps plan and design job accommodations
Identifies appropriate medical care providers	Reviews appropriateness of care	Facilitates smooth claims handling and payment
Supports labor-management communication about prevention needs	Serves as patient advocate	Evaluates outcomes

work-related condition or nonoccupational ailment.[45] For organizations pursuing "integrated disability management" spanning work-related and nonoccupational conditions, the case manager plays a vital role in orchestrating preventive services and benefits provided under workers' compensation and short-term and long-term disability insurance programs.[29,30]

Significant potential for incorporating prevention services into workers' compensation managed care plans exists in organizations that combine insurance and medical management functions. For example, many major workers' compensation insurers and third-party administrators, such as Travelers, Liberty Mutual, and Crawford & Co., have established active functions in both managed health care and workplace loss prevention. Likewise, some health care systems, including Kaiser-Permanente, Harvard-Pilgrim, and Tufts, have formed units devoted to worksite accident prevention and workers' compensation insurance. In theory, bringing together these disparate functions under one organizational structure holds promise for better harmonizing preventive activities with the delivery and management of medical services for injured workers.

Whether this promise is realized may be determined, in part, by how financial incentives are structured. Some commentators have argued that capitated managed care introduces new incentives for providers to engage in prevention approaches since a per-capita payment system shifts the financial risk for the health of an enrolled population to the provider. Ronald Loeppke of Phycor, Inc. has described a managed care plan in which workers were provided enhanced benefits, providers were offered a nondiscounted fee schedule, and the employer was guaranteed no annual increase in per-employee health care during the 1-year duration of the plan, with the proviso that any cost savings (compared to the previous year) would be shared equally among all three groups.[19] Aligning financial incentives in this way, argues Loeppke, motivates all parties to strengthen accident prevention measures and improve the quality of care, thereby ultimately lowering costs. In structuring such capitated managed care plans, however, precautions must be taken to ensure that the financial incentives actually promote intensified efforts to prevent accidents rather than encourage underreporting of cases or inappropriate shifting of occupational cases to the group health sector.[28]

In addition to these private-market initiatives, state regulators have tried to increase the emphasis on prevention in workers' compensation managed care plans. Approximately 23 states, including California, Florida, Oregon, and New York, have adopted requirements for the certification of workers' compensation managed care organizations.[9] Several of these contain explicit provisions regarding preventive services. California's, for instance, specifies that any certified workers' compensation health care organization must provide a variety of prevention services, including employee education, medical screening, and prompt reporting of sentinel health events (see Appendix).[5]

In the general health field, accreditation organizations and consumer advocacy groups have been active in promoting the establishment of requirements for preventive services in managed care organizations, but no similar movement has developed in the occupational health arena. Standards for the formation and operation of workers' compensation provider networks adopted in 1997 by the American Accreditation Health Care Commission do not address safety or accident prevention.[1] The commission's project to develop performance measures for workers' compensation managed care organizations, launched in 1998, will tackle this issue. Meanwhile, the National Association of Insurance Commissioners is supporting a study examining whether specific language in contracts between purchasers of workers' compensation managed health care and managed care organizations can assure the delivery of high-quality care, including preventive services, by the provider organization.[24] Preliminary indications from this study suggest that few managed care contracts currently contain such provisions.[8]

Overall, workers' compensation managed care organizations are increasingly offering services traditionally provided by insurers and third-party administrators,[16] but the provision of safety and prevention-oriented services remains limited. In the National Trends Survey of workers' compensation health care delivery programs completed by the University of Washington in 1997, 15 of 26 respondents (58%) indicated that their programs address injury prevention.[35] The most commonly reported prevention services included onsite safety inspections, tracking of injury/illness trends to identify concerns, onsite safety training, general health promotion programs, prevention education for employees, and employer incentives to develop safety programs. However, in general, respondents characterized prevention activities as less effective than other managed care services offered by their organizations.

Similar levels of prevention activity have been reported in other surveys of workers' compensation managed care. The 1996 survey of HMO managed workers' compensation strategies conducted by Milliman & Robertson, Inc. found that 61% of workers' compensation HMOs provide loss prevention and safety consultation services, up from 19% in 1995 and 13% in 1994.[12] A survey conducted by the California State Division of Workers' Compensation in 1996 found that 65% of workers' compensation health care provider organizations in California offer prevention programs.[31]

RECENTLY ESTABLISHED PREVENTION PROGRAMS

A brief description of some recently established prevention programs will help illustrate the range of preventive services being offered through workers' compensation managed care plans.

Johns Hopkins Health System

An internal managed care arrangement was initially established at Johns Hopkins Hospital in Baltimore in 1992 to cover the hospital's own employees, and it was eventually extended to cover the entire Johns Hopkins Health System and Johns Hopkins University workforce.[4,21] The managed care program consists of a preferred provider network, the use of medical management guidelines, return-to-work protocols, and comprehensive nurse case management. Part of the case manager's function is to identify serious cases that may be caused by unfavorable ergonomic conditions. For those cases, a full ergonomics assessment and hazard abatement survey is conducted by an industrial hygienist trained in biomechanics. In addition, a return-to-work plan is developed emphasizing the identification of modified duty and job accommodation opportunities to bring injured workers back to productive employment. Experiences during the first 3 years of Johns Hopkins' managed care arrangement have yielded positive results, with a 23% reduction in per-capita losses and fewer days of work disability.[4]

Kaiser Northwest

In 1991, the Northwest Division of Kaiser-Permanente established a state-certified managed care organization in Oregon called Kaiser-on-the-Job (KOTJ).[10,11] KOTJ uses a closed-panel HMO provider organization structured around dispersed occupational health clinics staffed with board-certified occupational medicine physicians. KOTJ is distinctive in that it contains various strategies to prevent workplace injury and illness. It features a proactive case management approach in which a nurse/physician case management team is assigned to work with an employer to review return to work programs and identify opportunities for prevention. The team completes a high-level safety hazard review, examines high-risk areas, and collects job descriptions for analyzing regular and modified duty positions. Preventive services offered by KOTJ, but not within their standard managed care contract, include direction of onsite medical services and first-aid, immunizations, biological monitoring and medical surveillance, preplacement examinations, periodic respirator and emergency responder examinations, and worksite health promotion. Various other prevention services are offered by KOTJ, including hearing conservation programs, employee education sessions, ergonomics interventions, and driver qualification tests.

Federal Office of Workers' Compensation Programs

In 1998, the Office of Worker's Compensation Programs of the U.S. Department of Labor will launch a pilot managed care program at several federal agencies for government workers covered under the Federal Employees' Compensation Act.[41] The managed care program will feature an intensive form of nurse case management with structured delivery protocols and specialized training in ergonomics risk assessment. The nurse case managers participating in the pilot program will be expected to evaluate ergonomic stressors that may be contributing to a patient's disability and provide appropriate recommendations to agency management for workplace changes that will reduce the exposure and facilitate the patient's return to the job.

Phycor

The Physicians Corporation (Phycor) is a physician management organization that has set up a unique managed care model. This model builds on the standard elements of the medical and utilization management found in many "gatekeeper" systems and adds an increased emphasis on prevention and health risk management, thereby constituting what Phycor calls a "healthkeeper" system.[19] It involves a hierarchy of occupational health services that focus on prevention, including case management, workplace health promotion, industrial hygiene, safety, and health education. As part of this managed care plan, Phycor physicians perform a prospective health risk assessment that identifies particular individuals for special prevention, screening, and early diagnosis protocols.

UNITE

The Union of Needletrades, Industrial and Textile Employees (UNITE) operates a comprehensive health center to provide primary care and occupational health services to 50,000 garment workers in New York City.[15] The UNITE health center employs an innovative model featuring a strong structural linkage between clinical care and prevention of workplace disorders. Health status questionnaires, occupational histories, and clinical examinations are used to identify cases that might be indicative of workplace problems. For every suspected occupational condition, a health and safety specialist acts as case manager, coordinating worker and employer education as well as workplace hazard abatement focused on exposure assessment and prevention. In this way, every case of occupational disease becomes a potential sentinel health event stimulating investigation at the worksite and follow-up aimed at hazard remediation.

THE FUTURE OF PREVENTION IN WORKERS' COMPENSATION MANAGED CARE

While the aforementioned examples display the promise of incorporating prevention into managed health care arrangements, the use of such techniques by most managed care organizations remains limited. The need to focus most primary prevention activities at the worksite introduces complexities for managed care plans regarding how to deliver and financially support such services. Managed care organizations may conclude that the market for primary prevention services is already saturated by the loss-control services offered through insurers, brokers, third-party administrators, private vendors, government inspectors, and employers' in-house safety and health staff. To the extent that health care plans incorporate preventive services, it may be more feasible to focus on secondary and tertiary prevention activities that are more clearly associated with the clinical process, such as medical screening and surveillance, preplacement and return to work assessments, early detection programs, and the provision of appropriate medical and rehabilitative care. Other functions that seem to be particularly appropriate for medical care organizations include records analysis to spot sentinel events and trends, employee health education, and programs to ensure the continuity and coordination of primary care and adjunctive therapies.

To contribute effectively in the prevention effort, managed care organizations must have the in-house expertise to understand issues of safety, ergonomics, industrial hygiene, toxicology, and an employer's regulatory requirements. In addition, to effectively use the medical data it generates or obtains from the workplace for prevention purposes, the care organization must build epidemiologic and risk analysis capability into its data system. Board-certified occupational medicine physicians and trained occupational health nurses can supply much of the needed expertise, and managed care organizations will need to rely heavily on these professionals to develop and manage their occupational medicine and workers' compensation services. None of these preventive services will be successful unless clear lines of communication are established between clinicians and those responsible for safety and health at the worksite.

The motivation for managed care plans to incorporate preventive services will need to come from a variety of sources. Certainly, a large part of their inducement will derive from basic market and competitive forces. However, it will also be necessary for state regulators to continue developing specific expectations for prevention services as part of their managed care organization certification standards, for accreditation agencies to include prevention activities as part of their performance measurement and quality assessment criteria, and for purchasers to demand that provisions for the delivery of preventive services be built into contract language with managed care organizations.

In the best scenario, the workplace prevention efforts undertaken by employers and safety consultants will be closely coordinated and meshed with the medical care and rehabilitation services offered by health care providers. One of the potential advantages of providing workers' compensation medical care within a managed care plan is the ability to consolidate medical services for a significant proportion of an employer's workforce within a single organizational and data collection system. To derive the full benefit of this arrangement, information about the health and medical

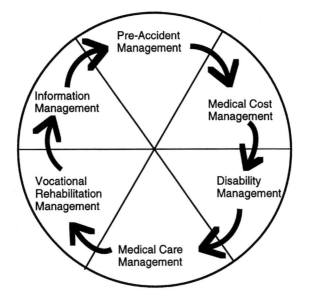

FIGURE 1.   Pre-accident management in a continuous feedback loop.

care provided to that population needs to be provided back to the employer to help guide their prevention efforts. If done properly, this approach can result in a continuous feedback loop that would establish what Liberty Mutual Insurance Company has called a "continuum of care" (Fig. 1).[18]

The migration of workers' compensation health care into managed care environments provides opportunities for devising new financial incentives and payment plans to provide an impetus for physicians and other medical providers to become more involved in the prevention effort. Certainly, little progress will be made in this area unless employers and managed care organizations can realize a meaningful financial return from the investment of time and resources needed to provide the service. This may require changing traditional purchasing practices, e.g., establishing multiyear rather than 1-year policies and health care contracts, as is now being explored by employers associated with the Pacific Business Group on Health.[32]

In the general health arena, managed care organizations have the potential to use nonoccupational health data to uncover potentially work-related conditions among employed patients. Several studies have demonstrated that a significant proportion of nonoccupational disorders show evidence of actually having been caused by workplace exposures.[23,47] For example, in a prospective cohort study of 79,204 members of an HMO, Milton et al. found that 21% of asthma cases were probably attributable to occupational exposure although none of them had been diagnosed by the HMO provider as occupational asthma or reported as workers' compensation cases to the state surveillance system or insurance carrier.[23] As employers increasingly contract with managed care organizations to provide both workers' compensation and nonoccupational health care for a workforce, there may be expanded potential for using general health care records to identify suspected occupational risks and initiate appropriate preventive action at an early stage.

While acknowledging the capacity for managed care arrangements to incorporate useful preventive services into occupational medical care, it also should be

pointed out that managed care plans, because of their inherent emphasis on cost reduction and utilization control, can potentially jeopardize workers' health by inappropriately restricting access to services, limiting the choice of providers, and
pressuring injured workers to return to work prematurely. If restrictive measures end
up compromising workers' trust in the medical system, preventive measures furnished by the health plan will likely prove to be ineffectual. Employers also may be
skeptical about paying for managed care plans to supply preventive services that
might be available less expensively through insurers, government agencies, or in-
house staff, unless the health plan can document the efficacy and cost-effectiveness
of the programs.

If workers' compensation is the last frontier for managed care,[38] prevention is
the last component to find its place into managed care arrangements for injured
workers. This chapter has described potential models and strategies for integrating
prevention into managed care plans; presented examples of managed care arrangements that have incorporated prevention into their occupational medicine services;
and offered suggestions to guide future efforts in this area. As new workers' compensation managed care plans continue to emerge, we hope that they take advantage
of the opportunities for linking medical care with the prevention of workplace injuries, illnesses, and disabilities in a way that is sensitive to the concerns of injured
workers and that facilitates research to assess the impact of these prevention activities on costs, outcomes, and the quality of care.

APPENDIX

State of California Certification Standards for Health Care Organizations
State Code of Regulations, Title 8

§9776. Workplace Safety and Health

(a) The HCO must maintain the capacity to work cooperatively and in conjunction with claims administrators, employers, and employees to promote workplace health and safety and to detect workplace exposures and hazards, including:

(1) education of employees and employers on health and medical aspects of workplace health and safety issues;

(2) consultation on employee medical screening for early detection of occupational disease, and assessment of workplace risk factors.

(b) An HCO shall include in contracts with claims administrators a provision which enables the HCO to obtain upon request information to allow appropriate provider decision-making regarding diagnoses, patient medical restrictions, early disease detection, or return-to-work, which may include:

(1) the employer's written Injury and Illness Prevention Plan, including the name and title of an individual responsible for implementing the plan;

(2) information concerning exposure levels for specified materials, and information, including Material Safety Data Sheets, concerning health, safety, and ergonomic risk factors in the workplace;

(3) the name and title of the individual responsible for loss control services for each employer.

(c) The HCO shall have in place a program for prompt reporting, to the employer or insurer loss control program and to the employer's designee responsible for the Injury and Illness Prevention Plan, of the following occupational injuries and illnesses: occupational asthma; cumulative trauma disorders of the upper extremities; lead poisoning; amputations (excluding amputations of the distal phalanges); noise-induced hearing loss; pesticide illness; electrocutions; asphyxiation; and burns and falls from heights requiring hospitalization.

(d) The HCO shall annually report to the insurer loss control program or to the employer's designee responsible for the Injury and Illness Prevention Plan, as designated in the contract between the HCO and the claims administrator, aggregate data on injuries and illnesses.

§9776.1 Return to Work Coordination

An HCO shall maintain a return to work program in conjunction with the employer and claims administrator to facilitate and coordinate returning injured workers to the workplace, to assess the feasibility and availability of modified work or modified duty, and to minimize risk of employee exposure after return to work to risk factors which may aggravate or cause recurrence of injury. The duties of the HCO shall be specified in the contract between the HCO and the claims administrator.

REFERENCES

1. American Accreditation Health Care Commission: Workers' Compensation Network Standards. Washington, DC, AAHCC/URAC, 1997.
2. American Association of Occupational Health Nurses: Position statement: The occupational health nurse as case manager. AAOHN J 42:155, 1994.
3. Bailey JE, Womeodu RJ: Prevention in managed care: Obstacles and opportunities. J Tenn Med Assoc 89:122–125, 1996.
4. Bernacki EJ, Tsai SP: Managed care for workers' compensation: Three years of experience in an "employee choice" state. J Occup Environ Med 39:1091–1097, 1996.
5. California Division of Workers' Compensation: Certification Standards for Health Care Organizations. State Code of Regulations, Title 8, §9776. San Francisco, February 14, 1996.
6. Childre F: Nurse-managed occupational health services. AAOHN J 45:484–490, 1997.
7. Dembe AE: Preserving workers' compensation benefits in a managed health care environment. J Public Health Policy 19:200–218, 1998.
8. Dembe AE: Contract provisions to ensure quality in workers' compensation managed care arrangements. Presented at the 125th annual meeting of the American Public Health Association, Indianapolis, November 11, 1997.
9. Eccleston SM, Yeager C: Managed Care and Medical Cost Containment in Workers' Compensation: A National Inventory, 1997–1998. Cambridge, MA, Workers' Compensation Research Institute, 1998.
10. Feldstein A, Breen V, Dana N: Prevention of work-related disability. Am J Prev Med 14(Supplement): 33–39, 1998.
11. Feldstein A, Marino G: Managed occupational health care in an HMO. HMO Pract 11:158–163, 1997.
12. Gallagher PA, Granahan WL: Report on Third Annual Milliman & Robertson Survey: HMO Managed Workers' Compensation Strategies and Products. Philadelphia, Milliman & Robertson, 1997.
13. Gellert GA, Dillenberg J: Incorporating prevention in managed care. JAMA 269:2505, 1993.
14. Gordon RL, Baker EL, Roper WL, Omenn GS: Prevention and the reforming U.S. health care system: Changing roles and responsibilities for public health. Am Rev Public Health 17:489–509, 1996.
15. Herbert R, Plattus B, Kellogg L, et al: The Union Health Center: A working model of clinical care linked to preventive occupational health services. Am J Ind Med 31:263–273, 1997.
16. HMOs increasingly offering comp services traditionally provided by TPAs, insurers. BNA's Workers Compensation Report 8:374, 1997.
17. Institute of Medicine: Role of the Primary Care Physician in Occupational and Environmental Medicine. Washington, DC, National Academy Press, 1988.
18. Liberty Mutual Insurance Company: Liberty Mutual's Continuum of Care (advertising brochure). Boston, Liberty Mutual Insurance Group, 1992.
19. Loeppke RR: Prevention and managed care: The next generation. J Occup Environ Med 37:558–562, 1995.
20. Martin KJ: Workers' compensation: Case management strategies. AAOHN J 43:245–250, 1995.
21. McGrail MP, Tsai SP, Bernacki EJ: A comprehensive initiative to manage the incidence and cost of occupational injury and illness. J Occup Environ Med 37:1263–1268, 1995.
22. Miller RH, Luft HS: Managed care plan performance since 1980: A literature analysis. JAMA 271:1512–1519, 1994. Worcester, Massachusetts, July 1997.
23. Milton DK, Solomon GM, Rosiello RA, Herrick RF: Risk and incidence of asthma attributable to occupational exposure among HMO members. Am J Ind Med 33:1–10, 1998.
24. National Association of Insurance Commissioners: Journal of Insurance Regulation Research Grant: Contract Provisions to Ensure Quality in Workers' Compensation Managed Care Arrangements. A.E. Dembe, Principal Investigator. Worcester, Massachusetts, July 1997.
25. Omenn GS: Prevention: Benefits, Costs, and Savings. Washington, DC, Partnership in Prevention, 1994.
26. Parkinson M: Reimbursement for preventive services. In Woolf S, Jonas S, Lawrence R (eds): Health Promotion and Disease Prevention in Clinical Practice. Baltimore, Williams & Wilkins, 1996, pp 525–542.
27. Pelletier KR: A review and analysis of the health and cost-effective outcome studies of comprehensive health promotion and disease prevention programs at the worksite: 1993–1995 update. Am J Health Prom 10:380–388, 1996.
28. Pransky G, Snyder T, Dembe A, Himmelstein J: Under-reporting of work-related disorders in the workplace. Ergonomics [in press].

29. Price M, Duplessie K, Powers B: Nurse-managed occupational health services without on-site clinical care delivery. AAOHN J 45:496–500, 1997.
30. Rieth L, Ahrens A, Cummings D: Integrated disability management: Taking a coordinated approach to managing employee disabilities. AAOHN J 43:270–275, 1995.
31. Rudolph L: Managed Care in California's Workers' Compensation System: A Survey of Current Practices. San Francisco, California Division of Workers' Compensation, 1996.
32. Rundall TG, Schauffler HH: Health promotion and disease prevention in integrated delivery systems: The role of market forces. Am J Prev Med 13:244–250, 1997.
33. Schauffler HH, Rodriguez T: Availability and utilization of health promotion programs and satisfaction with health plan. Med Care 32:1182–1196, 1994.
34. Schauffler HH, Rodriguez T: Managed care for preventive services: A review of policy options. Med Care Rev 50:153–198, 1993.
35. Schulman B, Schwartz S: Workers' Compensation/Occupational Health National Trends Study, Final Report. Olympia, WA, Washington State Department of Labor and Industries, 1997.
36. Showstack J, Lurie N, Leatherman S, et al: Health of the public: The private sector challenge. JAMA 276:1071–1074, 1996.
37. Simpson SJ, Purdy LS: Strategies for comprehensive nurse-managed care occupational health services. AAOHN J 45:491–495, 1997.
38. Stein G: Workers' compensation proves the brain and body are connected: Lessons for managed care. Managed Care Q 2:60–63, 1994.
39. Stokols D, Pelletier KR, Fielding JE: Integration of medical care and worksite health promotion. JAMA 273:1136–1142, 1995.
40. U.S. Centers for Disease Control and Prevention: Prevention and managed care: Opportunities for managed care organizations, purchasers of health care, and public health agencies. 44 (RR-14), November 17, 1995.
41. U.S. Department of Labor, Office of Workers' Compensation Programs: Maximizing outcomes in the federal workers' compensation system through integrated case management [unpublished communication], 1998.
42. U.S. Department of Health and Human Services: 1992 National Survey of Worksite Health Promotion Activities; summary. Am J Health Prom 7:452–464, 1993.
43. U.S. Preventive Services Task Force: Guide to Clinical Preventive Services: An Assessment of the Effectiveness of 169 Interventions. Baltimore, Williams & Wilkins, 1989.
44. Vogt TM, Kohatsu ND, Rutherford GW: Prevention in managed care. West J Med 161:63–64, 1994.
45. Washington Business Group on Health: Case Management: An Essential Element in Delivery Systems That Work. Washington, DC, WBGH, 1996.
46. Wilson MG, Holman PB, Hammock A: A comprehensive review of the effects of worksite health promotion on health-related outcomes. Am J Health Prom 10:429–435, 1996.
47. Windau J, Rosenman K, Anderson H, et al: The identification of occupational lung disease from hospital discharge records. J Occup Med 33:1060–1066, 1991.
48. Woloshin S, Schwartz L: Health of the public: The private-sector challenge. JAMA 276:1951, 1996.

ROBERT Z. BRUCKMAN, MD
JEFFREY S. HARRIS, MD, MPH, MBA

OCCUPATIONAL MEDICINE PRACTICE GUIDELINES

From Milliman & Robertson, Inc.
San Francisco, California (RZB)
and
J. Harris Associates, Inc.
Mill Valley, California, (JSH)

Reprint requests to:
Robert Z. Bruckman, MD
Milliman & Robertson, Inc.
595 Market Street
San Francisco, CA 94105

Practice guidelines are not new to medicine. Hippocrates may have written the first set when he developed the guiding principles for physician, teacher, student, and patient interaction.[10] Clinical and administrative guidelines are discussed and debated today in committees and meetings, in hospital and clinic lunchrooms, and in the medical literature. More than 900 articles appear yearly in databases of the English-language medical literature exploring the utility and effectiveness of clinical practice guidelines.

Practice guidelines, particularly those that are evidence- or normatively based, are used increasingly to promulgate, implement, and monitor health care policy. The rapid increase in the influence of guidelines has been called part of a third "revolution" in health care based on accountability that started in the early 1980s.[16] As a part of that change, guidelines, as "rules of the road," began to gain complexity.

The popularity of practice guidelines coincided with economic stresses on the health care system. In a sense, the conjunction of economics and the use of guidelines simply stems from the definition of quality in medicine, which includes efficiency and effectiveness.[6] Recent guidelines have emphasized efficiency and wise use of resources in the choice and progression of medical services.[17] Such uniform processes, especially when based on research or empiric evidence of efficiency and effectiveness, have the effect of reducing variability, errors, complications and costs.[2] Until recently, health systems gave such issues little thought, especially when reimbursed for their costs rather than at a market price, fee schedule, market-based system, or usual and customary fee screens.[18] Economics aside, however, authors of such guidelines are trying to give meaningful direction to the path that medical care takes.[4]

The terms *guidelines*, *care paths*, *care maps*, and *protocols* are often used interchangeably, but there are distinctions among them. *Guideline*, the broadest term, is generally used to define the evidence base, norms, or consensus (if evidence is lacking) for medical practice.[7] A more complete description and criteria for evaluation of guidelines have been described recently.[10,12] Examples of guidelines useful in occupational medicine include those published by the Agency for Health Care Policy and Research, Milliman & Robertson, and the American College of Occupational and Environmental Medicine.[1,3,11] Benchmarks can be derived from guidelines to provide a gauge of reasonableness for resource use and for managing disability that meets the medical needs of patients with a certain diagnosis. Guidelines generally underscore that the treatment they advise is for patients with uncomplicated conditions.

Care path and *care map* generally define day-by-day or moment-by-moment patient management activities that should occur within a structured framework, e.g., the specifics of treatment of adult acquired pneumonia or the management of a specific episode of acute low back pain. Here, the issue of uniformity in care is also a factor. That is, if all inpatients with repaired knee ligaments were treated according to a specific plan, confusion over nursing care, physical therapy, medications, and timelines should steeply decrease. This is turn should smooth the way for more effective posthospital case management in the patient's home or physical therapy center. The use of a care map or pathway can result in a high and efficient standard of care.

A *protocol* is generally a narrow step-by-step plan for accomplishing details noted in a care map or care path. Protocols facilitate good preparation of the patient and the doctor's support staff for the procedure and also can guide the practitioner. If everyone involved in a procedure knows their role, procedures tend to go well for the patient and for the staff.

TYPES OF GUIDELINES

All guidelines attempt to define or create health management policy. Many are at least partially based on high-grade medical evidence, which is commonly viewed as representing the "gold standard."[8] This approach cannot be applied completely or in all cases, however, because there is often a long lag time before such studies appear in the medical literature. In addition, many areas, particularly common musculoskeletal disorders, have not been well studied. Further, efficiency issues are infrequently addressed, but they can sometimes be deduced from the available studies.

Data-driven, or normative, guidelines are typically prepared by health management or health policy organizations that seek to define acceptable standards of care. When the data are examined, the median is commonly used to define a standard. Data-driven guidelines are popular because they are easy to defend. However, while this process is useful in preparing materials to be used in precertification and in assuring that a median level of quality is maintained, it is difficult to use data-driven guidelines to increase quality or efficiency. Normative practices are not necessarily the most efficient. Further, simply using the median or mean does not reveal the extent of variance around a single statistic. Such variance can often be markedly reduced to improve the efficiency and effectiveness of care. The data in normative databases can be used to generate control charts that present the variance and identify outliers, paving the way for organized quality improvement programs.[14]

Consensus guidelines are commonly prepared by and for medical specialty organizations. They seek to represent a common standard derived by acknowledged experts. Disagreements among participants have led to considerable time lags between initiation and completion of consensus. When diverse economic interests are not represented, consensus guidelines may not be credible in some circles. Moreover, if the experts are academics, they may make recommendations that practicing physicians will find hard to implement.

Best practice guidelines are a form of benchmarking based on direct observation of clinical practice patterns. Best observed practice guidelines have several advantages. They are based on real examples, and they can be used to gradually promote system improvement. As aggregate practice improves, more patient experiences will resemble the benchmark, reducing both the median and the level of variation. Such guidelines must maintain credibility through frequent and regular updates. Changes in technology, medical knowledge, and practices will change the benchmarks.

Physicians and Guidelines

The proliferation of guidelines over the past 15 years has led to some confusion among health care providers. It may not be easy to determine which guideline is most efficient and effective, but criteria are available.[10] In general, more specific guidelines, and those that rely on evidence or statistical correlations between observed practices and specific results, are more likely to lead to better outcomes. On the other hand, diverse guidelines may reach the same conclusion.

Other practical issues exist. On occasion, physicians may seek approval of "outside" guidelines by their specialty organizations before adopting and using them. (Guidelines generated by one's own specialty have a better chance of adoption.[5]) Such review and approval, which tends to be a protracted process, has been uncommon. Practitioners also have suspected that there is economic motivation for some guidelines.

Over time, guidelines have tended to develop on a national and international basis and pathways and protocols on a specialty-specific or local basis. This trend has assisted in defining national and international policy issues, which have an impact on the general direction of medical care while leaving specific judgments and patient care issues to local community control. Many medical groups have preferred to develop their own care paths and protocols at a local level. Local review or modifications improve the acceptance of guidelines. As long as the results are consistent with the evidence or national practices, there is no intrinsic problem with this practice.

Payors and Guidelines

The most interesting trend in guideline development and use during the past decade has to do with payors. Health plans tend to use guidelines as a means of instituting health policy for their members.[13] This trend is critical for the practice of occupational medicine: it is already causing a major change in the way it is practiced.

Until the late 1980s, health care organizations and workers' compensation payors had little reason to examine the delivery of health care services. As long as insurance premiums covered losses, there was no reason to examine what was paid for. Insurers simply focused on whether a health problem occurred in connection with work and on payment of bills. However, with the escalation of the cost of workers' compensation medical care during the 1980s, and more recently deregulation of insurance premiums, premium has failed to cover risk (e.g., the cost of loss). Loss/income ratios increased, and it became necessary to better manage risk or close operations. Most companies are trying to manage risk, but not always successfully. For example, as of mid 1998, 18 major insurers in California were on the watch list published by Firemark.[9] Losses have exceeded premium under open rating, and insurers have been slow to effectively manage care. If one examines risk in workers' compensation by studying the resources used to resolve groups of cases, it becomes clear that current medical system, with no meaningful use of guidelines and little case management, can produce similar results with vastly different costs. This understanding has led to a number of strategies calculated to decrease medical costs while maintaining quality outcomes. Only recently have payors begun to appreciate that discounted medical care has generally led to an increase in wage replacement costs and the volume of services: physicians have less time to address return to work issues if they try to maintain income by increasing volume.

Personal social issues and some employers' inattention to disability management also have permitted expectations regarding return to work issues to vary widely. Consequently, levels of absence from work are under control in some organizations and out of control in others.

USES OF GUIDELINES

Physicians are increasingly unafraid of guidelines as long as they are used correctly by all parties and are developed and maintained carefully and with professional integrity. Since managed care organizations (MCOs) and payors are using guidelines to assist with design of their preferred provider organization, exclusive provider organization, and panel selection process, the physician's competitive position is strengthened by involvement with the process of using guidelines. This can and should include modification of the guideline for local custom. Well-written guidelines may contain care maps and protocols that extend the range of medical options available to the occupational medicine physician in treating patients.

Some workers' compensation payors and MCOs examine physician practice patterns to find the highest quality, most efficient providers of health care services. One factor that is increasingly used is a willingness to comply with guidelines considered by the MCO to be a national standard. In fact, the requirement is often a part of the quality management clauses in provider network agreements.

This analysis only makes sense if all sides know the standards involved. It is appropriate for the physician and payor to share guideline information so that each understands the management framework expected of the other.

Comprehensive occupational medical guidelines track the occupational medical process to guide diagnosis, sequencing, and specific medical practices. Many guidelines address similar issues and follow similar timeframes. Practitioners and case managers should carefully analyze guidelines to decide which best serve their needs. Below, we outline the sections of a comprehensive guideline that would follow the occupational medicine process.

Red Flags

A number of guidelines address both the most common and most variant musculoskeletal diagnoses. To ensure that relatively uncommon but serious problems are not missed initially, the guidelines identify what are called "red flags," which are mechanisms, symptoms, or signs that could indicate serious injury or illness that

TABLE 1.   Potentially Serious Conditions Related to Low Back Pain

Fracture	Cauda equina syndrome
Dislocation	Progressive neurologic deficits
Tumor	Retrocecal appendix
Infection	Renal colic
Dissecting aortic aneurysm	Pregnancy complications

would require immediate attention. Table 1 lists some of the red flag conditions in low back complaints.

Diagnosis

A substantial number of misdiagnoses have been documented in workers' compensation cases. To prevent this, some guidelines include criteria for diagnoses, focusing on unique patterns of symptoms and signs for each. Guidelines also may describe the approach to the patient, including suggested history questions, physical maneuvers, or what information to seek (Table 2).

Comprehensive guidelines also contain criteria for initial tests needed to establish a diagnosis. While some apply to red flag conditions, most common complaints seen under workers' compensation do not require testing in the first 4 weeks, because the diagnosis can be made reliably by physical examination.

Work-Relatedness

Occupational physicians are often asked if a complaint is work-related. Making this judgment requires a careful history of the mechanism causing the problem, an accurate diagnosis, and knowledge of the epidemiology relating the problem to specific work factors or exposures. Comprehensive occupational medicine guidelines provide the latter information and explain the logic needed to establish a causal relationship according to accepted scientific criteria. This is another area of wide variance.

Treatment

Occupational medicine practice guidelines generally provide suggestions for sequential stages of treatment. Once the diagnosis is made, options are provided for initial treatment for each entity. The recommendations may be based on a review of

TABLE 2.   Evaluation of Ankle Injuries

1. Determine the type of trauma (inversion/eversion or dorsiflexion/plantar flexion).
2. Determine whether the problem is acute, subacute, chronic, or of insidious onset.
3. Determine the severity and specific anatomic location of the pain.
4. Grade the patient's pain on a scale of 0–5, with 0 being no pain and 5 being severe.
5. Assess the ability of the patient to bear weight.
6. Search for any evidence of an open or penetrating wound.
7. Search for any evidence of deformity (anterior/posterior or lateral/medial) of the ankle.
8. Test the range of motion of the joint (normal, mild, severe, or complete restriction).
9. Determine any present medication.
10. Determine any previous medical history, history of systemic illness, or previous ankle injury or disability.

Bruckman RZ, Rasmussen H: Workers' Compensation. Health Management Guidelines. Vol 7. Seattle, Milliman & Robertson, 1996; with permission.

TABLE 3.   Initial Treatment Guidelines for Low Back Pain

Recommendations	

Nonprescription Medications
  Acetaminophen (safest)
  Nonsteroidal antiinflammatory drugs
	Nonprescription Physical Methods
	  Adjustment or modification of work station, job
	    tasks, work hours, methods
	  Stretching
	  Specific low back exercises for range of motion,
	    strengthening
	  At-home applications of cold packs for a few
	    days, then hot packs
	  Relaxation techniques
	  Aerobic exercise

Prescribed Medications
  Nonsteroidal antiinflammatory drugs
  Short-term opiates if symptoms are severe
	Prescribed Physical Methods
	  1–2 visits for education, counseling, and
	    evaluation for home exercise (range of motion
	    and strengthening)

Options		

*Lumbar Disc Protrusion
  with Radiculopathy*
2–4 days of bed rest if
  symptoms are severe
	Lumbar Strain
	1–2 days of rest if symptoms
	  are severe
		Sciatica
		1–2 days of rest if symptoms
		  are severe

Spinal Stenosis
Instructions in body
  mechanics
	Postlaminectomy Syndrome
	2–4 days of rest if symptoms
	  are severe
		Regional Low Back
		1–2 days of rest if symptoms
		  are severe

From Harris JS (ed): Occupational Medicine: Practice Guidelines. Evaluation and Management of Common Health Problems and Functional Recovery in Workers. Beverly Farms, MA, OEM Health Information Press, 1997.

the available evidence (Table 3) or the experience of a managed care practitioner combined with an actuarial analysis of current practices (Table 4). It is particularly important to reinforce the need for patient education and discussion and to provide

TABLE 4.   Initial Optimal Treatment of Ankle Injuries by Primary Care Physician (PCP)

Sprains, sprain-fractures, contusions, and tendonitis: ICD-9 codes 726.71, 726.72, 726.79, 727.06, 727.81, 845.OX, 924.21
Path of care: therapy by PCP
Frequency of Path: 90% of all ankle sprains, sprain-fractures, contusions, and tendonitis

Procedure	Code	Frequency	Occurrence
Office/outpatient new detailed moderate	99203	56.00%	1
Office/outpatient new comp moderate	99104	24.00%	1
X-ray exam, ankle, complete	73610	78.00%	1
Pain injection	90782	5.00%	1
Ankle brace, air cast	AP002	80.00%	1
Strapping	AP024	10.00%	1
Trilateral splint (plaster/fiberglass)	AP032	8.00%	1
Apply short leg splint	29515	8.00%	1
Tape + ace	AP025	2.00%	1
Crutches	AP001	50.00%	1
ER visit focused mod complex	99283	12.00%	1
ER visit severe mod complex	99254	8.00%	1
ER charge, ankle sprain, etc.	ER001	20.00%	1

ICD = International Classification of Diseases, PCP = primary care physician, ER = emergency room.
Bruckman RZ, Rasmussen H: Workers' Compensation. Health Management Guidelines. Vol 7. Seattle, Milliman & Robertson, 1996; with permission.

TABLE 5. Uncommon But Accepted Procedures

Procedure	Code	Comments
X-rays, eversion or external rotation views	73610	Suggested by plain x-ray
X-rays, mortise views		
X-rays (other areas)	71610	To rule out associated foot injuries
MRI	73620	To diagnose osteochondral fractures
CAT scan	73721	Occasionally used to diagnose osteochondral fractures
Bone scan	73700	If question of tumor or infection. To help diagnose osteochondral fractures
Arthrograms	78300	Helpful for evaluation of ligament tears
Fluoroscopy	73615	
EMG	76120	
Nerve conduction studies	95860	If possibility of tarsal tunnel syndrome
Nerve conduction studies	95900	If possibility of tarsal tunnel syndrome
Narcotics, class II	95904	Indicated for a few days after major surgery and in cases of acute trauma

Bruckman RZ, Rasmussen H: Workers' Compensation. Health Management Guidelines. Vol 7. Seattle, Milliman & Robertson, 1996; with permission.

recommended content.[11] Discussion and education is widely underused, contributing to dissatisfaction and uninformed decision making, the latter of which can lead to significant overutilization and poorer functional outcomes.

Some guidelines also identify therapies that have not been proven effective. Calling out ineffective practices is important to improve inefficiency and prevent iatrogenesis (Tables 5 and 6).

Currently available occupational medicine guidelines describe a series of initial visits by primary care practitioners for common non-red flag conditions. If the patient has not substantially recovered in 4–6 weeks, the guidelines recommend a comprehensive reevaluation, which may include special studies, to ensure that a serious condition has not been missed. Some guidelines evaluate the efficacy of all diagnostic maneuvers, including special studies, typically with a combination of consensus and evidence review (Table 7).

TABLE 6. Unorthodox or Controversial Procedures

Procedure	Code	Comments
Biofeedback	90901	Unproven
TENS	64550	Unproven for extremity injuries
Surface EMG	95869	No proven value
PT passive modalities	97OXX	Unproven
Thermography	95762	May be of value in reflex sympathetic dystrophy
Phonophoresis, iontophoresis	97003	Unproven
Prolotherapy	20550	Unproven
Computerized strength testing	95999	Cost benefit ratio unacceptable
Trigger point injections	20550	Unproven
Systemic corticosteroids		Rarely indicated
Acupuncture	97800	Useful in some unresponsive chronic cases. Limit to 4 to 6 visits
Manipulation	97261	Not indicated for joints
Spray and stretch		Unproven
Electromagnetic field therapy		Unproven
Utrasound, diagnostic	76880	Unproven for joints

Bruckman RZ, Rasmussen H: Workers' Compensation. Health Management Guidelines. Vol 7. Seattle, Milliman & Robertson, 1996; with permission.

TABLE 7.   Ability of Various Techniques to Identify and Define Low Back Pathology

Technique	Lumbosacral Strain	Disc Protrusion	Cauda	Stenosis	Postlaminectomy
History	++	++	++	+++	+++
Physical exam	++	+++	++++	++	+++
Lab studies	0	0	0	0	0
Imaging					
Radiography	0	+	+	+	+
CT	0	+++	+++	+++	++
MRI	0	++++	++++	+++	++++
EMG	0	+++	+	+	+

From Harris JS (ed): Occupational Medicine: Practice Guidelines. Evaluation and Management of Common Health Problems and Functional Recovery in Workers. Beverly Farms, MA, OEM Health Information Press, 1997; with permission.

At this point it is important to again review risks for delayed functional recovery and barriers to return to work. Barriers and risks may originate with the employer (barriers), the patient (risks), or the treating physician (Table 8). In any of these cases, case management must be started to prevent further delay, debilitation, and possible iatrogenesis.

A primary treating physician who is not able to determine or treat the source of delayed functional recovery should refer the patient to a conservative specialist in the area of concern. There are occasions when a multidisciplinary team evaluation would be advantageous, but that is seen as a step beyond specialty evaluation and recommendations in current guidelines.

DISABILITY MANAGEMENT AND RETURN TO WORK

Effective return to work efforts require that expectations of physicians, employers, patients, and payors be addressed simultaneously. In most data sets, time lost from work, particularly for soft tissue complaints, far exceeds best practice or consensus guidelines. The role of social norms cannot be overestimated in this area. For example, in certain work environments all employees with a simple back ache may expect the same amount of time off work. With no drivers to the contrary, physicians may grant a patient's request for more time off following a complaint of this nature. As employers become accustomed to extended disability for certain health conditions, little attention is paid to managing protracted time off or developing modified work programs. Return to work is not the emphasis; therefore, its achievement is haphazard. Employers, physicians, and payors may miss numerous opportunities to establish some control over lost time.

Disability duration guidelines can be effective. For example, by simply suggesting that individuals return to modified work for a specific defined problem after 5 days, all stakeholders gradually lose their expectations that return to work will occur after 45 or 60 days. By defining an accepted optimal national standard, physicians

TABLE 8.   Physician Practices Possibly Delaying Functional Recovery

Significant departure from guidelines	Request for work hardening
Request for unusual tests	Request for pain management clinic
Excessive physical therapy	Request for rehabilitation program
Excessive pain medication	Preexisting medical problems
Physician request for consultation	Polypharmacy, narcotis, psychotropics

are empowered to suggest earlier return to work under a graded modified work program as compatible with an individual patient's injuries. By examining guidelines, employers understand the need to provide a modified work environment so that employees can return to work at an earlier time. Some workers' compensation MCOs, including payors, have found return to work guidelines to be such a powerful case management tool that they have redesigned management processes around their efficient use.

The Role of Modified Work

Effective return to work programs, and guidelines that provide a framework for them, use temporary transitional work as a key tool. Temporary transitional, or modified, work is a job or set of job duties that accommodate the physical or emotional limitations of the employee. Employers and physicians use such jobs to maintain social suport at the worksite and to gradually increase conditioning until the employee can return to his or her regular duties. The use of modified duty or transitional jobs assumes that the employee will gradually transition to more strenuous or demanding work until able to return to regular job duties. Employers offering temporary transitional work should see reduced time lost from work and reduced indemnity costs: workers reenter the workforce at low activity levels but are productive nonetheless.

Temporary transitional work may not be available in all situations. Even if available, an employee whose job requires heavy physical demands may need to stay on transitional work longer than one would anticipate before resuming full job tasks.

Return to Work Guidelines

Three types of guidelines are available to help providers and employers return workers to work. Comprehensive return to work guidelines include disability durations, activity modifications, and graded job function modifications. No available guidelines contain all three.

Physicians and employers can use disability durations to guide expectations about absence from work with or without modified duty. They can be derived from normative data,[15] best observed practices for uncomplicated cases,[3] or expert or consensus opinion.[11] An example of a normative disability duration guideline with suggested expert consensus benchmarks is shown in Table 9. The table contains three levels of work associated with activities such as standing or walking. Level 1 is the least demanding work and Level 3 the most demanding work related to the activity, body part, and injury. Level 1 describes activity that may be suitable for temporary transitional work for most workers if it is available from the employer. The table shows return to work estimates for each injury, expressed as both ranges and benchmarks for each level of work. The range indicates the soonest and latest a worker with the particular injury is expected to be able to return to work at that level. The guideline shown in the table anticipates that four-fifths or more of injured employees will be able to return to work within the specified range for the level of activity being considered. Benchmark days at each level represent the average number of days in which a worker would be expected to return to that level of work when a number of cases are studied. The benchmark serves as a guide but is not a maximum or standard by which to judge any individual case.

Case managers and physicians also should be alert for barriers to return to work. Table 10 lists barriers that should trigger case management discussions with the employer by the primary treating physician or a case manager.

TABLE 9. Ankle and Lower Leg Injuries: Return to Work Guidelines. Return to Work (Days) by Level of Activity

	Level 1 Range (Benchmark 1)	Level 2 Range (Benchmark 2)	Level 3 Range (Benchmark 3)
Sprain, sprain-fracture, contusion—Grade I ICD-9 Codes: 845.OX, 924.21	0–5 (2)	0–63 (28)	28–77 (63)
Sprain, sprain fracture, contusion—Grade II ICD-9 Codes: 845.OX, 924.21	0–8 (3)	3–28 (10)	14–35 (28)
Sprain, sprain-fracture, contusion—Grade III ICD-9 Codes: 845.OX, 924.21	7–14 (10)	14–42 (28)	35–63 (49)
Achilles tendonitis ICD-9 Codes: 726.71, 727.81 845.09	0–21 (1)	3–42 (14)	7–56 (42)
Anterior tibial tendonitis ICD-9 Codes: 726.72, 727.06	0–7 (2)	7–42 (21)	7–56 (35)
Posterior tibial or peroneal tendonitis ICD-9 Codes: 726.72, 726.79	0–7 (2)	7–42 (21)	7–56 (35)

Bruckman RZ, Rasmussen H: Workers' Compensation. Health Management Guidelines. Vol 7. Seattle, Milliman & Robertson, 1996; with permission.

Activity Modification

At the same time, providers should use activity modifications based on epidemiologic evidence to prevent aggravation of the condition.[11] This information is used in "work restrictions," although a more helpful term might reflect accommodation to use residual abilities. Some return to work tables show ranges of time in which a patient with a particular diagnosis and treatment for the specific body part is expected to be capable of each level of activity.

Graded increases in job duties based on physical exertion are useful to guide the transition back to the usual and customary job.[3] "Levels of activity at work" tables describe activities of regular jobs or possible temporary transitional work. These tables illustrate classifications of work based on the activity to be performed and the demands of different levels of such activity. Such guidelines are generally presented for each part of the body and should reflect the known aggravating factors used in activity modification guidelines. In jobs requiring customer contact or time pressure, a similar framework addressing mental and emotional demands would be useful. The physician's prescription should indicate which tasks, loads, and motions are to be included or excluded in a particular return to work prescription. In cases in

TABLE 10. Barriers to Return to Work

Noncooperative employer or supervisor
Conflict between patient and supervisor
Employer not honoring work restrictions
Disciplinary action at work
Downsizing of company

Bruckman RZ, Rasmussen H: Workers' Compensation. Health Management Guidelines. Vol 7. Seattle, Milliman & Robertson, 1996; with permission.

TABLE 11. Risks for Delayed Recovery

Demographics	Employment factors
Age	Job satisfaction
	Task enjoyment
Historical factors	Adversarial relations
Previous injuries	Job demands
Absence from work	Perceived work-relatedness
Past abuse	Alternate work available
Social factors	Injury factors
Family disabilities	Self-rated severity
Change in family role	Self-rated health
Family support	Expectations
Union membership	Severity of signs
Personal health	Delayed presentation
Chemical dependency	Chronic pain symptoms
Depression	Economic/legal factors
Emotional distress	Income
	Education
	Compensability
	Representation
	Litigation

From Harris JS (ed): Occupational Medicine: Practice Guidelines. Evaluation and Management of Common Health Problems and Functional Recovery in Workers. Beverly Farms, MA, OEM Health Information Press, 1997.

which more than one activity level is listed—reflecting the components of a single job—the highest level required should define expectations.

Most return to work tables do not address certain catastrophic injuries or multiple injuries. For multiple injuries, a return to work expectation may be based on the longest return to work time among the injuries, but synergistic disabilities or the availability of temporary transitional work may influence the result in specific cases.

Return to work guidelines that focus exclusively on workers' compensation have no entries for the definitive diagnoses of systemic diseases. Even though they may be disabling, chronic diseases are generally not work-related. General guidelines, however, do address most systemic disorders.

Analysis of Time Loss Using Guidelines

Return to work benchmarks can serve as an additional operational aid for case managers, network managers, and employers. They also may be used to assess the experience of a plan or of an employer. One method of analysis is to segregate the experience data into complicated and uncomplicated diagnostic groups using standard injury and diagnosis coding. The uncomplicated group experience can then be compared to return to work benchmarks. Such comparisons may be used to analyze network efficiency, workers' compensation management, and opportunities to improve return to work and reduce plan costs.

Delayed Recovery

The differences in the endpoints of the ranges of time off work in some guidelines are caused by a variety of factors, including specifics of work available at that level, severity of injury, and different rates of healing. Employment-related and psychosocial factors such as job satisfaction, supervisory relations, marital problems, alcohol or drug dependency, and financial problems may result in longer than indicated return to work times. Longer return to work times are often called "delayed

TABLE 12.   Behavioral Risks for Delayed Recovery

Anger	Symptoms and signs inconsistent with mechanism
Noncompliance	
Patient request for additional disability	Changing symptoms from original history
More symptoms than signs (symptom amplification)	Request for unusual tests
	History of frequent job changes

recovery," because they are not optimal. Table 11 lists risks derived from population studies.

Ideally, physicians or case managers should detect risks for delayed recovery early in the case and work with the patient to address each potential issue or problem. Delayed return to function can thus be prevented primarily.

Table 12 lists behavioral risks that are commonly believed to require attention but have not been studied.

SUMMARY

Practice guidelines have become accepted "rules of the road" for many illnesses and injuries. Guidelines can be the basis for performance measures if they include a development step summarizing the available evidence for efficiency and effectiveness of maneuvers, tests, and treatments. They are particularly valuable for entities that have high degrees of variance in diagnostic accuracy, testing, and treatment. Periodic revision of guidelines can keep professional knowledge bases up to date.

One must keep in mind that guidelines are just that—descriptions of normative data, observed best practices, expert consensus, or high-grade evidence. While they provide benchmarks for assessment and improvement, there may be good reasons why they do not apply to some patients. However, the exercise of justifying the differences can sharpen clinical judgment and improve outcomes.

REFERENCES

1. Bigos SJ, Bowyer OR: Acute Low Back Problems in Adults: Clinical Practice Guideline No. 14. Rockville, MD, US Department of Health and Human Services, Agency for Health Care Policy and Research, 1994, publication 95-0642.
2. Blumenthal D, Scheck AC (eds): Improving Clinical Practice: Total Quality Management and the Physician. San Francisco, Jossey-Bass, 1995.
3. Bruckman RZ, Rasmussen H: Workers' Compensation. Health Management Guidelines. Vol 7. Seattle, Milliman & Robertson, 1996.
4. Chassin MR: Practice guidelines: Best hope for quality improvement in the 1990's. In Harris JS, Belk HD, Wood LW (eds): Managing Employee Health Care Costs: Assuring Quality and Value. Beverly Farms, MA, OEM Health Information, 1992, pp 49–55.
5. Davis DA, Taylor-Vaisey A: Translating guidelines into practice: A systematic review of theoretic concepts and research evidence in the adoption of clinical practice guidelines. Can Med Assoc J 157:408–416, 1997.
6. Donabedian A: Quality and cost: Choices and responsibilities. In Harris JS, Belk HD, Wood LW (eds): Managing Employee Health Care Costs: Assuring Quality and Value. Beverly FArms, MA, OEM Health Information, 1992.
7. Field MJ, Lohr KN (eds): Clinical Practice Guidelines: Directions for a New Program. Washington, DC, National Academy Press, 1990.
8. Field MJ, Lohr KN: Guidelines for Clinical Practice. Washington, DC, National Academy Press, 1992.
9. Foppert D: Firemark Insurance Perspectives. The Workers' Compensation Insurance Industry. San Francisco, Joanne Stone Morrissey, 1998.
10. Harris JS: Clinical practice guidelines: Development, use and evaluation. J Occup Environ Med 39:23–34, 1997.

11. Harris JS (ed): Occupational Medicine: Practice Guidelines. Evaluation and Management of Common Health Problems and Functional Recovery in Workers. Beverly Farms, MA, OEM Health Information Press, 1997.
12. Harris JS, Bombardier C: Practice guidelines. In Harris JS, Loeppke RR (eds): Integrated Health Management: The Key Role of Occupational Medicine in Managed Care, Disability Mangement and Integrated Delivery Systems. Beverly Farms, MA, OEM Press, 1998.
13. Harris JS: Payers' use of practice guidelines. In Harris JS, Loeppke RR (eds): Integrated Health Management: The Key Role of Occupational Medicine in Managed Care, Disability Management and Integrated Delivery Systems. Beverly Farms, MA, OEM Press, 1998.
14. McEachern JE, Makens PK, Buchanan ED, Schiff L: Quality improvement: An imperative for medical care. In Harris JS, Belk HD, Wood LW (eds): Managing Employee Health Care Costs: Assuring Quality and Value. Beverly Farms, MA, OEM Health Information, 1992, pp 207–214.
15. Reed P (ed): The Medical Disability Advisor: Workplace Guidelines for Disability Duration. 3rd ed. Horsham, PA, LRP Publications, 1998.
16. Relman A: Assessment and Accountability: The third revolution in medicine. N Engl J Med 319:1220–1222, 1988.
17. Shapiro DW, Lasker RD, Bindman AB, et al: Containing costs while improving quality of care: The role of profiling and practice guidelines. Annu Rev Public Health 14:219–241, 1993.
18. Starr P: The Logic of Health-Care Reform. Knoxville, TN, The Grand Rounds Press, 1992.
19. Work Loss Data Institute: Official Disability Guidelines: Length of Disability Data by IC-9 CM from CDC and OSHA plus NHDS Hospital Length of Stay. Riverside, CT, Work Loss Data Institute, 1997.

BARTON MARGOSHES, MD

DISABILITY MANAGEMENT AND OCCUPATIONAL HEALTH

From the Liberty Mutual Insurance
   Company
Boston, Massachusetts

Reprint requests to:
Barton Margoshes, MD
Vice President, Liberty Mutual
   Insurance Company
Medical Director, Risk Services
175 Berkeley Street
Boston, MA 02117

The estimated national income loss in 1994 due to lost time from work was $81.1 billion, of which $49.4 billion was replaced by income-protection programs including sick leave, group insurance, temporary disability insurance under statutory state provisions, individual insurance, workers' compensation (WC), and Social Security disability insurance.[12] This estimate represents only the direct costs associated with disability.

The total cost of disability includes both direct and indirect costs, with the direct, or disability, costs representing only the tip of the iceberg. Some experts include the medical costs in the direct costs. Indirect costs, which are associated with a disability other than the direct wage or salary replacement costs, include hiring and training of replacement workers, overtime, lost productivity, increased administrative and supervisory costs, and lost revenue opportunity. While these costs are difficult to calculate and are employer-specific, it is conservatively estimated that indirect costs are two to four times higher than the direct costs of disability.

A recently published study of the financial impact associated with occupational injuries and illnesses in the United States for 1992 found that total direct (medical and indemnity) and indirect costs were estimated to be $171 billion.[13]

The estimated direct cost of disability for an employer averages 8% of payroll.[18] This expense can have a significant impact on a corporation's profits. Many U.S. corporations operate with a profit margin of 5% or less. Given this margin, a corporation must generate $20 in revenue to cover $1 in disability costs. It becomes quickly apparent that disability costs need to be controlled and managed for a corporation to be competitive.

HISTORY OF MANAGED DISABILITY

Disability management has become a major focus for controlling costs and improving productivity in corporate America. For years, employers considered absence a cost of doing business and an uncontrollable expense. However, two major social and economic trends have resulted in disability management becoming a commonplace cost-containment intervention.

The first trend was the advent of managed care. National health expenditures as a percent of gross domestic product reached double digits in the 1980s and early 1990s. In fact, in 1993 national health expenditures were equal to 13.9% of the gross domestic product.[19] In response to the "health care crisis," managed care organizations such as health maintenance organizations grew rapidly. The premise of managed care is that medical costs can be contained and quality improved through the application of business management techniques, including quality control, utilization management, and competitive pricing. Largely as a result of the increased use of these managed care principles, the rise in medical inflation has moderated from double-digit growth to 5.5% in 1995 and 3.5% in 1996.[20]

The second trend contributing to the increased interest in disability management was the downsizing initiatives of major U.S. corporations in the 1990s. This focused attention on employee census and worker productivity. With a leaner workforce, the impact of absenteeism became more acute and evident. Corporations with high rates of absenteeism were at a competitive disadvantage due to the costs associated with disability and lost productivity. While this impact on competitiveness always existed, it was not recognized as a major influence until relatively recently.

With medical inflation under control, corporate managers began to focus on controlling the costs associated with disability. A logical supposition was that the costs of disability also could be managed through applying many of the same management techniques as in managed medical care. While this was not a new strategy in controlling workers' compensation disability, it was a new strategy for corporate managers responsible for group health disability.

Managed WC, a further refinement of the traditional approach to managing WC costs, integrates medical and disability management principles. Under WC laws, the employer is responsible for paying both the medical and disability costs (indemnity costs). In the early 1990s, WC preferred provider organization (PPO) networks were formed similar in design to group health PPOs to control medical costs. Similar to the group health medical managed care system, a clinical case management infrastructure was developed in WC to perform utilization management and return to work management.

A distinction should be made between an impairment and a disability. An impairment as defined by the World Health Organization is "any loss or abnormality of psychological, physiological, or anatomical structure or function."[23] A disability is defined by the American Medical Association as "an alteration of an individual's capacity to meet personal, social, or occupational demands, or statutory or regulatory requirements, because of an impairment."[2] In the context of WC and group health, a disability is the inability to function to one's fullest capacity in the workplace due to the existence of an impairment.

Disability management can be defined as "a systematic approach to identifying, evaluating, and coordinating the delivery of disability-related services to individuals; the objective is to improve return-to-work outcomes for employees who become disabled and financial results for employers."[17]

Disability management can be viewed in both an occupational and a nonoccupational context. Disability caused by occupational injuries and illnesses is covered by WC indemnity payments (wage replacement), while disability from nonoccupational injuries and illnesses is covered by short-term and long-term disability. The indemnity portion of WC is determined by the individual state WC regulations. Group disability eligibility and compensability are determined by the disability policy contract. The legal and reimbursement issues may differ between the two systems, but the basic issues involved in disability management are the same. For example, the employee's functional ability to perform his or her job remains the same concern whether the employee has an occupational or nonoccupational disability. The optimal endpoint of disability management is the successful return to work of the individual at the appropriate time to his or her regular job. Unfortunately, this is not always possible or realistic. Other outcomes include return to modified duty, return to a different job, return to a different employer, or the determination of a permanent total disability.

Like any system, the disability system has its own vocabulary (Table 1). It is important to define and understand the terminology to effectively communicate within the system.

BASIC PRINCIPLES OF DISABILITY MANAGEMENT

Disability management is a comprehensive approach to integrating programs and services to help control employers' disability costs while helping employees who have been disabled return to full functionality and productive work as soon as they can.[17] To accomplish this goal efficiently and effectively, the health practitioner should understand some basic principles, including the following:

- Prevent exacerbation and aggravation
- Focus on functional ability rather than pain
- Set realistic recovery and return to work expectations
- Specify limitations and abilities
- Assess medical and psychosocial factors
- Communicate effectively with the patient and employer
- Consider vocational rehabilitation when indicated
- Practice recurrence management.

Effective disability management begins with prevention. Disability management too often begins after an employee has already developed an injury or illness and missed work. An effective disability management technique is to prevent the injury or illness.[3] This requires loss prevention strategies and interventions such as worksite health and safety programs, attention to ergonomic and industrial hygiene issues, and establishing stay at work and proactive return to work programs. Prevention programs should stress employee accountability and be relevant in occupational and nonoccupational settings. For example, safe climbing techniques learned in the workplace should be followed at home. Likewise, promoting healthy lifestyles can have a positive impact on work safety and productivity.

Preventive measures also should include the examination of the employer's policies and procedures and the employee benefit plan. Policies and procedures should be in place and enforced to promote early reporting, direction to the appropriate health care provider, and the ability to accommodate an employee in a modified capacity (transitional duty) until he or she is able to return to full duty. The benefit plan design is often overlooked as an important factor in contributing to excessive absenteeism. Some group benefit plans pay disability benefits for prolonged periods at up to 100% of salary, or an employer may supplement WC payments with

TABLE 1.   Definitions of Disability Management Terms

Case Management

A systematic approach to identifying, coordinating, implementing, and evaluating the delivery of health care to an individual to meet quality-of-care and cost-containment objectives.

Claims Management

A comprehensive approach to handling claims that includes ongoing assessment of the employee's disability, assessment and coordination of medical and vocational rehabilitation sources, and determination of the employee's eligibility for other benefit plan offsets to reduce the cost of the claim.

Disability—Workers' Compensation

A physical or psychological condition that occurs in or results from the workplace and that actually or presumptively results in a loss of earning power. Disabilities may be partial or total, temporary or permanent.

Disability, Permanent Partial

A disability in which some portion of earning power is lost and the loss is expected to last for the individual's lifetime.

Disability, Permanent Total

A disability in which all earning power is lost and the loss is expected to last for the individual's lifetime. In many states, workers' compensation laws specify certain injuries as permanent total disabilities even if the injured person is able to do some work. Compensation may be limited by time or amount, or it may run for life.

Disability, Temporary Partial

A disability in which some portion of earning power is temporarily lost but from which complete recovery is expected. Benefits are generally based on a percentage of the difference between the person's predisability wage and what he or she can earn during disability.

Disability, Temporary Total

A disability in which all earning power is temporarily lost but from which complete recovery is expected. Benefits are payable until the individual returns to employment at some level of predisability earnings.

Disability—Group

Long-Term Disability Plan

Benefit plan that replaces a portion of income (usually 50%, 60%, or 66⅔%) lost because of an injury or illness that lasts for an extended time and prevents an employee from performing all the material duties of his or her job. After a waiting period (e.g., 90 or 180 days), benefits are payable until the employee retires or reaches a specified age, provided the disability is continuous.

Short-Term Disability Plan

A plan that replaces a portion (usually 50%, 60%, or 66⅔%) of income lost because of an injury or illness that prevents an employee from performing the duties of his or her job. Benefits are usually paid following a waiting period (e.g., 7 days) and may continue for various periods: 1 week, 13 weeks, 26 weeks, 52 weeks, or until long-term disability benefits become payable.

Disability Case Management

A systematic approach to identifying, evaluating, and coordinating the delivery of disability-related services to individuals; the objective is to improve return to work outcomes for employees who become disabled and financial results for employers.

Duration Control Guidelines

Guidelines on the characteristic duration of different types of disabilities according to diagnoses, symptoms, and occupational factors; used to evaluate occupational and nonoccupational disabilities and determine expected return to work dates.

Early Intervention

Initiation of a variety of "case management" and stay at work or return to work efforts as soon as possible after an actual or potentially disabling event occurs. It involves communication among employees, physicians, employers, claims administrators, and rehabilitation specialists.

Impairment

Any loss or abnormality of psychological, physiologic, or anatomic function.

Indemnity

In workers' compensation, the benefit paid to replace lost wages; generally a tax-free replacement of two thirds of the predisability wage, up to a maximum.

Loss Prevention

Activities that focus on preventing injuries or illnesses; typically refers to ergonomics, safety, and wellness programs.

Managed Care

A system of health care delivery that seeks to influence utilization and cost of services while measuring performance. The goal is to control costs while providing access to high-quality care.

Managed Disability

A comprehensive approach to integrating all disability benefits, programs, and services to help control the employer's disability costs while returning the employee to work as soon as possible and maximizing the employee's functional capacity.

Table continued on facing page.

TABLE 1 (Cont).   Definitions of Disability Management Terms

Return to Work Program
An employer-sponsored effort to assist employees who are recovering from a disability. Accommodations may include limited hours, modified tasks, or entirely different jobs. The objective is a safe and gradual return to full regular employment.

Salary Continuation
An uninsured plan provided to a salaried workforce for periods of illness or injury ranging from 1 week to several months. The benefit period may be tied to service, job performance, and union contracts. Benefit amounts—typically 100% of earnings for some period, then a lower percentage (e.g., 60%)—may be coordinated with workers' compensation and other group disability benefits. Also called sick leave.

Transitional Return to Work Program
A program to enable employees who have been disabled to return to modified work with retraining options. The onsite program coordinates the efforts of company-based physical therapists, physicians, department supervisors, occupational health nurses, and supplier-provided disability management services.

Transitional Work
Changes in the work environment to allow an employee who has been disabled to return to work at a job that is less physically or mentally demanding then his or her previous assignment. Modifications may include job restructuring, assistive devices, workstation modifications, reduced hours, or reassignment to another job. Also known as modified work or light duty.

Twenty-Four Hour Program
A program that integrates management, payment, and coverages for group health (medical), group disability (short-term and long-term disability), and workers' compensation benefits. The objective is to better serve employees and employers and reduce administrative costs by dissolving the boundaries between occupational and nonoccupational benefits.

Workers' Compensation Program
State-mandated system under which employers assume the cost of medical treatment and wage losses for employees who suffer job-related illnesses or injuries, regardless of who is at fault. In return, employees are generally prohibited from suing employers, even if the disabling event was due to employer negligence. U.S. government employees, harbor workers, and railroad workers are not covered by state workers' compensation laws but instead by various federally administered laws.

From The Language of Managed Disability, William M. Mercer, Incorporated, Met DisAbility, Washington Business Group on Health, 1995; with permission.

short-term disability. This can result in the employee receiving more than 100% of his or her salary. Such practices do not promote incentives to return to work and therefore make effective disability management difficult.

One must understand that the initial visit to the physician has a significant influence on the outcome. At the initial visit, the treatment plan is often established and return to work expectations are set. An appropriate treatment plan aimed at maintaining or restoring function as soon as possible is the sine qua non of a successful initial office visit. Several practice guidelines are available that provide diagnostic and treatment recommendations for management of common disorders such as low back pain and other occupational disorders.[1,4] Because disability is a functional concept, the provider should focus on the patient's abilities rather than disabilities. An overemphasis on pain alone may lead to prolonged inactivity and disability.[22]

The provider should make every effort to keep the employee at work, if medically appropriate. This requires close communication with the worksite to explore alternative work opportunities that are consistent with the patient's limitations. The importance of avoiding a disability is illustrated in a recent study by Hashemi et al. of WC low back pain claims. The study found that, in general, half of the claimants who remain on disability at the end of "n" weeks will be off disability at the end of "6 × n" weeks. For example, half of the claimants who miss 1 week of work because of low back pain will be off disability at 6 weeks.[11]

If, however, a patient is disabled, periodic evaluations of the patient's functional ability should be performed and results communicated to the employer to facilitate an appropriate return to work outcome. One should understand that recovery may be influenced not only by medical factors but also by psychosocial factors.

The return to work decision requires intimate knowledge of the employer's policies and procedures, job demands, modified duty availability, and other workplace issues. It is not reasonable to expect the physician to know all of these details. The physician, however, is often asked by the employer or insurer to determine whether an employee can return to work. It is the employer who decides whether the company can safely accommodate the employee given the employee's limitation. The physician's role should be to delineate these limitations. The physician can help the employer with the return to work decision by matching the functional requirements of the available job with the limitations and functional ability of the patient. This interactive communication can help allay the patient's and employer's concerns regarding reinjury and promote an optimal outcome. This discourse also may reduce the potential for conflict among the provider, the patient, and the employer. Disability case managers can help by coordinating information and communicating expectations among the employee, employer, provider, and disability carrier.

Vocational rehabilitation should be considered if it becomes apparent that the impairment will be permanent and that the patient can no longer perform the requirements of their job. It is important to make a timely decision to begin vocational rehabilitation efforts rather than continuing ineffective medical management.

Recurrence management is designed to identify and correct the factors that contributed to the disability. It may include loss prevention, ergonomics, or industrial hygiene interventions. One cannot ignore the psychosocial issues contributing to the disability, and a plan to address the psychosocial issues should be part of the recurrence management strategy. As part of the preventive strategy and philosophy, recurrence management is an important element in a comprehensive disability management program.

RELATIONSHIP BETWEEN MEDICAL CARE AND DISABILITY

A dynamic relationship exists between medical care and disability; the process and outcome of one affects the process and outcome of the other. Maximum efficiency can be achieved when there is a proper balance between the appropriate timing and use of medical services and the duration of disability. Medical treatment strategies can influence the duration of disability. If a provider takes an overly conservative approach to treatment, the period of disability is likely to be prolonged. On the other hand, unnecessary diagnostic testing and excessive or inappropriate treatment can prolong disability. Likewise, an employer's ability to accommodate an injured worker in a modified capacity (transitional duty) can influence the treatment plan. For example, if an employer requires that an employee return to his or her regular strenuous job and does not have a transitional duty program, it is likely that the physician will order expensive treatment modalities such as extensive work hardening.

The total cost of care includes the medical costs and the disability costs regardless of who is paying or whether the disability falls under group or workers' compensation. In the group health model, where the medical and disability costs are frequently managed by different entities, inefficiencies may occur. There is better coordination of the medical care and disability management in the workers' compensation system because, by definition, the payment and management source is one vendor or department.

Over the past several years considerable interest has been generated in a fully integrated medical and disability system. The so-called "24-hour program" integrates medical care and disability management in both the WC and group health systems. In other words, one entity has responsibility for the group health medical plan, group health disability plan, and management of the medical and indemnity portions of WC. The theory is that this fully integrated system will streamline the administrative expenses, provide a single point of entry for treatment, coordinate information, and improve outcomes. This system makes intuitive sense, but due to its complexity and corporate buyers' internal organizational issues, few large-scale successes have been documented.

Integrated disability is a hybrid of the 24-hour concept in which occupational and nonoccupational disability is managed by one entity but the medical care is not fully integrated into this system. Integrated disability has gained some recognition because many employers offer their employees multiple group medical plans. The coordination and control of multiple medical plans is quite difficult and expensive. Therefore, excluding the medical portion of the 24-hour systems has some appeal.

FACTORS INFLUENCING THE LENGTH OF DISABILITY

Many factors influence the duration of disability and the return to work outcome, including medical, social, economic, occupational, and psychological factors. The practitioner needs to evaluate the impact of these factors on the outcome.

Medical Factors

Within a specific diagnosis there can exist significant variability in the length of disability. Some of the reasons for the variability include the following:[15]
- The severity of the illness or injury
- The individual's response to treatment
- The course of recovery
- The stage at which the illness or injury is detected and treated
- The availability of effective treatment
- Whether the treatment is medical or surgical.

Age clearly has an effect on healing, recovery, and return to work. Older patients tend to take more time to recover and return to work. One study found that workers older than 60 averaged 7% longer off work than workers between 25 and 54.[8]

Comorbid conditions can influence healing and recovery, but not all comorbid conditions equally affect recovery from the primary condition. For example, diabetes may affect the recovery from surgery but have no adverse effect on recovery from a back sprain.

Medications also can influence the length of disability. Medications that have adverse side effects may delay a return to work. Some side effects, such as sedation, may have safety implications and therefore prolong disability.

All of these factors need to be considered when estimating the duration of disability. Published disability duration guidelines give an estimate of reasonable disability durations for specific conditions.[7,15] The guidelines consider the medical condition or procedure and the physical requirements of the job to which the patient will return. It is helpful for the practitioner to consult these guidelines to help set the return to work expectation with the patient.

Nonmedical Factors Influencing Outcome

Psychosocial and occupational factors influencing the return to work outcome are increasingly recognized as playing a significant role. The practitioner must be aware of these factors and how they may contribute to a patient's motivation and successful return to work.

Workplace issues should be evaluated when determining case management strategy. The worker's relationship with the supervisor and coworkers can influence a worker's incentive to return to work. A recent poor appraisal, downsizing, job transfer, labor strife, or disciplinary action also can affect outcome. Bigos et al. reported that nonphysical factors such as job task dissatisfaction and distress may affect the reporting of back injuries and patients' responses to medical treatments.[5,6] Workplace policies and procedures also can have a significant effect on the return to work outcome. The ability to accommodate a worker in a modified capacity will facilitate an early return to work and reduce the duration of disability.

Early reporting of an injury and subsequent disability is often mentioned as a necessary component of a successful disability management program. Liberty Mutual Insurance Company has found in an unpublished study examining WC claims that when the first report time lag increases, disability duration and overall claims costs also increase. An injury reported 15–21 days after the accident will typically have 19% longer disability duration than an incident reported within 7 days. The same holds true in group disability. If an absence is not reported promptly, it essentially goes unmanaged until it becomes known to the disability management group. At such time, the return to work expectations are well entrenched in the treatment plan, and it is difficult to effect a change in this expectation if the original return to work date is not realistic or does not take into account the availability of modified duty.

Litigation also can increase the duration and costs associated with a disability. In another unpublished study, Liberty Mutual Insurance Company examined all lost-time WC claims from 1992–1995 reported to their company. Temporary total disability on litigated claims was more than three times longer than nonlitigated claims.

In a study performed in Wisconsin in 1989 and 1990, the Workers' Compensation Research Institute found that workers who had long periods of disability had the following nonmedical characteristics: had job tenure less than 6 months, had periods of unemployment in the year or 2 before injury, did not return to the preinjury employer, worked at smaller firms, and were represented by an attorney.[8]

Psychological distress and psychopathology have been studied as they relate to chronic back pain and disability.[9,10,21] Psychological factors such as depression and anxiety play a role in recovery and ultimately in the return to work outcome. The practitioner should evaluate psychological factors and develop an appropriate intervention strategy, which may involve a referral to a mental health professional for treatment.

"Red flags" are often present that indicate that psychosocial issues are interfering with recovery and return to work, including noncompliance, missed appointments, symptom magnification, and a lack of physical findings associated with subjective complaints. It is useful for the practitioner to evaluate why these problems are present. Speaking to a family member, the patient's supervisor, or case manager will often clarify the situation.

Another nonmedical issue affecting return to work outcomes is so-called information asymmetry, a situation in which the worker, supervisor, and treating health professional do not have critical information to make a reasonable decision. The health care provider may not know that there is a modified duty option available, and this can influence his or her decision to return a worker to work. One of the most important functions in disability case management is coordinating the information while maintaining patient confidentiality.

OUTCOMES

Because the goal of disability management is return to work and improved function, the costs and savings associated with return to work form the basis of disability measurements. A disability management program can be measured by the percentage of temporarily disabled employees returned to work, wage/salary replacement costs, medical costs, duration of disability, savings, and return on investment. The ability to capture these costs depends on the system under which one is operating. For example, it is relatively easy for a WC carrier to calculate the medical and indemnity costs associated with a specific claim. However, in the group arena medical costs and disability costs are captured and managed by different vendors. It is quite difficult to identify which disability costs are associated with a specific disability claim in the group health system.

The duration of disability is often measured in "days of disability," which are figured by calculating the difference between the last day worked and the return to work date. Some payors use the duration of disability payments as a surrogate for disability duration. This is less accurate because it does not take into account an elimination period, if one exists, and interruptions in absence. In calculating the duration of disability it is important to distinguish between a return to modified duty or full duty; this distinction has financial and productivity implications. The duration of disability also may be used to estimate the indirect costs associated with lost productivity.

Savings are often reported but are imprecise at best. The most frequently used method is to calculate the difference between the doctor's estimated return to work date and the actual return to work date. The difference in days is then multiplied by the average disability payment. Theoretically the savings are attributable to those involved in the disability management process, including the provider, employer, and disability manager. Ideally one should look at the disability incidence rate over time, and the reduction in disability dollars paid is an indicator for success. This requires accurate baseline data, which are often absent.

The return on investment is a simple calculation whereby the calculated savings are divided by the cost of performing the disability management process. One cannot forget that there are administrative costs associated with disability management. If one spends more on managing the disability than is saved by an appropriate return to work outcome, one has gained at best a Pyrrhic victory.

CONCLUSION

Many of the same strategies and techniques used in medical managed care are being used today in disability management and have led to improved outcomes. Bernacki and Tsai demonstrated that employing a comprehensive approach to workplace injuries can result in demonstrable savings. Applying preventive and managed care techniques to the workers' compensation system reduced per-capita loss by 23%.[3]

Managed workers' compensation, along with the regulatory reform that has occurred in many states, has been credited with dramatically reducing the medical and disability costs in workers' compensation.[14] The annual growth rate in the average medical cost per lost-time case has been reduced from 12% during 1980–1990 to 5% during 1990–1996. The growth rate in the average indemnity cost per lost-time case has been reduced from 9% during 1980–1990 to 0% annual growth during 1990–1995.

A 1996 survey of 251 employers on the issue of integrated disability management found the following:[16]

- Occupational and nonoccupational disabilities are often treated very differently even though appropriate treatment and a timely return to work are equally important for both.
- Only a quarter of all survey respondents coordinated their overall disability approach, but many were coordinating selected elements of their programs.
- Coordination of disability programs with medical care is far from universal. A total of 47% of respondents coordinated workers' compensation with medical care while only 27% coordinated short-term and long-term disability with the treatment received under the employee's medical coverage.

This study illustrates that even though employers demonstrate awareness of and interest in managed disability, there remains a significant opportunity to affect the costs associated with disability through a comprehensive, integrated managed disability program.

REFERENCES

1. American College of Occupational and Environmental Medicine: Low back complaints. In Harris JS (ed): Occupational Medicine Practice Guidelines: Evaluation and Management of Common Health Problems and Functional Recovery in Workers. Beverly Farms, MA, OEM Press, 1997, pp 14-1–14-30.
2. American Medical Association: Guides to the Evaluation of Permanent Impairment. 4th ed. Chicago, AMA, 1995.
3. Bernacki EJ, Tsai SP: Managed care for workers' compensation: Three years experience in an "employee choice" state. J Occup Environ Med 38:1091–1097, 1996.
4. Bigos S, Bowyer O, Braen G, et al: Acute Low Back Problems in Adults. Clinical Practice Guideline No. 14. Rockville, MD, Agency for Health Care Policy and Research, 1994, AHCPR publication 95-0642.
5. Bigos SJ, Battie MC, Spengler DM, et al: A longitudinal, prospective study of industrial back injury reporting. Clin Orthop 279:21–34, 1992.
6. Bigos SJ, Battie MC, Spengler DM, et al: A prospective study of work perception and psychosocial factors affecting the report of back injury. Spine 16:1–6, 1991.
7. Bruckman RZ, Rasmussen H: Healthcare Management Guidelines. Vol 7. New York, Milliman and Robertson, 1996.
8. Galizzi M, Boden LI: What are the Most Important Factors Shaping Return to Work? Evidence from Wisconsin. Cambridge, MA, Workers' Compensation Research Institute, 1996.
9. Gatchel RJ, Polatin PB, Kinney RK: Predicting outcome of chronic back pain using clinical predictors of psychopathology: A prospective analysis. Health Psychol 14:415–420, 1995.
10. Gatchel RJ, Polatin PB, Mayer TG, Garcy PD: Psychopathology and the rehabilitation of patients with chronic low back pain disability. Arch Phys Med Rehabil 75:666–670, 1994.
11. Hashemi L, Webster BS, Clancy EA, Volinn E: Length of disability and cost of workers' compensation low back claims. J Occup Environ Med 39:937–945, 1997.
12. Kerns WC: Cash benefits for short-term sickness, 1970–94. Social Security Bulletin 60:49–53, 1997.
13. Leigh PJ, Markowitz SB, Fahs M, et al: Occupational injury and illness in the United States. Estimates of costs, morbidity, and mortality. Arch Intern Med 157:1557–1568, 1997.
14. National Council on Compensation Insurance: Issues Report. Boca Raton, Florida, NCCI, 1997.
15. Reed P: The Medical Disability Advisor: Workplace Guidelines for Disability Duration. 3rd ed. Boulder, CO, Reed Groups Ltd., 1997.
16. Staying at Work: Value Creation Through Integration. New York City, Watson Wyatt Worldwide, 1997.
17. The Language of Managed Disability. Washington, DC, William M. Mercer, Inc. Met DisAbility, Washington Business Group on Health, 1995.
18. UNUM Insurance Co., unpublished data.
19. Vincenzino JV: Health care cost: Market forces and reform. Statistical Bulletin Metropolitan Insurance Company 76(1):29–35, 1995.

20. Vincenzino JV: Trends in medical care cost-revisited. Statistical Bulletin Metropolitan Insurance Company 78(3):10–16, 1997.
21. Waddel G, Main CJ, Morris EW, et al: Chronic low back pain, psychological distress and illness behavior. Spine 9:209–213, 1984.
22. Waddell G: A new clinical model for the treatment of low-back pain. Spine 12:632–644, 1986.
23. World Health Organization: International Classification of Impairments, Disabilities, and Handicaps. Geneva, WHO, 1980.

JANE C. HALL, RN, MPA, CCM

STATE OF THE ART
CASE MANAGEMENT

From AON Consulting
San Francisco, California

Reprint requests to:
Jane C. Hall, RN, CCM
AON Consulting
333 Bush, Suite 600
San Francisco, CA 94105

Case management is one of the tools that is used in the implementation and maintenance of managed care programs. The impetus for the growth of formal case management was the exponential growth in medical costs and an increasing awareness and appreciation for the direct and indirect costs of disability. Employers, insurers, and payors had an abrupt wake-up call, to which they responded by creating incentives for employees to select a managed care model of health care delivery. While workers' compensation did not experience the explosive move to managed care models seen in group health, it has come under much closer scrutiny in recent years, leading to the current focus on absence management, integrated disability management, and a search for the tools to implement a totally integrated health care model.

Occupational case management focuses heavily on returning the injured or ill person to productive work at the earliest possible time, consistent with the individual's restrictions. In addition, the case manager often acts as a benefits administrator for the employer and as a patient advocate for individual employees. The case manager may assist with job analysis, supervisor education, return of the employee to modified or full duty, and follow-up during the recovery period.

Case management has been in existence since the first time that a person took care of another person. It then grew to one person taking care of a group of people. This altruistic model was adapted by business and industry in the United States when the steel mills in the early 1900s hired a nurse to take care of their employees and their families. The Visiting Nurse Association gave birth to a community-based model of case management, and the military advanced the concept by forming a corps of nurses to provide care to military personnel. The evolution of case management was furthered in the formal sense by the advent of utilization review, discharge planning, and today's rapidly growing models of managed care. Examples of case management are now found in most areas of health care.

THE ORIGINS AND DEVELOPMENT OF CASE MANAGEMENT

The metamorphosis of case management into a formal profession and practice with defined standards and credentialing is a relatively new phase. In early 1990 a group in Rolling Meadows, Illinois, chartered an association for the certification of case managers. This body provides certification based on education and experience.[6] Many occupational health constituents, wishing to apply for case management credentials, are finding their applications being rejected by the credentialing body. One key reason is that the job descriptions of occupational health nurses frequently do not directly refer to their case management role. The job descriptions must be written to reflect the case management process of assessment, planning, implementation, coordination, monitoring, and evaluation.

The Case Management Society of America (CMSA), founded in 1991, formulated and published standards of practice in 1995. The CMSA defines case management as "a collaborative process which assesses, plans, implements, coordinates, monitors and evaluates the options and services required to meet an individual's health needs, using communication and available resources to promote quality, cost effective outcomes."[6]

TYPES OF CASE MANAGEMENT MODELS

Telephonic and Field Models of Case Management

Case management services are delivered either by telephone or in the field. The most effective models use a combination of services from each in a seamless manner. With telephonic case management, a group of case managers in one location traditionally perform an initial phone assessment and then follow-up with frequent telephone calls to the stakeholders. Delivering this service costs considerably less than the field case management model. Field case management refers to services that are performed in person with the patient, physician or other vendor, adjuster, and the employer. Different skills are needed to use each of the models. In telephonic case management the nuances of verbal communication assume greater importance; the case manager's listening skills must allow him or her to correctly interpret what is being said without the benefit of nonverbal communication. Field case managers must be able to read body language. Both groups must be effective at establishing rapport, negotiation, and patient advocacy. Best practices in telephonic and field case management include the following:

- Development of the most cost-effective case plans consistent with the medical and disability goals
- Timely identification of risks for delayed recovery followed by appropriate communication and interventions
- Monitoring of patient compliance with the treatment plan and early identification of barriers to compliance
- Monitoring of outcomes against medical and disability management criteria
- Negotiation of earliest possible return to work within medical restrictions

Internal Versus External Models

Case managers work and are employed in a multitude of settings: insurance companies and third party administrators, employer worksite, hospitals, and agencies. They also may be self-employed. If the case manager is employed by the payor or the employer, the model is called an "internal model." The case manager may be the nurse or medical management coordinator for the company. The advantages are that the case manager will know the ill or injured worker, know the job requirements from a physical standpoint, and usually will be able to effect positive return to work programs. On the negative side, employees may see the nurse as representing the company and feel that he or she does not have their best interest at heart. This may result in a less satisfied client and a higher litigation rate than if the case manager is external to the company.

An "external model" exists if the case manager is self-employed or employed by an agency. The use of such case managers, while often beneficial, is expensive and should be judicious. In addition, the external case manager should be managed as any other vendor would be, with agreed responsibilities and clearly defined expectations for performance outcomes.

Background Knowledge and Skill Mix

Most case managers in occupational health have a nursing or rehabilitation background. Because the certification process is relatively new, many case managers are not yet certified. As competition among vendors of case management services increases, the requirement for certification will be mandated by those who are paying for case management services.

Case Management Skills

The knowledge bases of nurses and rehabilitation professionals readily lend themselves to the case management process. As within any group of individuals, there will be a range of skills and expertise. The best skills for positive outcomes have been defined as "agreeableness followed by intellect, conscientiousness, extroversion, and emotionality."[7] Other skills that lead to positive outcomes include negotiation, communication, empathy, creativity, flexibility, attention to detail, strategic thinking, organization, enthusiasm, and computer literacy.

Differences of opinion exist regarding what professional and educational qualifications a case manager should have. The certification requirements have changed over time, but in the future can be expected to include postgraduate education, experience consistent with demonstrable medical and disability functions, business knowledge, and computer literacy. The utilization of outcomes and metrics will help the case manager and other stakeholders to move toward excellence rather than allow cases to become stagnant.

Roles and Responsibilities

CASE MANAGER AND THE PATIENT

The case manager is first and foremost the advocate for the employee. To be successful in this role, the case manager must be able to readily establish rapport with the patient. This may not be a simple matter, because some patients will suspect the case manager of acting on behalf of the insurance company or insurer. As the general population increasingly experiences managed care, the case manager initially may be viewed as the person who can deny care. The ability to establish rapport and involve the patient as the critical stakeholder in the recovery process is the prerequisite for success.

CASE MANAGER AND THE PHYSICIAN

Physicians also may view the case manager with suspicion. They have experienced denial of payment for treatments, hospitalizations, and other services in the form of utilization review. Physicians tend to dislike anyone else being responsible for "overseeing" the care of their patients. Some physicians, however, have seen benefits to their patients and to themselves in the assistance of the case manager in negotiating the utilization review and claim management systems to obtain the maximum benefits for their patients.

CASE MANAGER AND THE ADJUSTER

The interaction between the case manager and adjuster can be especially challenging. The adjuster, who has the overall financial responsibility for the case, generally does not have a medical background. What makes sense to the case manager medically and financially may not be understood by the adjuster as anything other than an expense.

Some companies have taken advantage of the system by using case management to enhance their own revenues. An unmanaged case management program may actually escalate costs by allowing unfocused activities and keeping the case management portion of the case open longer than necessary. On the other hand, some claim adjusters use case managers judiciously to produce positive case outcomes. By defining the desired services and overseeing the case administratively, the use of the case manager is beneficial for all parties.

THE CASE MANAGEMENT PROCESS

The elements of the case management process closely follow those of the business management model as defined by CMSA (see page 706).

Assessment

In the assessment phase, the case manager gathers information on the physical, emotional, and social aspects of the patient's condition and the goals of all the stakeholders, including the patient and his or her family. This may necessitate a series of interviews telephonically or in person with the patient, patient's family, physician, employer, and claim adjuster. In the initial interview with the patient, also referred to as the client, permission is obtained to speak with the necessary parties to assist with the planning of care. This authorization should be given in writing to avoid any future liability that might arise from alleged breaches of confidentiality. The case manager must always retain advocacy for the patient. In the assessment process, the case manager must be an adept listener and observer. Interviewing skills and knowledge of body language are requisite to obtaining the information necessary to provide the groundwork for the plan of care. Basic information such as the age and gender of the patient, previous physical and mental health, working conditions, and family relationships will identify areas for more in-depth investigation. Identified comorbidities will need further assessment to determine if they are likely to contribute to delayed recovery or will be barriers to the care plan. The role of the patient in the family is especially important in determining additional assistance that may be needed during the recovery process. For instance, if the patient is a parent who assumes total care of young children for part of the day, alternative care may need to be arranged if the patient has a condition that would preclude the lifting of the children during the recovery phase. In occupational health, the usual activity of the patient during nonwork hours is often not given adequate attention and, when delayed recovery occurs, the family situation is often overlooked as a cause.

During the assessment process, the case manager must contact the employer to obtain a functional job description, determine the company's attitude toward modified work, and establish rapport to support the earliest possible return to work for the client. The relationship between the supervisor and the client is important because a high correlation has been demonstrated between the supervisor/client relationship and the early return to work of the injured or ill person. If a negative rapport exists, the case manager will note that a "red flag" exists for prompt return to work. The employer is not entitled to personal medical information but is entitled in a workers' compensation case to know information directly relating to the condition and recovery of the employee. When personal medical information is an overlay to the case, the case manager must use caution to avoid conveying any information that should be maintained as confidential.

While much of case management is conducted telephonically, catastrophic cases, cases of delayed recovery, and cases with identifiable barriers or red flags (risk factors) warrant a home visit. The assessment performed in the home should include identification of physical barriers such as stairways, noise factors, and walking hazards. The usual physical responsibilities of the individual should be identified, including child care, elder care, laundry, and grocery shopping. The attitude of others in the home toward the ill or injured person should be evaluated for codependency, supportive or nonsupportive behaviors, and religious or cultural values and beliefs with regard to recovery.

Case managers are often used on a one-time basis to accompany the patient to the physician visit. The purpose of the visit may be to help the case manager and patient understand the treatment plan, to obtain the physician's assessment of the restrictions needed for the person to return to work successfully, or to determine the physician's expectations as to the need for surgery. Some physicians are resistant to the interaction of the case manager in these respects and actually pose a barrier to the successful case management plan. More education is needed to assure physicians that the case manager is a patient advocate—even if the case manager is employed by the third-party administrator. When an insurer or third-party administrator has denied a particular service under its utilization management prerogative, it is often the case manager working in partnership with the physician who is able to facilitate resolution that is agreeable to the patient and physician. The key to this is a full assessment by the case manager with full contributing information from the physician.

The assessment process also clarifies the payors involved in the medical and disability management process. A full understanding of the usual and customary services to be provided, plan limits, and the appeals process is critical during the implementation process. The case manager should identify any areas where coverage for an expected service is not immediately available. The assessment process is carried out when the case manager initially opens the case and may be done subsequently in the case process when barriers or unexpected events occur. The entire process is interactive and requires flexibility and reprioritization of goals as the situation changes. Table 1 outlines a sample case management assessment and evaluation checklist.[2]

TABLE 1. Sample Case Management Assessment and Evaluation Checklist

Information to Be Obtained	Rationale
Age	Age affects recovery time, rehabilitation.
Gender	Gender may play a role in recovery time.
Years of service with the company	Raises issues such as motivation to return to work and interest in medical retirement.
Length of time in current position	In-depth knowledge of a position will aid in developing opportunities for modified work
Previous workers' compensation injury	If yes, the case manager will want to determine employee's attitudes as a result of that experience: previous history in return to modified work, litigation.
Current injury, diagnosis, and treatment	In addition to gathering the particulars, it is important to note any areas in which the employee, provider, or adjuster lacks full information.
Diagnostic testing	Determine what tests have been conducted and the results; also review inappropriate tests and tests that might be expected but have not been done.
Medications (a) Appropriateness of use (b) Use of other personal medications (c) Outcomes of (a) and/or (b)	Some personal medications may have an additive or negative combination effect. Patients may not be taking medication in the appropriate timeframe or manner, thus delaying recovery. Medications that seem ineffective or have side effects should be brought to the attention of the physician.
Physical medicine modalities and results	Modalities should be scientifically based, and if a patient is not showing progress after 4–6 weeks, a reevaluation by the physician should be initiated.
Expectations as to disability duration Physician Patient Family	Expectations of disability may subtly influence the recovery.
Psychosocial variables	Family and social issues may be incentives or disincentives in the recovery process. This is an area in which case managers may frequently uncover hidden agendas—issues that would have delayed recovery if not addressed.
Communication	Employee's failing to receive a timely workers' compensation payment, or uncertainty as to how the workers' compensation system works, has one of the highest correlations with the employee's initiation of litigation. The case manager fills a vital role as liaison with the employee, providers, employer, and third-party administrator.

From DiBenedetto DV, Hall JC: Workers' Compensation and Disability Case Management. The OEM Report 9(12), 1995; with permission.

Barriers to Recovery

Red flags or barriers to recovery frequently can be identified in the assessment process. These are factors of the case that, if not addressed, may result in poor clinical outcomes, delayed recovery, and delayed return to the activities of daily living and work. Barriers in occupational health cases might include one or more of the following:

- Catastrophic injury such as amputation, severe burns, and head or spinal cord injuries
- Previous litigated workers' compensation cases
- Patient dislike of the treatment facility or physician

- Drug or alcohol use
- Disability beyond 6 weeks
- Communication problems
- Patient resistance to return to work
- Poor rapport with supervisor
- Supervisor unwilling to take employee back with restrictions
- Failed back syndrome
- Reflex sympathetic dystrophy
- Frequent request for change of treating physician

Evaluation and Planning

Following the assessment, the case manager will evaluate the plan options to select the areas where intervention will support the best outcomes. Short-term and long-term plans are delineated. Measurable timelines and outcomes will be established based on the goals of the stakeholders as identified in the assessment process. The timelines and expected outcomes will be shared with all of the stakeholders. If barriers have been identified, contingency plans may need to be formulated. The goal for all parties is to have no negative surprises in the recovery of the individual. Critical to this phase of the process is ongoing communication with the patient and other stakeholders to ensure that all needs are being met and that there is consensus on the plan prior to implementation.

Implementation

Implementation of the case management plan takes place with each of the stakeholders. The case manager must monitor all facets of the case plan and timelines and provide regular feedback to the stakeholders regarding what is and is not working appropriately. Proposed changes to the plan go through the assessment and evaluation stage before they are enacted. The case management skills of negotiation, facilitation, creativity, and flexibility are often challenged at this point in the process. The process should be one of forward movement of the case. If the case appears to be in stasis, further assessment and evaluation are necessary to identify why the case has failed to progress. New barriers must be identified and addressed with all parties. Most failures at this juncture in the process are due to unidentified red flags and frequently are psychosocial in nature.

Monitoring

Monitoring is often considered the only step in the process that case management provides. If such a perception exists—if the case manager is only providing documentation of the case activity or lack thereof—a change in case manager is needed. Case managers should be proactive, results-oriented, and their monitoring of the case an ongoing report card of case flow, activity, and results according to the preestablished goals and metrics. Common examples of case management monitoring that result in positive changes in the course of the case include the following:

- Identification of overutilization of physical therapy or medication
- Noncompliance with the medication or treatment regimen
- Disability duration that exceeds the guidelines for the diagnosis without apparent reason
- Psychologic overlay
- Substance abuse
- Family is supporting an illness model rather than a recovery model

TABLE 2. Medical Case Management Metrics

Metric	Best Practice
Diagnosis verified	Diagnosis verified by appropriate test or observations. If diagnosis is not verified, case manager will challenge diagnosis until it is verified.
Evidence-based practice protocols	Ten most common diagnoses will have practice protocols.
Existence of "red flag" alerts case manager to institute or increase case management	Case manager has established criteria or indicators for increased case acuity.
Case manager has specific diagnosis-based disability-duration guidelines to follow.	Low variances from disability-duration guidelines
Resources used for hospital and ambulatory care	Most appropriate resources are identified and used.
Average number of disability days per diagnosis	Documented decrease in disability days
Case cost with case management	Decreased case cost with case management
Case notes/documentation	Well-documented treatment plan, decision making
Hospitalization	Low hospitalization rates (below 5%) coupled with good outcomes
Readmission	Low readmission rate (below 1%)
Medical management	Treatment process changes based on case management information
Individual (worker/patient) satisfaction	Improved patient satisfaction with case management (using a survey tool)

From DiBenedetto DV, Hall JC: Workers' Compensation and Disability Case Management. The OEM Report 9(12), 1995; with permission.

Table 2 provides a sample of case management best practices and case management metrics. Benchmarking against best practice or against similar entities is one way to demonstrate process improvement.

Ethics

The standards of practice for case management are a guide to professional practice. Ethics for the case manager is a "gray area" because no standard of practice or case law has been delineated. Because this is an evolving field, practitioners need to adhere closely to community standards of practice as well as the professional written guidelines. A reasonable rule of assessment where ethics are concerned might be: "The actions contemplated are in the best interest of the patient and take into account the needs of other stakeholders without compromising quality of care." Patient advocacy is the primary responsibility of the case manager. Advocacy does not imply that the case manager will always do what the patient wants but rather that the case manager will advocate services that are in the best interest of the patient. This may bring the case manager into conflict with the payors or providers. It is at this point that the ethics of the case need to be explored by the case manager in conjunction with other professionals. Legal prudence must be exercised and care taken to avoid breaches of confidentiality or self-supportive behaviors.

COST BENEFIT OF THE CASE MANAGEMENT PROCESS

Case costs in the workers' compensation and health benefits areas are affected by direct and indirect costs of both the medical expenditure and indemnity or disability/lost time areas. An essential role of the case manager in occupational health is helping individuals return to work. This part of the overall injury/illness process lends itself to excellent cost-benefit results. To estimate the cost savings for management of using a modified duty program, the following analysis can be performed:

1. Obtain from human resources or payroll the figure for the "average daily wage." If most of the workforce is nonexempt, that figure should be used. If most employees are exempt, the overall average figure is appropriate.

2. Add the number of restricted work days from the Occupational Safety and Health Administration log for both injury and illness.

3. Multiply the sum of restricted work days for the year by the average daily wage to obtain the direct benefit dollars attributable to the modified work program.

Not so easily quantified are the savings from the indirect cost of lost work days, such as replacement labor, training time by supervisors, and less productivity from inexperienced replacement workers. The indirect costs are usually two to ten times higher than the direct costs. A more exact cost of a workers' compensation claim can be calculated using a guideline that is customized to the individual company (Fig. 1).

The cost of disability to the employee can be calculated using the worksheet shown in Figure 2. Case managers use such information to encourage employees to

Check All That Apply	Disability Components	Average Employer Cost
	Workers' compensation indemnity payment/case average	
	Average medical costs/day/injured worker	
	Salary continuation/average cost/case	
	Average LTD costs/day/injured worker	
	Average rehabilitation costs/case	
	Average labor replacement wages/day	
	Average supervisor hourly wage × number of hours of orientation	
	Average per day total of overtime payment to other worker(s) to maintain department daily productivity in the absence of the disabled worker	
	Average unit cost of lost productivity with/without replacement labor	
	Average lost opportunity cost	
	Average turnover cost	
	Average human resources costs in time to recruit/arrange temporary help, orient to policies, etc.	
	Average permanent disability settlements	
	Average legal costs	
	Total	

FIGURE 1. Worksheet to help determine the cost of a workers' compensation claim.

Check All That Apply	Employee Cost Components	Employee Cost
_____	Lost wages that are not covered by workers' compensation or other wage	
_____	Lost wages from inability to do a usual second job	
_____	Lost wages from inability to receive overtime wages	
_____	Decreased accrual of paid time off	
_____	Increased cost of meals(s) from cafeteria subsidy	
_____	Increased utility costs	
_____	Unreimbursed rehabilitation costs	
_____	Litigation costs	
	Total	

	Nonquantifiable
	    Disturbance of work/family routines and roles
	    Spousal impact
	    Loss of ego strength/pride	

FIGURE 2.   Worksheet to determine true costs of disability to an injured employee.

return to work. The longer an individual is out of work with a disability, the less likely it is that he or she will ever return to productive employment.

The benefit of using case management has not often been captured in a standardized financial model. One company with documented financial savings is Southern California Edison, which reportedly has saved $5–8 for each dollar spent on health care case management.[7] In 1995 the *Wall Street Journal* reported that International Rectiflier Corp. experienced a reduction of 25%, or $1.1 million, with the use of two nurses and a part-time medical director to monitor cases, review bills, and counsel employees.[9] Chrysler Corporation reportedly saved 160,000 nonworkers' compensation disability days in the 2 years after initiating the use of WorkAbility, a relational software program that delineates disability durations.[4] Nurses and physicians interact with the treating physicians to effect compliance with the specified disability duration or negotiate the plan based on individual patients needs.

Metrics for the evaluation of case management effectiveness should include patient satisfaction, cost of medical care, number and cost of lost work days, litigation rate and costs, physician satisfaction, and claim administration satisfaction.

INTEGRATED BENEFITS

In the future, case management will deal with integrated benefit services. To provide a seamless service, many case managers will be called upon to cross the current boundaries of occupational and personal health care. Data management technology and skill requirements will be combined with the ongoing worlds of medicine and cost-containment. Outcomes for case management practices will be monitored, and utilization of services will be predicated on delivery guarantees of specific outcomes. Occupational health practitioners will have fewer problems with the transitions than general health care case management practitioners. This is due in large part to the natural occupational health focus on prevention, disability management, and cost-effective delivery of services. Trends away from the conventional onsite, hands-on medical and nursing services will be balanced with new demands for the knowledge and skills of occupational health professionals as case managers.

REFERENCES
1. Cohen EL: Nurse Case Management in the 21st Century. St. Louis, Missouri, Mosby, 1996.
2. DiBenedetto DV, Hall JC: Workers' Compensation and Disability Case Management. The OEM Report 9(12), 1995.
3. Harris JS (ed): Evaluation and Management of Common Health Problems and Functional Recovery in Workers: The ACOEM Occupational Medicine Practice Guidelines. Beverly Farms, Massachusetts, OEM Press, 1997.
4. McDonald M: You can control your disability costs. Business and Health May 1990, pp 21–36.
5. McMahon B, Shrey D: The Americans With Disabilities Act: Disability management and the injured worker. J Workers' Comp 4:9–28, 1992.
6. Mullahy C: The Case Manager's Handbook. Gaithersburg, Maryland, Aspen Publishers, 1995.
7. Quick B: Relationship between personality traits and job satisfaction for case managers. J Care Management 3(5):81, 1997.
8. Resnick R: Case management evolves into a quality care program. Business and Health, September 1992, p 56.
9. Rogers B: Occupational Health Nursing. Philadelphia, WB Saunders, 1994.
10. Rundle R: How one company controls health costs: Office nurses. Wall Street Journal, August 4, 1995.
11. Vander Kolk C: Litigated Disability Cases: A Guide to Utilizing the Vocational Expert. Atlanta, Georgia, Elliott & Fitzpatrick, Inc., 1993.

LAURENCE A. MILLER, MD

NETWORKS IN WORKERS' COMPENSATION MEDICAL DELIVERY

From the Community Care Network
La Jolla, California

Reprint requests to:
Laurence A. Miller, MD
Chief Medical Officer
Community Care Network
5251 Viewridge Court
San Diego, CA 92123

A steadily increasing percentage of workers' compensation cases are cared for within medical networks. The process of enhanced channeling of cases to network providers and increased monitoring and control of cases by these organizations has paralleled the experience in group health programs. This chapter summarizes the history, content, and motivating forces for the development of networks. Terminology and internal function of these entities are explained. The reasons for association with networks, ways of evaluating proposed contracts, and the future role of networks in the managed care system are discussed.

HISTORY OF NETWORKS

Physician networks delivering general and specialized care have a long history. Informal and formal associations of health care providers have played a prominent role in medicine. Among the earliest examples were the guilds of Medieval Europe and, more recently, relationships ranging from scientific societies and teaching institutions to more organized, profit-directed organizations. Contemporary developments have included the establishment of groups of physicians to treat practitioners of certain trades or employers, such as the Kaiser Foundation during World War II, and unofficial panels that served large national employee groups, such as railroad workers and shipbuilders.

During the 1980s, for-profit and non-profit entities began playing an increasingly prominent role in negotiating relationships with providers and hospitals. Initially, many groups were vehicles for labor and industry to contract rates with various aspects of the health care delivery system. For example, Community Care Network (CCN), one of the nation's largest preferred provider organization (PPO) networks, began as a non-profit organization for the purpose of negotiating rates with providers in San Diego. Through a series of mergers, buyouts, and expansions, which resulted in the establishment of a $100 million charitable foundation, the network has grown to include more than 250,000 health care providers, facilities, and ancillary delivery groups. Aside from its non-profit roots, CCN is not atypical of the genesis of many large national networks.

Other networks were created in the 1980s and early 1990s with similar intent but purely on a for-profit basis. Many concentrated on a specific geographic region, were specialty oriented, or proposed a unique delivery model. More recently, for-profit, publicly traded companies composed of multiple clinics have appeared. Some have been very successful, with the capacity to dominate the provision of primary workers' compensations care in certain geographic areas.

It is difficult to estimate the number of medical networks in the United States due to the multiplicity of structures and forms they take. More than 75% of all health care contacts are believed to involve some form of affiliation between payor and provider. In occupational medicine these run the gamut from health care delivery systems of varying sizes to large national PPOs with hundreds of thousands of health care delivery points. Today, many networks include primary care clinics, hospitals, surgery centers, specialized caregivers, vendors of durable medical equipment, pharmacies, and most participants in the occupational health care system.

Why Networks?

What has driven the development of these networks? Some of the factors include the following: (1) discounted fees and the implied medical cost saving, (2) control of the workers' compensation case, (3) quality assurance, and (4) managed care services. Reduced costs as a result of **discounted fees** have been the primary reason for the genesis and use of networks. Recently, this logic has come under much criticism because of the implication that, in states with a low fee schedule relative to physician costs, discounts off the fee schedule would be compensated for by overutilization by physicians. While agreeing that in some situations this has occurred, this author's experience is that on the basis of utilization rates, a discount of 10% yields true savings of 7–8%. Most physicians in workers' compensation do not change their practice habits for a specific patient; nor are they aware of what discount, if any, applies to a specific patient. Therefore, most purchasers and payors view these savings as real and not compromising the quality of care. A reduced medical cost of 10% can represent savings of millions of dollars to a large employer.

Control of the workers' compensation case has been another reason for the success of networks and continues to be of great importance today. Payors correctly theorized that by directing the worker to a group of caregivers that were knowledgeable about the type of injury, familiar with the reporting requirements of the system, and objective relative to the disability aspects of the case, they could restrain total costs. This appeared to be especially true in states with unusually adversarial legal environments and significant fraud rates. The assumption was that in-network referrals avoided many of the problems associated with a random, nondirected choice of physician.

In addition, the networks' **ability to monitor the quality** of its providers has been another development in their favor. Earlier, larger networks had few quality of care criteria by which to evaluate physicians. About 2–10% of doctors were not accepted into the networks based upon malpractice history, licensure, or legal problems. More recently, however, quality of care has gained increasing importance as the primary driver for certain types of networks. As data, especially the integration of disability and indemnity information, become more available, greater emphasis will be placed on outcomes measurements to help choose which physicians will become network providers.

A further compelling reason for the success of networks in workers' compensation has been the integration of other **managed care services** into the networks' package. Not only is there generally a unique association or discounted network of providers, but many networks provide bill review, case management, utilization management, and other associated services. This has made these entities a formidable force in the control of workers' compensation cases. Managed care in workers' compensation is beginning to resemble its group health sister, only without the health maintenance organization (HMO) and capitated payment of physician components. However, systems similar to HMOs and capitation may be on the horizon for workers' compensation.

Three Generations of Networks

As networks have evolved, so has the increasing use of the concepts of first-, second-, and third-generation networks. A first-generation network is one that has not used a great deal of selectivity in credentialing physicians. The intent is to recruit the greatest number of physicians as possible into the network to create a broad geographic coverage and a high density of physicians. In a second-generation network, some profiling of physicians occurs, and the focus is on improved outcomes. A third-generation network has specific profiling, both before selection and on a continuing basis. The intent is to use outcome variables for selection, which results in a small group of physicians, usually drawn from the first-generation network. The idea is that third-generation physicians will provide more cost-effective, outcome-focused care. Data compiled by CCN seem to support the concept of the effectiveness of a third-generation network.

THE CREDENTIALING OF NETWORKS

Credentialing is the process by which agencies document, screen, and select health care practitioners for inclusion in networks. The intent and goals of the organization will define the detail and extent of the credentialing process. For example, agencies that take direct risk (both financial and in health care decision-making) will have labor-intensive, frequent, detailed, and highly selective credentialing. Organizations not considered "at risk" will not be as obsessive about credentialing.

A number of basic elements are included in most, if not all, credentialing processes. Physicians need to understand that these are basic network requirements and having this information available in legible form will greatly simplify the credentialing process. These items include the following:

1. License: when, where, duration, status
2. Training
3. Specialty status
4. Practice associations and locations
5. Malpractice coverage
6. Malpractice history
7. Time in practice
8. Office setting and special skills (languages)
9. Practice capabilities: special physical examination, audiometry, Department of Transportation testing, and others.

There are two approaches to the credentialing process. One is primary source verification, which means that the issuing body verifies all important information. This method requires that state boards, malpractice carriers, and others are directly contacted for information. Primary source verification also can rely on documents supplied by the applicant physician. First-time credentialing using this method can be expensive, costing $50–250 per applicant.

The second approach, delegated credentialing, is the reliance upon another organization's credentialing process as being adequate, and there is automatic acceptance of providers into the network. This occurs when a smaller organization applies for inclusion into the larger network. If the credentialing from the smaller organization is equal in depth and extent to the larger organization, acceptance of that process as being sufficient for credentialing purposes may take place.

Recredentialing is normally mandated by an organization on a routine basis. For many networks recredentialing is performed every 2 years and frequently does not require primary source verification. Some groups, especially those at risk, will recredential providers yearly.

Credentialing, as well as network creation, can be performed directly by the network or by contract with a second party. Many companies have been founded that offer assistance or a complete turnkey operation to the credentialing process. An example is a large national network that wants to rapidly develop a network in a specific state. The process requires delineation of type, number, and location of physicians. If the network does not have an office or personnel in that state, the process may be contracted to a second party, which would then identify, screen, and enroll the physicians in the network. Physicians and facilities need to be aware that solicitation may not always come directly from the contracting network. A careful review of contracting agreements will identify the contracting network and its goals.

An agreement will contain many items that will directly affect a physician's practice, including the following:

1. What is the network (is it different from the contracting agent)? Is it local, regional, or national? What is its reputation?

2. What is the financial arrangement between the network and the physician? Is this a discount arrangement? If so, how is this calculated?

3. What is the duration of the agreement? How can the physician break the agreement?

4. Hold-harmless clauses: what are the liability ramifications?

5. Is the relationship with a directly contracted network or another entity?

6. Is utilization management binding on the facility or network?

7. What agency is the payor? Is it the network, its owner/manager, or another agency?

8. Exclusivity: how close are competing providers to the physician's location?

9. What are the referral requirements? Must referrals always be in-network, and how does that affect a physician's practice?

Scrutiny of these items for the potential impact on a physician's practice should consider both short-term and long-term implications.

JOINING A NETWORK

The evolution of managed care in the United States has followed a well-established path over the past two decades, a journey with which not all practicing physicians have been comfortable. One universal stage in this evolution has involved the enrollment of physicians into various forms of provider networks or associations.

Many physicians have refused to participate because they refuse to accept discounts, refuse to allow potential review or control by other organizations, and believe that such organizations do not represent the best interests of providers or patients. Although these beliefs represent cogent, logical, and even ethical reasons for not joining some networks, in the most competitive workers' compensation markets the channeling capabilities of networks and the increasing power of managed care has resulted in the steady disappearance of physicians or groups that do not participate in networks. Practicing physicians in today's managed care environment must acknowledge the potential impact of networks on their economic survival.

Margins and Discounts

When an individual physician or clinic decides to join a network, they should ask the amount of the discount that the network is asking the provider to take. The discount can approach a break-even point for the group or practitioner and can make care of workers' compensation cases unprofitable. To realistically evaluate the financial impact of network participation, an objective evaluation of the margins involved in running a practice is required. The trade-off is the possibility of increased business volume of another nature. Many of these services are undiscounted or based on special contracted rates between an employer and the provider. Some services of this type include Department of Transportation physicals, return to work physicals, drug testing, and the primary care treatment of problems covered by group health insurance. Physicians occasionally accept discounts for workers' compensation that are below the level at which they can make a profit, because they understand that linkage with a network may lead to other benefits, including increased market share.

Practitioners or groups can find that their bills are reduced at varying rates by a payor, a situation that can result from "stacking" of physician rates. Stacking is the process by which multiple networks are used by a single payor, and the lowest contracted rate to the provider or facility is that which is paid. Because providers and hospitals have multiple contracts with various networks, this essentially leads to their receiving the lowest possible reimbursement. Stacking has been viewed as inherently unfair to the provider or facility and has been objected to by ethical networks.

NETWORK CAPABILITIES

Direct Contracting by Provider Groups: A New Development

Direct contracting by provider groups should not be confused with the use of the term *direct contracting* for the contracting process involved in connecting physicians to a network. In the former case, *direct contracting* refers to networks or groups of providers signing contracts for services directly with primary payors. This might mean that a large employer would sign a contract delineating services and prices with clinics or medical groups. Such relationships have always existed between providers and employers, but the relationships rarely went beyond one or two service sites. The capacity exists today for such contracts to go outside a confined region, to encompass a full range of services on a statewide or even nationwide basis. While inherently attractive to provider groups because the managed care "middle man" would appear to have been eliminated, direct contracting requires provider-based utilization management services at significant added cost. Moreover, a potential feature of such direct relationships is new payment methodologies, which require more managed care to be competitive with traditional networks.

Channeling, Exclusive Contracting, and Marketing Advantage

Nearly all networks publicly acknowledge that they attract physicians by offering the potential of increased market share through channeling of patients to their practices. While some states allow employer control of where injured or ill workers can be treated, most state laws allow employer control for only a limited time or not at all. Interestingly, statistics do not seem to support the effectiveness of employer control, even where it has been allowed.

The increased importance and effectiveness of managed care programs in channeling workers to specific physicians has changed the previously ineffective and disinterested efforts of the past. CCN has found that channeling to networks, even in states without complete employer control, can approach 95% in special programs. This furnishes new evidence for the capacity of networks to channel more patients to member physicians. Participating physicians need to independently judge whether the contracting organization has the capacity to actually get patients to his or her practice. Most networks without a comprehensive utilization management capability will not be able to accomplish this feat. The term for what percentage of injured workers in a given program are actually cared for by a network provider is *penetration rate*. With large national networks, penetration can vary from 10–90% depending on the geographic area and the managed care program. Channeling and penetration rates are increasing across the country as managed care becomes more effective and state laws allow for new forms of employer control through state-certified managed care organizations.

Bill Review

Many networks have the capacity to perform bill review for clients. Those that do not will frequently have access to bill review data for profiling and quality assurance functions. Bill review entails receiving provider and facility bills and reviewing for certain criteria. For one of the criteria, price, the standard may be the state fee schedule or a percentage of reasonable and customary fees. Other automated rubrics scan for "upcoding" and "unbundling" of services, and frequency (intensity) of visits. Because the federal government and some states set standards in these areas, items can be easily reviewed and the results justified. However, many physicians have not learned that such systems of review exist. Not only are their bills being reduced, but some of these habits are being recognized as quality issues by the networks, which are using this information to identify physicians practicing outside of community standards. Third-generation networks rarely include physicians who overbill, upcode, or deviate radically from fee schedules.

Quality Assurance, Profiling, and Benchmarking

Quality assurance, profiling, and benchmarking are gaining increasing importance in networks. Initially, a remarkable incident of poor quality practice or other legal issue was required before a provider would be deleted from a network. Such incidents usually only came to light after a public exposition because mechanisms were not in place to notify the network. Moreover, early networks had no ability to routinely monitor a provider's practice habits. This has changed with the integration of bill review and other data into the quality assurance process. It is now possible for networks to monitor not only for gross types of practice problems (malpractice suits, deaths, readmissions to hospitals) but also to define the general treatment habits of physicians. For example, sophisticated networks can determine how many physical therapy visits a provider orders for patients with a given ICD-9 code or if the doctor routinely orders magnetic resonance imaging for all patients with low back complaints. Ways exist to profile physicians even before they are examined for possible inclusion in a network; there are controls for patient mix (severity), specialty, and other variables. Because the workers' compensation system is becoming increasingly oriented to outcomes, the process of how a physician practices to get patients well often is irrelevant. Quality assurance is present in most organizations and is making expanding use of profiling tools that rely on bill review data for some screening of providers.

RECENT CRITICISM OF NETWORKS

Networks frequently have come under attack for excluding certain physicians. In the group health arena, the claim has been made that ethnic, racial, or other nonrelevant criteria have been used in credentialing. Recent articles suggest otherwise, and it has been this author's experience that the most important variables in physician solicitation are board certification and location of practice.[1] Physicians need to be aware of the practical requirements purchasers and payors of health care have placed on networks. Broad geographic coverage is a necessity for success. Board certification of physicians is always desirable, especially in states with high litigation rates. In addition, board-certified specialists who deal with musculoskeletal injuries, the bulk of workers' compensation injuries, are in the greatest demand. A purely workers' compensation network would have few obstetricians, for instance, but many orthopedists and neurologists. The use of primary care physicians and the gatekeeper concept are discussed below.

NEW MODELS

Networks are increasingly using new models of distributing care of injured workers. The payment for these services will shift some risk to providers, as has occurred in group health.

The Gatekeeper Model

Different referral patterns have been used in workers' compensation with varying degrees of success. Channeling injured workers directly to specialists has been one method. Other attempts have involved using group health providers who were not experienced in workers' compensation. This has proven particularly disastrous, with astronomical costs. More recently, the gatekeeper concept of referring patients to a primary care physician or clinic knowledgeable in workers' compensation has been popular. The assumption is that the providers will be able to care for most of the common and short-duration injuries and that more complex problems are sent to specialists for further evaluation and care. This model has been remarkably successful, and many organizations consider the gatekeeper the model of choice.

The popularity of the gatekeeper model means that there is a continuous demand for knowledgeable primary care practitioners in workers' compensation networks. Many of these practitioners have backgrounds in family practice, internal medicine, and emergency medicine. Most networks require primary care practitioners to have experience or advanced training in the workers' compensation system.

Centers of Excellence and Specialty Organizations

The limited number of costly and specialized diagnoses in workers' compensation has led to the identification, based on outcomes, of centers of excellence for the referral of specific "high-cost" injuries. Some of these centers have linked up with nationwide networks for the care of such problems as back injuries and chronic pain. In other cases, networks have been asked to identify these centers and give them special prominence. Initial attempts at identification were not based on total outcomes but only on medical costs. Recent efforts to define these centers by examining medical costs, indemnity costs, patient functionality, and patient satisfaction have met with some success.

Various specialities, especially those that deal with specific diagnoses in a circumscribed fashion, are beginning to create national organizations. The association of certain specialties into a network is not new. Behavioral health professionals, chiropractors, and other specialties have formed effective and nationally dispersed networks. This is a potential model for what may occur in workers' compensation. National associations of specialist physicians already exist that address the specific needs of the workers' compensation health care system, including associations of spine surgeons, neurologists, and pain centers. Some of the associations have been formed with a singular economic motive of gaining market share without any indication of improved outcomes. However, managed care companies now have data access abilities that can identify these entities and channel patients to more appropriate practitioners. While the state-specific nature of workers' compensation has been somewhat of a barrier to national success, there are indications of an emergence of national specialist networks and centers of excellence.

Physician and Facility Reimbursement

Networks are frequently the vehicle through which new reimbursement methodologies in this realm are tried. Capitation, case rates, bonus plans, and risk/gain-share programs are being tested and refined by payors and networks with increased frequency. The data as to how these programs affect outcomes are not yet available.

The Future

The recent establishment of third-generation networks with great success in limiting medical and indemnity costs without any perceived sacrifice of functional outcomes suggests the form that national networks will take in the future. Most qualified physicians will be a part of multiple major networks, but only a few providers will be enrolled in the smaller, more select networks. To most physicians, this will make no difference because most American health care is paid for by group health plans. However, to those who specialize in the care of workers' compensation patients, a focus on joining the selective third-generation networks may be advisable.

The present success of large national PPOs does not mean that the current status of such networks will last forever. Challenges are being mounted from direct contracting by smaller regional medical groups and companies owning clinics. With the addition of more clinics with a larger spectrum of services, these organizations can bypass traditional networks for some local and national business.

The growth of HMOs has led to their greater involvement in workers' compensation, which is one of the few areas in today's health care market where a billed dollar is not discounted. This lesson has not been lost on HMOs, as their margins decline and the potential for integrated health care services (24-hour care) is realized. Early HMO forays into workers' compensation met with poor results because they tried to provide occupational health services using group health providers. Recent changes to that approach by such organizations as Kaiser Permanente have led to better results and the capacity for HMOs as organizations to assume greater responsibility for workers' compensation services. We can expect this process to continue as HMOs spread into new markets.

CONCLUSION

Networks have steadily increased in absolute number, national coverage, and number of physician members. Despite recent criticism, they are increasingly being used by payors to control costs, quality of care, and case outcomes. Practicing physicians need to be aware of the importance of networks in the workers' compensation managed care system to survive as individual or group practitioners.

REFERENCE

1. Bindman AB, Grumbach K, Vranizan K, et al: Selection and exclusion of primary care physicians by managed care organizations. JAMA 279:675–679, 1998.

JOHN A. IGOE
JEFFREY S. HARRIS, MD, MPH

24-HOUR PROGRAMS: GREAT IDEA OR UNREALISTIC?

From Igoe Associates
San Raphael, California
and
Harris Associates, Inc.
Mill Valley, California

Reprint requests to:
John A. Igoe
Igoe Associates
24 Summit Avenue
San Raphael, CA 94901

When managing occupational health care, questions of the relationships between occupational and nonoccupational health risks, actions, and conditions inevitably arise. Apparently work-related health effects often cannot be managed predictably and reliably without considering the rest of the worker's life and health, since many effects are multifactorial. Conversely, do conditions and exposures at work affect general or family health?

Certainly just as salient for many people are the economics of care and health such that the separation of coverage increases the cost of care. Apportionment of causation or financial responsibility may not be appropriate or even logical. Should care, management, and coverage be combined?

The concept of *24-hour* has been proposed and even implemented as a solution to health care fragmentation, quality problems, financial issues, and productivity improvement. The concept can refer to a single source of care; coordinated benefits policies or coverage among workers' compensation and group health; possible disability, life, accidental death, and disability insurance; or true combined policies. However, regulatory and practical barriers exist, some of which are significant and some more conceptual. Proof is lacking that the posited effects on access, disputes, litigation, fraud, administrative costs, and quality of care do in fact occur. This chapter discusses definitions, similarities, and differences among clinical and financial arrangements, the logic supporting *24-hour* in its various forms, regulatory issues, practical implementation, and evidence to support combined care and disability management.

DEFINITIONS

The *24-hour* concept can refer to continuity of care or to comprehensive financial (insurance) coverage. The initial concept labeled as *24-hour* was that one would obtain health care from the same provider regardless of the cause of the problem. Another variant on the concept of continuous access to care was that access (usually synonymous with financing) was assured without reference to causation. In its purest sense, 24-hour care simply means assured access to care. The single provider concept superficially makes sense medically, but there are issues of training and perspective, response to employer needs, effective prevention, and return to work components for occupational health. Even in organizations that provide occupational and nonoccupational health services, separate physicians and facilities usually handle occupational and nonoccupational complaints.

The initial insurance or financial concept of *24-hour* was to issue a combined, single insurance policy backed by one company. With a single policy, causation disputes and double-dipping would be eliminated. However, there are significant regulatory and administrative barriers to this approach. With the exception of Texas and New Jersey, where traditional workers' compensation insurance is not required, it is not legally possible to issue a single policy. In most states, the department of corporations or a similar entity regulates managed care, self-insured health and life insurance, and workers' compensation health care organizations. Departments of insurance fully regulate health and life insurers and property and casualty insurance. There are different reserve requirements, performance standards, and standards of market conduct and ethics.

As a result, most 24-hour coverage has been achieved by issuing separate policies that provide matching but nonoverlapping coverage. More than one carrier usually is involved, because few insurers have both property/casualty (workers' compensation) and life and health (health) licenses. In some cases, there is a behind-the-scenes determination of causation and allocation of benefits by the employer, broker, managing general agent, or insurers. Large employers who wish to reduce the friction and employee relations problems caused by disputes about work-relatedness have developed most such programs. They also wish to maintain a single health-related database and coordinate benefits for maximal efficiency and cost-effectiveness.[10]

PARALLELS AND DIFFERENCES

Workers' compensation benefits cover far more than medical care as defined in most group health agreements and for a longer time—up to the lifespan or life expectancy of the injured worker. Group health contracts are generally for 1 year. Under almost all workers' compensation statutes, benefits also are mandated for temporary and permanent lost income, rehabilitation, some legal costs, and durable medical equipment. Accommodations for permanently disabled workers also may be covered. Life insurance and scheduled accidental dismemberment coverages are required in most states. All of these additional benefits and services can create incentives that affect the demand and provision of medical care. Therefore, to completely parallel workers' compensation coverage, one would need to provide incidental, short- and long-term disability, accidental death and dismemberment, dental, life, rehabilitation, long-term care, and group health insurance. To manage care under such a scenario, one would need to manage disability as well as medical and dental care.

In addition the standard for medical coverage under group health managed care—which now comprises more than 90% of group health benefits—is "medically necessary" service to maintain or restore health according to proven best practices. Under most if not all workers' compensation statutes, the standard is "reasonable and necessary care" to "cure and relieve" the effects of an illness or injury. Using the latter standard, a good deal more care, particularly palliative care, cosmetic procedures, marginally beneficial rehabilitation, and quasiexperimental procedures, have been performed and paid for under workers' compensation.

Another problem arises from the fact that workers' compensation is fully funded by the employer, while most health plans call for the employee to assume part of the burden. In group health and dental insurance, costs are generally shared with employees and dependents through copayments, deductibles, and lifetime maximums for specific benefits. There are also defined, limited benefits in a number of areas. Cost-sharing has been demonstrated to make employees somewhat price-sensitive, reducing the use of discretionary, and often unnecessary, services.[11] In fact, lack of cost-sharing is felt to be a reason that workers' compensation costs have increased at a much faster rate than those in group health or disability. Nevertheless, the strict statutory requirements of the workers' compensation laws would require a careful pricing scheme that would not result in any additional burden to the employee or relieve the employer of its burden under the workers' compensation laws.

Finally, dependents as well as employees are typically covered by group health and dental benefits, but the employee alone is covered by workers' compensation, disability, life, and AD&D policies. This is another area where parallelism does not exist.

PUBLIC POLICY LOGIC

The Clinton Administration's national health care reform initiative proposed financial coverage of care regardless of cause, effectively combining medical coverage and/or care for work- and nonwork-related illnesses and injuries. Advantages of combined care are believed to include improved care for work-related problems, reduced double billing, and a decrease in disputes and litigation about causation and coverage. It is clear that care for work-related problems is on average more expensive and of lower quality than when it is not paid for by workers' compensation.[8,12]

For employees without health insurance, comprehensive or combined care was thought to provide access to care more effectively than shifting nonoccupational issues to workers' compensation. In fact, combined care may have been a means to expand health insurance to uninsured employed workers. This was clearly the case in the design of the health care organization legislation in California and probably the 24-hour pilots in California and Oregon.

However, none of these initiatives have attracted substantial employer participation; nor have commercial 24-hour products garnered substantial market share. No jurisdiction has mandated their introduction. The slow adoption of combined coverage and care has puzzled some observers but is seen as a logical situation imposed by implementation and regulatory barriers.

THE CLINICAL LOGIC OF 24-HOUR CARE

Logic and knowledge of the dynamics of health, work, and illness would lead one to conclude that a single source of care should mean better care. One reason is that a single source of information about an individual should ensure that the provider has more complete knowledge of all influences on his or her health.[1,13] Advocacy of a single health-related database tied to worksite based care and case management for workers' compensation, group health, and disability[15] is becoming more widespread among occupational health professionals, many of whom also have a family practice or public health background.[3] This concept builds on the growing acceptance of worksite health promotion and primary care at work. From a corporate benefits standpoint, knowing all the costs associated with an employee or family unit enables the employer to better manage the aggregate cost of benefits and manage cases more effectively.[4,5,10]

Information needs to reflect knowledge about work and health. Work affects health, and health affects the ability and motivation to work.[14] For example, factors at work can affect general medical and psychosocial conditions, whereas general health, family situations, health risks, and coping skills can affect the ability to work, interest in working, and susceptibility to exposures at work.[7] Another reason for a single source of care is that a strong relationship with a patient or an entire family can lead to better outcomes.[16] This "whole person/social group approach" has long been a cornerstone of family practice and is now becoming the basis of cost-effective occupational medical care for common complaints among workers.[2,6]

Combining care can eliminate needless activities and disputes about the (often unknowable) cause of complaints that are thought to be work-related, as several employers have discovered. Making the distinction is laborious and often speculative. Physicians often do not take the time to perform the rigorous analysis and study of the literature needed to render an accurate probability or opinion.

BUSINESS AND FINANCIAL REASONS

Combining coverage allows employers and insurers to more accurately predict and manage their risks and burden of illness and injury. A number of employers are now using the "total burden of illness" approach to understand the complete impact of health on work. It is easier to do on a real-time basis with a combined database containing clinical and financial information.

A total burden of illness analysis also allows one to understand the effects of jobs, work design, and supervision on costs and productivity. Analysis can allow one to pinpoint working conditions associated with ill health.

Those who have adopted a combined coverage approach perceive clear financial advantage. Workers' compensation insurers have been buying most of their coverage from the same reinsurance markets that provide protection to health insurers and managed care companies. The combined buying power of the two coverages should result in significant reductions in price.

Costs of internal claims administration also can be reduced. About 60–70% of the payments being made under workers' compensation coverage are being made to the same providers and in a similar manner as those made by the health care provider. A properly designed and managed system would significantly reduce the duplicate costs involved in running two operations.

DISCUSSION AND ANALYSIS

Do the benefits of 24-hour care, or 24-hour coverage, outweigh the disadvantages? How realistic are the promises of better care? Will workers give up anything significant in combining care or coverage? The following analysis explores these and other important questions.

Health Care Delivery Issues

Whether better care will result depends on the training and competence of the providers. Much occupational health care is provided by primary care physicians.

Only about 2000 of the estimated 10,000 physicians who care for injured workers are board-certified in occupational medicine. If the provider of combined care can use the whole person/whole family perspective and also manage the disability and the work and social factors that may have caused the patient to seek health care, a superior form of care would result.

Disability management has been a neglected area, in part because it has been fragmented or ignored. Of those involved with disability management, occupational health professionals are generally most familiar with effective disability management. A combined or integrated approach to disability management makes sense if the appropriate care is available.

The converse could also be true. Physicians managing all health care issues must be skilled and knowledgeable about occupational exposures, prevention, the effects of work organization and management on health, disability management including modified duty, and general medicine. There is a substantial psychosocial and economic aspect to the prevention, diagnosis, and treatment of occupational health problems. In addition, family and personal issues can be expressed as or affect complaints about work, particularly musculoskeletal and psychosomatic complaints. Even without this overlay, most work-related complaints are musculoskeletal, an area subject to significant misdiagnosis and overtreatment.[9] Family physicians, emergency physicians, and internists, who handle most general health complaints, often lack the training and experience to appreciate or manage these issues. Communication with employers, disability management, and causality determinations are particular problems.

In addition, many physicians do not like workers' compensation cases, believing that substantial malingering or manipulation is involved. Some have expressed disinterest in working with lower socioeconomic-level patients, who sustain most complaints. Some dislike the conflict, communication with insurers, and paperwork inherent in the workers' compensation system. Their administrative systems may not be set up to deal with these requirements. Finally, the workers' compensation fee schedules in many states are low and have not been adjusted in some time. Most fee schedules do not allow time for reasonable discussion and counseling when there is psychosocial overlay or symptom amplification.

Another practical issue is determining work-relatedness. Accurately determining the contribution of work exposures or influences to complaints such as low back pain can be a time-consuming, conjectural, and frustrating exercise that most physicians would prefer to avoid. Opining on the relative effects of worksite conditions and actions and personal risks and behaviors is often of no great medical benefit to the worker; the treatment is the same. Benefits issues are involved, but health issues are usually moot unless there is clear epidemiologic or experimental evidence that work-station or job redesign might prevent exacerbation or recurrence. Understanding the contribution of work may make a significant difference for secondary and tertiary prevention.

Administrative and Benefits Issues

The major benefits issue seems to be a concern that workers not lose the broad coverage afforded under workers' compensation. The broad mandate and unmanaged nature of workers' compensation has led to overtreatment that has measurably harmed workers. Some of this has occurred in attempts to prove permanent disability, on which basis plaintiffs' attorneys are paid. Some overtreatment is due to the "cure and relieve" standard that has been discarded under more scientifically based managed care. The concern for equitable wage replacement is justified as long as disability is valid and well managed. In any event, erosion of benefits is an issue that must be addressed. On the other hand, some benefits are now state-mandated under group health, such as mental health coverage, that are not necessarily covered by workers' compensation, automobile, or other property/casualty insurance. Benefits would need to be updated.

Under a combined program, workers who previously had no health or disability benefits would be likely to have them in a truly parallel program. Employers have expressed concerns that this would increase their costs, particularly for seasonal or part-time workers. Access would be improved but at a cost to individual employers. However, an offsetting reduction in workers' compensation costs would occur for health problems that were previously shifted to workers' compensation or automobile insurance as the only source of coverage. This effect has been estimated actuarially at 10–15% of the premium.

Some economies may be achieved, especially for hospital, pharmacy, step-down, or home health care, by leveraging the use of group health managed care contracts for workers' compensation and automobile insurance as well. (Most state workers' compensation fee schedules cover physician, laboratory, radiology, and physical medicine outpatient services only.) Significant cost-shifting to the latter two, which typically have paid fee for service rates, has increased costs by several fold. Using extant managed care contracts closes that loophole, reduces employer or payer costs, and creates pressure for greater efficiency and effectiveness.

Combined coverage or care clearly would reduce or eliminate causation disputes, which create ill will, litigation, and friction among employers, employees, and providers. If all health problems were covered, the blaming of the worksite for health issues, which is strongly correlated with litigation and delayed recovery, would be mitigated to some extent.

Combining coverage also should reduce paperwork, which has become a major cost and headache for all concerned parties. Claim filing, payment, and the paperwork involved in deciding causality and recovery funds can consume more than 25% of overhead in many cases.

It appears that employers would rather have a single source of information about employees' absence from work and health care so that they can better manage costs and quality. These are concerns of at least potential fraud, double claim filing, and questions about the quality of care provided to workers with work-related complaints. There are in fact concerns with overall health care quality, especially cost-effectiveness. Creating a single source of information would at least bring the overall picture into focus. One caveat is that current information is likely to be incomplete, creating some underwriting and pricing risk. New information applications that capture clinical and complete administrative data may be needed.

Regulatory and Legal Issues

Plaintiffs' attorneys have opposed combined care on the basis of erosion of benefits. However, litigation and recovery is rare in group health and disability insurance. The benefits are clear. If this philosophy were used for all health and lost-time issues, litigation would drop precipitously, as it did in Texas when employers were allowed to create a parallel set of coverages outside the traditional workers' compensation system. Surgical rates also dropped sharply.

Enabling regulations or legislation will be needed to allow combined coverage. Combined care can be provided without these changes, but the burden of paperwork would remain until abated by regulatory reform.

CONCLUSION

Twenty-four hour care would provide holistic, more effective care if the providers had the skills to manage occupational and nonoccupational health complaints. A single provider would consider the work, social, and psychological issues underlying a number of complaints. Invasive treatment that is not justified would be avoided. Prevention could be focused on underlying causes. Combining care could leverage favorable managed care contracts with providers.

Truly parallel coverage would integrate disability and consider the known risks of delayed recovery, many of which are psychosocial. There is a significant opportunity to better manage all disability. Causation issues would become secondary or nonexistent.

Regulatory and statutory requirements would need to be reexamined and revised to allow combined coverage. Unnecessary reporting would be eliminated.

A combined medical and financial record would be needed to effectively manage a combined system. In turn, payers and providers would have a complete picture of each worker to better pay for and manage his or her health.

REFERENCES

1. Besserman RA: System architecture and scope. In Harris JS, Loeppke RR (eds): Integrated Health Management: The Key Role of Occupational Medicine in Managed Care, Disability Management and Integrated Delivery Systems. Beverly Farms, MA, OEM Press, 1998.
2. Comstock MA: Human asset risk management. Occup Med State Art Rev 13, 1998.
3. Dalton BA: Productivity management. In Harris JS, Loeppke RR (eds): Integrated Health Management: The Key Role of Occupational Medicine in Managed Care, Disability, Management and Integrated Delivery Systems. Beverly Farms, MA, OEM Press, 1998.
4. Dalton BA, Harris JS: A comprehensive approach to employee health management. J Occup Med 33:338–347, 1991.
5. Harris JS: Strategic Health Management. San Francisco, Jossey-Bass, 1994.
6. Harris JS: The ACOEM Occupational Medicine Practice Guidelines. In Harris JS, Loeppke RR (eds): Integrated Health Management: The Key Role of Occupational Medicine in Managed Care, Disability Management and Integrated Delivery Systems. Beverly Farms, MA, OEM Press, 1998.
7. Harris JS: The economics of occupational medicine. In McCunney RS, et al (eds): A Practical Approach to Environmental and Occupational Medicine. 2nd ed. Boston, Little, Brown & Co., 1994.
8. Harris JS: Workers compensation. In McCunney RS, et al (eds): A Practical Approach to Environmental and Occupational Medicine. 2nd ed. Boston, Little, Brown & Co., 1994.
9. Harris JS, et al: Occupational Medicine Practice Guidelines: Evaluations and Management of Common Health Problems and Functional Recovery in Workers. Beverly, MA, OEM Press, 1997.
10. Harris JS, Carr R, Fass P, et al: The corporate medical department and managed care. In Harris JS, Loeppke RR (eds): Integrated Health Management: The Key Role of Occupational Medicine in Managed Care, Disability Management and Integrated Delivery Systems. Beverly Farms, MA, OEM Press, 1998.
11. Harris JS, Custer WS: Health care economic factors and the effects of benefits plan design changes. J Occup Med 33:279–286, 1991.
12. Harris JS, Iskowe DI, Goldstein SR, et al: Workers' compensation: Business as usual may mean going out of business. NCCI Digest 4(3):25–43, 1989.
13. Harris JS, Miller LA: Sources and uses of occupational medicine data. In Harris JS, Loeppke RR (eds): Integrated Health Management: The Key Role of Occupational Medicine in Managed Care, Disability Management and Integrated Delivery Systems. Beverly Farms, MA, OEM Press, 1998.
14. Kuhnen AE, Harris JS, Aidinoff S, Kahn JS: Stress related disorders. In Harris JS, et al (eds): Occupational Medicine Practice Guidelines: Evaluation and Management of Common Health Problems and Functional Recovery in Workers. Beverly Farms, MA, OEM Press, 1997.
15. Peterson KP, Loeppke RL: Population health management. In Harris JS, Loeppke RR (eds): Integrated Health Management: The Key Role of Occupational Medicine in Managed Care, Disability Management and Integrated Delivery Systems. Beverly Farms, MA, OEM Press, 1998.
16. Rakel R: Textbook of Family Practice. 4th ed. Philadelphia, WB Saunders, 1994.

STEVEN C. SCHUMANN, MD
DAVID GUNN
DALE PRATT

DATA MANAGEMENT IN OCCUPATIONAL MEDICINE

From The Stolas Group, Inc.
Fresno, California

Reprint requests to:
Steven C. Schumann, MD
President and CEO
The Stolas Group, Inc.
6061 North Fresno Street
Suite 104
Fresno, CA 93710

The ostensible goal of a health care provider is to deliver the best medical service to the largest number of people who, as a consequence, would enjoy optimal wellness. This is true in occupational medicine, where an additional caveat is that wellness should be delivered within the shortest time with the lowest possible medical and indemnity costs. Occupational medicine occurs in an environment that is defined by the workplace and driven by not only the doctor-patient relationship but also peripheral participants such as employers, payors, and others with a vested interest in the process and the outcome.

While the goal of optimizing wellness has not changed, much evolution has occurred during the past few decades in the characteristics of health care management. The core relationship of physician-patient has shifted from individuals to institutions and includes a cadre of specialists, ancillary personnel, and organizations. Diagnostic emphasis on the physician's clinical skills has become centered on the clinical laboratory, the imaging center, and other testing venues. Reimbursement formats, once typically fee-for-service, now include a variety of provider risk models.

The change is the result of the interaction of many crosscurrents that influence health care delivery, including medical, political, economic, and technical forces. In essence, the evolution has been from micro to macro, individualized to systematized, and independent to networked and consolidated. It features authorization, analysis, automation, and algorithmization.

The product of this evolution has been given a name: managed care. Managed care is the result of the confluence of business interests and medical interests in developing a system that responds to the effects as well as requirements of those factors. Wellness becomes the goal of medical services that are delivered with the net income in mind. Better services are to be delivered more efficiently and less expensively. Health care becomes a commodity.

If some of this change has been the consequence of advancing medical technology as well as economic interests, much of the reorganization and management of health care in the future likewise will be driven by technology. In T*he Digital Economy*, Don Tapscott states: "We are at the dawn of an Age of Networked Intelligence—an age that is giving birth to a new economy, a new politics, and a new society. Businesses will be transformed, governments will be renewed, and individuals will be able to reinvent themselves—all with the help of the new information technology."[6]

Managed care is managed data. The information system is a critical component of the evolving medical marketplace. Essential ingredients include the ability to capture, process, and report data that enhance effective practice management. To function in a managed care environment requires a thoughtful approach to integrating the management information system (MIS) into the practice operation. In many ways, the information system may determine how the medical practice is conducted.

In few medical specialties is information management as important as in occupational medicine. Not only are the usual clinical and financial records maintained, but a plethora of reports and outcomes summaries are needed for employers and payors. Mandated health care services demand recording and reporting. In addition, occupational medicine has not escaped the grip of business necessity; marketing analyses, sales reports, profit and loss summaries, and similar economic outputs drive a need for sophisticated data management.

The purpose of this chapter is to review the role of the information system in optimizing the occupational medicine practice and achieving the practice's goals in a managed care marketplace. We present practice goals that can serve to direct the practice and define its intended process.

In anticipation of developing an MIS for an occupational medicine practice, several considerations should influence the decision-making process:
- The MIS must support the achievement of the practice goals. If not, it serves little purpose in the health care delivery system.
- The MIS must recognize the dual requirements of medical and business interests in the practice and must assist in optimizing operational activities and efficiencies of both.
- Both practice management and system technology are processes that are in evolution, and one must attempt to anticipate their progress in designing an MIS.
- Not all data are useful. The goal of the MIS is to assist in revealing data that permit management and care delivery decision making that will enhance the program.

STRATEGIC THINKING: IDENTIFICATION OF PRACTICE GOALS

If data management is expected to support practice goals while participating in the managed care environment, what are those goals? Several exist at various strata.

The primary goal for all medical practices is the maintenance or achievement of wellness, i.e., assisting in optimizing the employee's health prior to injury or illness as well as returning the employee to the same level of health. Certainly, both providers and consumers of health care services would agree that the most important consideration is medical care to help the patient become as well as possible.

Additional goals that might be considered secondary, although not in a qualitative sense, include quality care, consumer satisfaction, and profitability.

Quality care is the delivery of superior medical services. It does not necessarily correlate with maintaining wellness, but it often does. Literature-based evidence and consensus in the medical community identify this quality.

Consumer satisfaction reflects that consumers' needs are being met adequately. Consumers of occupational health care services include patients, employers, and insurance carriers. Needs vary among the groups.

Profitability is the result of net revenue exceeding expenses. Ideally the facility or program is profitable. If not, the outstanding medical program is unlikely to survive in a competitive business environment unless other considerations predominate.

Characteristics also exist that are not ends in themselves but rather features that assist in assuring operating efficiencies. They include expedition, cost-effectiveness, and efficiency.

Expedition is the assurance that care and service are delivered in a timely manner. Clearly the service component of health care delivery is a critical issue, particularly to the consumer.

Cost-effectiveness relates to achieving the greatest success in accomplishing practice goals for the lowest cost.

Efficiency reflects optimizing the use of facility resources with the least energy.

Not all medical or operational activities in the clinic will result in the accomplishment of these goals. However, it is critical to focus on these goals when making management decisions. The information system exists as a support piece in the attempt to accomplish as many of the practice goals as possible. The information system brings great power to clinical practice management and can be exceptionally useful in successfully achieving the goals.

TACTICAL THINKING: USING DATA MANAGEMENT TO ACHIEVE PRACTICE GOALS

In general, the categories of useful consequences of the MIS include management reports, operating efficiencies, services delivery, and value-added products (Table 1).

Management Reports

Management reports include medical and financial summaries. Medical reports are composed of first reports, supplemental and discharge reports, permanent disability reports, and summaries of surveillance data. This information typically is stored in the form of free narrative text and is printed as it is stored.

Financial reports include summaries of activity, often by the provider or facility. This information is stored in a format that allows retrieval and comparison of data elements.

Reports are particularly useful when they include a history of employer referrals, progress of the patients, and referral trends by employers and payors. Cost accounting reports assist in negotiating and managing financial risk programs such as case rate and capitation models.

TABLE 1. Information Support of Practice Goals

Goal	Reports			Operations	
	Medical	Outcome	Financial	Case Management	Clinic Efficiency
Wellness	√	√		√	
Quality care	√	√		√	
Consumer satisfaction		√		√	√
Profitability		√	√	√	
Expedition				√	√
Cost-effectiveness		√	√	√	
Efficiency				√	√

Operating Efficiencies

Many office functions can be performed much more efficiently by the information system than manually. The MIS should be designed in anticipation of patient flow and with the intent of creating operating efficiencies. Patient demographics must be collected and entered in an efficient manner that prevents a bottleneck in the waiting room. The data entry process should consume only a few minutes. Systems that require more time will not effectively speed patient flow. Use of existing patient demographic data will speed the creation of a new file for a subsequent injury. Previous files of employers and payors will hasten data entry and ensure accuracy. No piece of information should be collected and entered more than once.

Autofaxing saves substantial staff time in the clinic. Rather than printing documents and standing at the fax machine, staff members can use the information system to send the documents to a fax print queue, and they may be transmitted at a later time.

Use of templates and macros will help the physician or therapist dictate medical records. Macros are words, sentences, paragraphs, or pages that are stored and are retrievable using a predetermined code. Templates are similar to macros but contain fields for variable elements of data. Automated input devices, described below, help the provider to hasten the charting process and occasionally obviate the need for a transcriptionist. Scheduling capability permits the most efficient use of clinic resources.

Services Delivery

Two practice components, medical case management and outcomes analysis, essentially have become requirements from both an operating and reporting standpoint. Not only are they essential ingredients in managing an efficient occupational medical practice, but their absence often is perceived as reflecting an incomplete health care delivery system.

Most patients will follow a predictable clinical course if standardized medical care is provided. Consistent use of treatment protocols and algorithms will result in consistent care and, subject to endogenous and exogenous variables affecting the individual patient, generally leads to a predictable outcome. However, some patients will deviate from the predictable course and become "outliers." Medical case management is (1) the identification of outliers as early as possible in the course of care and (2) applying appropriate alternative diagnostic and treatment strategies.

Outliers are identified by sorting the clinical database of records for patients who exceed one or more of the parameter values. When the outlier is identified, the case management nurse can take appropriate steps in conjunction with the treating physician to alter the care plan. This process occurs only if the MIS contains identifiable elements of data that can be recognized and measured. Accomplishing this process requires the use of standardized data rather than data in free narrative text form.

Another feature of the MIS is generation of outcomes reports. Outcomes analysis has become an increasingly important concern of the employer, payor, and practitioner. This area of practice assessment is exceptionally difficult in the absence of sophisticated data processing. Significant areas of outcome analysis include the following:

1. **Consumer satisfaction:** the opinion of the patients, employers, or insurance carriers that care is delivered satisfactorily. The perception by these consumers of adequacy of service is a subjective decision based on their own values. Weaver provides an excellent summary of this measurement.[7]

2. **Indemnity resource consumption:** the use of temporary or permanent disability benefits, vocational rehabilitation, or death benefits.

3. **Medical condition:** the change in the patient's symptoms, signs, or other findings at the conclusion of care compared to at the initiation of management or another event.

4. **Financial and medical resource consumption:** measurement of the use of practice resources in the provision of care, particularly for identifying the cost of services to determine the practice's ability to accept financial risk.

5. **Cost-effectiveness ratio:** assessment of the "costs" of care compared to the "effectiveness," recognizing the often subjective quality of these terms. A recommendation for cost-effectiveness analysis has been described by Siegel et al.[5]

Outcomes analysis requires collection and processing of discrete elements of data. Standardized data, collected as tabled elements rather than from free narrative text, are required. Summarizing collected information, then, generates outcome reports. The report may be in the form of a "profile report" that provides means, modes, or medians, or it may be an "exception report" that identifies individual patients or trends that exceed a standard. An example is in the application of medical case management above.

Wolfe offers an excellent review of goals for computerization in a discussion of information management in the occupational medicine clinic.[8]

Value-Added Products

Information itself has value to the consumers of occupational health services. The health care industry spent $8.5 billion on information systems in 1994, and predictions anticipated 50% growth in 1995.[4] One reason is the generation of reports. Occupational medicine is one of the few areas where the guarantor is not the consumer of the essential service. The patient consumes the service, but the insurance company receives reports of that service, its characteristics, and its outcome.

As a consequence, it is critical to generate useful reports for employers and insurance carriers. In some cases the reports are mandatory summaries of activity; in other cases the reports themselves have value and represent a source of revenue for the clinic.

SELECTION OF THE MANAGEMENT INFORMATION SYSTEM

If a group has formulated a set of practice goals for its occupational medicine program in a managed care environment and has a vision of how the MIS will participate in the development and delivery of health care services, decisions then must be made concerning the implementation of information technology.

Selection of the information system should be undertaken with caution. Issues include consideration of existing systems to which the system may be required to interface. The information technology support group, if present, may have a preference for a particular hardware or operating system.

Other participants in the health care delivery system may offer opinions. The interests of the medical providers, operators, administrators, and others may not always coincide.

Projection for growth of the system must be made. The preferred software application may or may not be capable of expansion.

Finally, one must remember that not all data are useful. The product of the information system is the assistance it renders in achieving practice goals. To that end it must have several characteristics. Data must have integrity, i.e., be consistent from provider to provider. It must be valid, actually meaning what it is interpreted to mean. Finally, it must be meaningful; it must have application to the practice management.

Seen in another light, data are numbers. Information is data that permit decisions to be made. Knowledge occurs when data are used to make helpful decisions, and wisdom is demonstrated when good decisions are the outcome. Select the system wisely.

MAJOR COMPONENTS OF A MANAGEMENT INFORMATION SYSTEM

The major components of an MIS include the hardware platform, the operating system, and the specific software applications. In addition, consideration is given to input devices, remote connection, system configuration, and scalability.

Historically, the primary consideration in the selection of an MIS was to focus initially on the application and subsequently on the hardware and operating system. With the consolidation and evolution of the computer industry, however, determination of the hardware platform and operating system are as important as the application itself.

Hardware

Hardware refers to the physical equipment upon which operating systems and software applications function.

Hardware can be categorized on a functional basis as mainframe, minicomputer, or personal computer. Mainframe and minicomputer platforms run what most companies would consider their legacy systems (mission critical), and many are converting these applications to run on personal computers. The primary characteristics of mainframe and minicomputer systems are high cost, reliability, and centralized operations.

Personal computers have become the dominant platform today due, in large part, to the rapidly increasing power of the processors that are used and lesser cost compared to mainframes and minicomputers. A common industry observation is that the processing power of computers will double and cost will halve every 18 months.

Computers can be distinguished on the basis of the central processing unit (CPU), the component where data processing occurs. All other components within the computer can be considered as connecting the user with the CPU. CPUs may be viewed as Intel products and "others." Intel Corporation is the largest manufacturer of processors and has largely set the standard for personal computers. Other producers include Advanced Micro Devices and Cyrix.

A third form of hardware distinction is single- versus multiprocessor systems. Single-processor systems have only one CPU. Multiprocessor systems have more than one, which permits data processing at a faster rate and allows some processors to specialize in specific tasks. Multiprocessor systems must have the support built in by the operating system. Multiprocessor systems are either symmetrical multiprocessor systems or asymmetrical multiprocessor systems, wherein processing functions are distributed arbitrarily or systematically, respectively.

Operating System

Operating systems control the hardware by providing instructions that determine the functions to be performed. The operating system accepts requests for action from the software application programs and transmits the requests to specific devices or components.

The major operating systems with significant market share include Novell, Microsoft Windows, and Unix.

During the late 1980s and early 1990s, Novell was the undisputed leader in network operating systems. It enjoyed most of the network market. However, it has suffered with the development and maturation of the Windows operating systems, which are easier to install and administer. Novell has been burdened by having its operation confined to Intel processors. Its market share has eroded substantially.

Microsoft's current products include Windows 3.1, Windows 95, and Windows NT. Windows 95 has become the most commonly installed desktop operating system. Its user interface is regarded generally as being substantially improved over Windows 3.1. Businesses progressively are migrating to Windows NT Workstation for important functions, including security and full 32-bit subsystems.

The Windows operating systems have benefited from aggressive marketing by Microsoft, and they are superior products. Windows NT compares favorably to Novell products as a full-featured system that allows modular, object-oriented functionality. Its kernel includes such modules as file system drivers, network drivers, and graphic device drivers. Its hardware abstraction layer permits interface to both reduced and complex instruction set computing processors.

Unix has been the standard for processing large volumes of data in the minicomputer environment. It has been used with text-based terminals or on high-end engineering workstations used for CAD/CAM applications. It is also used in large database server applications. It can be considered both a desktop and a network operating system. Unix is limited, however, by its lack of graphical interface other than X-Window. This window application is available only as an expensive, sophisticated, high-end program that is difficult to maintain. Unix is largely confined to large, multiuser environments but is being challenged substantially by Windows NT.

Databases

Databases are storage areas for data. In typical single-user desktop applications, data are stored in files and retrieved as such. Earlier versions of larger databases were flat file managers with no relational database capability, i.e., groups of data elements could not be combined for comparison and reporting.

Current databases store much larger volumes of information and are capable of retrieving such information for a variety of processing and reporting functions. Databases vary in size and features. The Access database has a simple and functional user interface but poor scalability and poor multiuser capability. SQL Server and Oracle are large databases that have excellent scalability, performance, and multiuser function.

Software Applications

Software applications are the user-selected programs that perform the desired functions. Just as hardware and operating systems have advanced significantly, so too have software applications.

Applications are fundamentally a series of instructions to the computer. Many languages have evolved. Some are considered low-level languages that essentially are a series of binary instructions. Others are high-level languages similar to English in complexity.

Among the most sophisticated languages is C++. Although sophisticated and challenging to use, C++ is most commonly employed to write complex and mission-critical programs. For example, C++ is used by Microsoft to develop its Office applications, Windows NT, and, in fact, the C++ programming application itself.

An alternative is Visual Basic, which is found in many corporate development situations where the emphasis is on faster development and the applications are not used outside the developer's environment.

Configuration

Configuration refers to the organization, connections, and operation of the hardware, the operating system, and applications. Configuration implies the management of the components in the interest of optimal system function. The functional goal of the system is to deliver the fastest speed of data processing with the least disruption and at the lowest cost.

Hardware considerations include the amount of random access memory (RAM), speed of the processor(s), speed of the hard drives, and other components. The faster that data move through the system, the faster processing occurs.

The network influences system speed through bandwidth and hardware connections to the local or wide-area network. Modem speed and connections influence remote communication.

The software applications themselves can influence system performance. Some are written for a file server environment where files are stored on the server and all processing occurs on the workstations. This allows distribution of some processing functions but requires significant data to be moved through the network. On the opposite end of the spectrum is the "host-based" system, in which all processing is done at a central mainframe or a Unix "box."

In the middle is the client/server system, in which processing is done both at the server and the client, or workstation. This configuration most readily permits the distribution of processing tasks between the two. Efficiency and speed are maximized by such steps as locating some executable and/or screen files on the workstation, obviating the need to transmit them between the server and client. In fact, additional speed and efficiency in a client/server setting are achieved by using more than one server and designating server functions. Servers may be specified for special functions such as printing, faxing, or back-up. A database server may be used for maintaining the database and responding to requests from the client applications.

By transmitting just the requests between the client and server instead of the entire database, network traffic is minimized. Allowing the database server to control the database also helps maintain the integrity of the database.

Additional configuration considerations include distributed processing among several processors in a server or the use of clustered servers where processing is distributed among several servers.

Input Devices

Input devices, four of which are described below, are increasingly important components of the system regarding care delivery efficiencies.

1. **Voice recognition:** the ability of the computer to recognize a normal speech pattern and generate text or the proper computer commands from that pattern. It allows medical personnel to dictate directly into documents without requiring a transcriptionist.

2. **Voice synthesis:** the reverse of voice recognition. This application outputs text files through a speaker. It allows individuals to receive text such as e-mail by the telephone.

3. **Computer telephone integration:** a process that links the telephone and computer systems into one application. When a patient telephones the clinic, the system identifies the caller and the application loads the appropriate record.

4. **Pen-based computing:** a technique by which data are captured and entered in the system as the data are generated manually by the provider.

Scalability Testing

With increasing health care delivery consolidation and networking, the need to process data on an expanded scale grows. As a consequence, the issue of scalability of software arises. This refers to the ability of the software application, operating system, and hardware to operate with sufficient speed for a particular volume of data. The application that manages the data for a small local or wide-area network may not effectively support a much larger network with several hundred workstations.

Scalability testing is the process of determining the capability of the combination of software application, operating system, networking software, and hardware to function with reasonable speed with an increasing volume of user data. Unfortunately, the ability of the system to function adequately is not continuously linear—at some point one of the system components will begin to suffer. Which component will begin to fail depends on the characteristics of each and the manner in which they are combined.

The testing process involves several steps:
- Selection of the software application to be used
- Selection of the operating system, networking software if used, and hardware
- Configuration of the system components
- Calculation of the amount of data generated by the users
- Calculation of the rate at which data will be inputed and processed
- Simulation of that volume during a period of time

Calculation of the amount of data to be processed is a difficult task that requires a high level of sophistication and understanding of the system components. Not all applications generate the same amount of data. In addition, there is not necessarily a direct relationship with the number of workstations. In some environments with many workstations, the workstations may be periodically idle. In other situations, fewer workstations may be continuously busy and generating a larger volume of data.

TABLE 2. Data Volume Calculation for Scalability Testing

	Category	Activity	Visit Type					
				Occupational Medicine			*General Practice*	
			TOTAL	*Injury*	*Follow-up*	*Exams*	*New*	*Follow-up*
	Number of Patient Visits		1000	150	300	150	300	100
Data Volume Manipulated	Registration	Patient selection	x	x	x	x	x	x
		Demographics	x	x	x	x	x	x
		Case information	x	x	x	x	x	x
		First report entry	x	x	x	x	x	x
		Visit entry	x	x	x	x	x	x
		Injury worksheet (F)	x	x	x	x	x	x
		Charge sheet (F)	x	x	x	x	x	x
		Labels (F)	x	x	x	x	x	x
	Discharge	Diagnosis	x	x	x	x	x	x
		Work status	x	x	x	x	x	x
		Referral	x	x	x	x	x	x
		Appointment	x	x	x	x	x	x
		Charge posting	x	x	x	x	x	x
		Invoice (F)	x	x	x	x	x	x
		Work status (F)	x	x	x	x	x	x
		Clinical report	x	x	x	x	x	x
	Transcription	Visit notes	x	x	x	x	x	x
		Supplemental report	x	x	x	x	x	x
		Surveillance	x	x	x	x	x	x
	Billing	Charge posting	x	x	x	x	x	x
		Receipt posting	x	x	x	x	x	x
		Open/close batches	x	x	x	x	x	x
		Audit reports	x	x	x	x	x	x
		Invoices (F)	x	x	x	x	x	x
		HCFA/UB92 (F)	x	x	x	x	x	x
		Clinical reports	x	x	x	x	x	x
		Work status	x	x	x	x	x	x

x = variable field, F = form

Further, the volume of data generated varies. Some periods of the day, days of the week, and months of the year are busier. The system needs to support the greatest amount of data to which it will be subjected.

"Testing software" that simulates the data entry process is often required. For example, if the operating environment contemplates 300 users on a network, it may not be practical to arrange 300 workstations for testing. Rather, testing software is used that effectively inputs data at a rate simulating the appropriate number of workstations.

Table 2 shows a format that can be used in the calculation of data volume. It assumes 1,000 patients per day, which are distributed between occupational medicine and general practice. General practice patients are included because many occupational medicine clinics also provide urgent care and other primary care services. In this table, the distribution is 60% occupational medicine and 40% general practice patients. However, the ratios are easily changed and the proportion of the patients and number of visits can be modified to reflect the anticipated volume and mix.

Once the patient volume and visit mix are calculated, the actual volume of data is determined. Four general categories of data entry and processing are listed: registration, discharge, transcription, and billing. Within each category are included

TABLE 3. Data Flow Rate Calculation

Patient Processing	Occupational Medicine			General Practice	
	Injury	Follow-up	Examinations	New	Follow-up
Quantity per hour	x	x	x	x	x
Time interval (minutes)	x	x	x	x	x
Time interval (seconds)	x	x	x	x	x

x = variable field

the various activities. Virtually all data management events from the clinics will fall within one of these activities. Under "Visit Type," columns are fields designated by "x" for the amount of data for each of the activities. Calculated values subsequently are based upon the review of many records in a typical practice management database.

With the volume of data and rate of patient flow known, the next step is calculating the actual amount of data to which the system will be subjected in a specific time. Table 3 provides the format.

Thereafter, the testing process is undertaken by submitting the calculated amount of data to the configured system. Measurements of the system response are made.

If the system performance is determined to be inadequate, manipulations are made in how data management occurs. Changes that may be made include increases in size or capacity of the processor or hard drive, increases in RAM, distribution of software application processing functions between the server and workstations, enhancement of transmission capacity of the modem and wide-area network links, and internal function of the software application.

THE INTERNET

The Internet plays an increasing role in the development of information systems in the occupational medicine environment. Among the most significant areas are the following:

- Access to data at the clinic level, e.g., current surveillance regulations, appropriate treatment guidelines, employer examination requirements, and others.
- Facilitation of health care delivery and administration using a Web-based solution. Providers, employers, and insurance carriers would contribute appropriate information and be able to retrieve as appropriate.
- Communication between the provider and the consumers, i.e., employer and insurance carriers, concerning authorization, reporting, status, and decision support.

The advantage of the Internet as a vehicle for communication is that it obviates the requirement for long-distance telephone calls and the requirement at either the provider or consumer sites for multiple lines to ensure access. For the provider to make information available, many simultaneous calls would necessitate a number of lines being available. Similarly, at the consumer site line connections would be required at all locations where data might reasonably be acquired.

Several good articles concerning the Internet in the managed care environment are provided by Fine.[1]

CONCLUSION

It is the intent of the occupational medicine physician to deliver the best medical service to the largest number of people who, as a consequence, will enjoy optimal health; the provider does so within the shortest time with the lowest possible medical and indemnity costs.

The advent of managed care places some restrictions on the occupational medicine provider, requiring greater efficiency while practicing in a competitive environment. Medical and economic interests converge.

To have a focus for program development, the successful occupational medicine practice defines the practice goals. One of the substantial entities available to assist in accomplishing practice goals in a managed care environment is the management information system. Information management is used to optimize reporting, operations, and services delivery, and to create value-added products.

The information system should be selected based on the practice goals and the technical issues that will assure that the system is most likely to be effective.[2,3]

REFERENCES

1. Fine A: Managed Care Q, Winter 1998.
2. Harris JS, Guillen K: Information systems for health care delivery: Business process models, goals, and design. In Harris JS, Loeppke RR (eds): Integrated Health Management: The Key Role of Occupational Medicine in Managed Care, Disability Management and Integrated Delivery Systems. Beverly Farms, MA, OEM Press, 1998.
3. Harris JS, Miller LA: Sources and uses of occupational medicine data. In Harris JS, Loeppke RR (eds): Integrated Health Management: The Key Role of Occupational Medicine in Managed Care, Disability Management and Integrated Delivery Systems. Beverly Farms, MA, OEM Press, 1998.
4. Miller JL: Is "value" the new frontier? Integrated Healthcare Report 1–11, February 1996.
5. Siegle JE, Weinstein MC, Russel LR, et al: Recommendation for reporting cost-effectiveness analysis. JAMA 276:1339–1341, 1996.
6. Tapscott D: The Digital Economy: Promise and Peril in the Age of Networked Intelligence. New York, Donnelly & Sons, 1996.
7. Weaver M, Patrick DL, Markson LE, et al: Issues in the measurement of satisfaction with treatment. Am J Managed Care 3:579–594, 1997.
8. Wolfe K: Information management and computer applications in the occupational health clinic. In Herington T, Morse L (eds): Occupational Injuries. St. Louis, Mosby, 1995, pp 53–71.

LINDA RUDOLPH, MD, MPH

PERFORMANCE MEASURES IN OCCUPATIONAL MEDICINE: A TOOL TO MANAGE QUALITY

From the California Division of
    Workers' Compensation
San Francisco, California

Reprint requests to:
Linda Rudolph, MD, MPH
Medical Director
California Division of Workers'
    Compensation
45 Fremont Street, #3130
San Francisco, CA 94105

The use of managed care in occupational medicine is increasing rapidly, in large part due to the desire of employers and insurers to better control workers' compensation costs. However, recognition is growing that indiscriminate cost-cutting may have an adverse impact on the quality of care.[4]

Increasingly, large purchasers, including the federal government, are turning their focus to the concept that the value of health care equals quality divided by cost. Therefore, value-based purchasing requires a mechanism to measure both cost and quality. On the cost side of the equation, employers and insurers can monitor their own monetary and productivity costs associated with health benefits, workers' compensation premiums, absence days, and other factors. However, measuring the quality of health care is extremely challenging.

The interest in assessing quality of care is not limited to purchasers and consumers. Medicine is evolving toward a focus on medical effectiveness and outcomes and on evidence-based care.[8] Numerous studies suggest the persistence of wide variations in medical practice, some of which raise questions about the quality of care.[27] Health care providers and managed care organizations are struggling to identify the parameters of quality care and striving to improve performance in the face of increasing financial and time constraints.

This chapter provides an overview of basic concepts of quality of health care and approaches to assessing and improving the quality of occupational health care through the use of indicators or performance measures.

The Institute of Medicine defines *quality of care* as the degree to which health services for individuals and populations increase the likelihood of desired health outcomes and are consistent with professional knowledge.[14] Poor quality of care may increase morbidity and mortality, decrease ability to function after an injury, and fail to improve the public health.

Aspects of poor quality of care include the following.

1. **Shortcomings in interpersonal care.** The nature of interactions among the physician, health care personnel, and the patient influences the development of patient trust in the physician, the extent of patient understanding, and the willingness of the patient to follow instructions or return for follow-up care. In occupational health, shortcomings in interpersonal care additionally may affect the patient's trust in the appropriateness of return-to-work recommendations, the understanding of work restrictions, and the likelihood of litigation.

2. **Shortcomings in the technical aspects of care.** Overuse of ineffective therapeutic modalities, use of inappropriate treatments, and underuse of effective treatments contribute to poor outcomes. Several studies suggest that overuse may be a problem in workers' compensation medical care, particularly in the care of common musculoskeletal problems such as low back pain.[15,17,28] Overuse may increase complications and iatrogenic poor outcomes[9] or may simply drive up costs of care. Although managed care organizations tend to focus on identification of overutilization, several recent studies in the group health arena suggest that underuse is also a significant problem.[3] Further studies in occupational medicine are warranted.

Deficiencies in the skill and judgment of individual providers also lead to poor quality of care. There is considerable evidence that, at least in the performance of coronary artery bypass grafting (CABG), high volume is associated with lower mortality.[10] Studies of the association between volume and, for example, outcome after low back surgery, are lacking, as are assessments of the appropriateness of selected procedures.

3. **Shortcomings in the organizational aspects of care.** The health care delivery system influences both the initial access to care and access to specialty care, continuity of care, and coordination of care. The traditional workers' compensation fee-for-service system, in which the injured worker, claims examiner, or attorney has often managed care, has been characterized by fragmented, uncoordinated care.

In assessing the quality of care, experts have focused on three aspects of care: structure, process, and outcomes.[7] Structure includes the organization of the health care delivery system, the nature of the provider network, and the facilities that are available, i.e., the overall physical and organizational context in which health care providers actually provide care. Process refers to everything that happens between the provider and the patient, including communications, medical decision-making, diagnosis, and treatment choices. Outcomes reflect changes in health status that occur subsequent to the delivery of care and that can be attributed to the health care that was provided.

To evaluate or monitor the quality of care, there must be both a standard of care to use as a benchmark and a standardized method for evaluation. Performance measures, or quality indicators, provide a tool to monitor the extent to which the health care providers meet a standard of care; they are signs that can point to problems, indicate changes in complex systems, or compare different areas or groups.[13] Several examples of specific occupational medicine performance measures are provided beginning on page 750.

Properly developed and used, performance measures and quality indicators can be used by health care providers, managed care organizations, purchasers, consumers, and health care regulators. Such measures can provide insight into the strengths and weaknesses of care delivery systems, providing useful information for quality improvement efforts and for selection of health care.[6,16,22]

In the group health arena, several organizations have devoted considerable resources to the development of performance measures, including the National Council on Quality Assurance, the Joint Commission for the Accreditation of Healthcare Organizations, and the Foundation for Accountability.[18,20] These performance measures, for the most part, focus on diagnoses and services that have high impacts on cost and outcome, such as postoperative CABG mortality, mammography and immunization rates, screening for complications of diabetes, and hospitalization for asthma. They provide little help in the evaluation of the quality of occupational medical care, because, with few exceptions, they are not relevant to the practice of occupational medicine.

The first step in developing performance measures is determining what one wishes to assess and in what population. Clearly, performance measures for occupational medical care should address work-related illnesses and injuries. High-frequency diagnoses in occupational medicine include low back pain, fractures, dermatitis, upper extremity complaints and cumulative trauma of the upper extremities, and eye injury; however, less frequent events may have particularly serious consequences (e.g., occupationally related cancer) or may be particularly amenable to quality improvement efforts (e.g., treatment of occupational asthma).

Performance measures are most reliable when they are used to assess outcomes in specific populations; understanding the population of interest thus provides additional important information for the development of performance measures.[23] Knowledge of population characteristics is also important in identifying risk adjusters, which may be critical in the analysis of data used for performance measurement. Generally, occupational medicine patients are between the ages of 16 and 65 and sufficiently healthy—at least prior to injury—to be working; the population is characterized by ethnic, linguistic, and literacy diversity. The usual patterns of general health care for this population vary tremendously, ranging from rich group health benefits to no usual health care.

Occupational medicine encompasses a wide scope of activities, including primary prevention, clinical diagnosis and treatment, and disability prevention and management. Performance measures should address the breadth of occupational medical practice and may pertain to the structure, process, or outcomes of health care.

Ideally, the quality of the structure and process will contribute to the nature of the outcomes; however, this is not always the case. In selecting performance measures, it is important to assess the extent to which a particular structure or process is truly associated with an outcome of interest. There is good evidence, for example, that immunizations really do prevent polio; therefore, immunization rates of children are a reasonable indicator of quality of pediatric care, as a proxy for measuring polio case rates. Surgery utilization rates, however, are not a reasonable proxy for measuring outcome after back surgery.

When using outcome measures, it is important to consider key contributors to outcome that may lie outside the health care provider's domain. Adolescent pregnancy rates, for example, certainly reflect factors other than the quality of counseling by pediatricians. Return to work outcomes similarly reflect workplace conditions and employer policies that are beyond the control of the individual physician. Thus, although the physician may play an important role in the return to work process, good return to work outcomes also require employer policies and behaviors conducive to return to work.

TYPES OF PERFORMANCE MEASURES

Listed below are some examples of the types of performance measures that might be used to assess the quality of occupational medicine services and, also, some of the problems in using performance measures. These examples are illustrative of the range of issues that warrant examination if we are committed to developing performance measures and using them to improve the quality of occupational medical care.

Access

Simple measures of access include time from injury to first doctor's visit (which can be obtained from medical bill data) or standard patient satisfaction survey questions regarding geographic convenience and waiting time in the doctor's office.[5] However, assessing access in occupational medicine also should include a measure of the extent to which workers with occupational illness have access to the workers' compensation system. This poses a larger measurement problem because it is impossible to routinely and systematically identify occupational illnesses that are treated outside of the workers' compensation system.

Clinical Diagnosis and Treatment

Process quality indicators for clinical diagnosis and treatment, including provision of clinical preventive services, must be carefully derived from professionally developed and accepted clinical guidelines of care. Medical services utilization rates may be difficult to use as quality indicators unless there is reasonable evidence regarding what constitutes an appropriate rate of services or there is clear-cut evidence of services that should or should not be provided in particular patient groups. Clinical indicators must be carefully defined.[19] Examples of possible clinical performance measures are provided in Table 1, based in large part on clinical standards of care presented in The American College of Occupational and Environmental Medicine *Occupational Medicine Practice Guidelines*.[11]

Prevention

Occupational medicine is a preventive medicine specialty, and high-quality occupational medical services should play a role in the prevention of occupational injury and illness.[1] Components of the process of care may be important indicators of the quality of preventive services. Failure to take a good occupational history makes it difficult to identify hazardous exposures, which warrant intervention. However, taking a good history is not sufficient and may not lead to primary prevention interventions. Thus, examining the occupational physician's records to assess the frequency with which an occupational history is taken also may not be a good measure of the quality of prevention services.

A better measure for occupational medicine prevention may be (1) the record of communicating recommendations for primary prevention to the employers of injured workers or (2) the number of times a provider has visited a worksite in the prior year. The Association of Occupational and Environmental Clinics asks applicants for membership to describe a primary prevention intervention in which the clinic has been involved.[2] Employer surveys could be another source of information about primary prevention efforts by an occupational medicine provider.

TABLE 1. Examples of Performance Measures Used in Occupational Medicine

Carpal Tunnel Release Surgery	Acute Low Back Problems

1. Was there an adequate trial of conservative care prior to surgery?
   a. % patients with appropriate activity restrictions for at least 1 month prior to surgery
   b. % patients with localized injection of lidocaine or corticosteroid prior to surgery
	1. Were appropriate assessment techniques used?
	   a. % medical records with documentation of screening for serious underlying condition
	   b. % patients with plain radiographs of lumbar spine in absence of red flag
	   c. % patients with computed tomography or magnetic resonance imaging in first month in absence of red flag

2. Was appropriate nerve conduction velocity testing performed prior to surgery?
   % patients with documented decreased nerve conduction velocity
	2. Was appropriate conservative care provided?
	   a. % patients with chart documentation of patient education/counseling
	   b. % patients with appropriate analgesic prescribed (acetaminophen, nonsteroidal antiinflammatory drugs, aspirin)
	   c. % patients with bed rest greater than 4 days
	   d. % patients with oral corticosteroids prescribed
	   e. % patients receiving transcutaneous electrical nerve stimulation
	   f. % patients receiving trigger point or ligamentous injections

3. Has counseling been documented regarding outcomes, risks, and benefits prior to surgery?
   % patients with counseling documented in chart
	3. If performed, was surgery appropriate?
	   a. % patients with chart documentation of discussion of treatment options
	   b. % patients with documented clinical evidence of nerve root compromise

Other measures of preventive services include the proportion of high-risk health workers who receive necessary immunizations (e.g., hepatitis B), the proportion of exposed individuals who receive appropriate biologic monitoring (e.g., blood lead testing), the proportion of exposed individuals who receive appropriate medical screening for early disease detection (e.g., audiometry and pulmonary function testing), or the proportion of cumulative trauma cases in which appropriate work restrictions or modifications are prescribed.

Outcome

Outcome measures provide the only indicator of the extent to which health care actually affects health status. A number of outcomes are of considerable interest, including easily measured clinical outcomes of both preventive and treatment interventions (e.g., decreases in blood lead levels after intervention to reduce lead exposure; improved nerve conduction velocity after carpal tunnel release surgery).

Patient-perceived outcomes such as frequency and severity of pain or functional impacts of injury at work and at home are clearly extremely important outcomes, requiring surveys of injured workers. Patient satisfaction with medical care is another important outcome, which, in the workers' compensation arena, may affect not only patient compliance with treatment but also employer control over medical care, litigation, and disability outcomes.[24] Measures of employer satisfaction, such as with adequacy of communications regarding appropriate work restrictions, also may provide insight into the quality of occupational medicine.

The use of outcome measures requires careful attention to other factors that also may affect outcome. In the analysis of hospital mortality rates, for example, intensive effort has been exerted to develop methods for risk adjustment that consider patient demographics, severity, and case mix to allow more confidence in using these rates to compare the quality of care among hospitals.[12] Different risk adjustment methods, however, may yield different results when comparing hospitals' mortality experiences. This should give investigators pause when considering the use of some outcome measures of great interest in occupational medicine, particularly given the complexity of the workers' compensation system. Rates of injury and illness, for example, are the outcomes most reflective of the success of prevention efforts and could certainly be used to assess the quality of preventive services. However, it is the responsibility of the employer, not the physician, to maintain a workplace free of hazards; claims rates also may reflect aspects of labor-management relationships. Injury rates may thus not be a fair indicator of the physician's performance with regard to prevention. Indeed, using injury rates as a performance measure for the health care provider organization could create incentives to provide services only to employers with good safety programs.[25]

Some purchasers and managed care organizations view return to work outcomes as a paramount measure of occupational medicine quality, even proposing that physician reimbursements be tied to return to work outcomes. However, even the best disability management skills on the part of a provider may not result in a good return to work outcome if the supervisor is unwilling to cooperate. Without a method for risk adjustment that considers the nature and severity of injury or complaint, the specific job and characteristics thereof, and the willingness of the employer to implement appropriate work modifications or restriction, return to work is an inconclusive measure of occupational medicine performance.

Performance measures may be extremely useful in improving the quality of care and facilitating the health care choices of consumers and purchasers. However, to be useful, information derived from performance measurement must be understandable and meaningful.[21] Employers must pay considerable attention to worker concerns, literacy levels, and presentation formats.[26] For physicians and health care organizations, a level of buy-in is required that may be facilitated by an inclusive measures development process by a credible organization and by a nonpunitive approach to discussion of performance measurement results.

The use of quality indicators is a new phenomenon in health care. In occupational medicine, developing meaningful and valid performance measures will require a concerted effort involving health care providers, employers, labor representatives, and public health experts. Embarking on that effort will provide the information that is needed to improve the quality of preventive and treatment services for workers.

REFERENCES

1. ACOEM Committee on Ethical Practice in Occupational Medicine: Committee report: Commentaries on the code of ethical conduct. J Occup Med 37:201–206, 1995.
2. Association of Occupational and Environmental Clinics: Criteria for Clinic Membership. Washington, DC, AOEC, 1992.
3. Chassin M: Assessing strategies for quality improvement. Health Affairs 16:151–161, 1997.
4. Chelimsky E: The political debate about health care: Are we losing sight of quality. Science 262:525–528, 1993.
5. Consumer Assessment of Health Plans Survey. AHCPR Pub. No. 97-R013. Rockville, MD, U.S. Department of Health and Human Services, Agency for Health Care Policy and Research, 1997.

6. Corrigan J: How do purchasers develop and use performance measures. Med Care 33(suppl): JS25–JS30, 1995.
7. Donabedian A: The Methods and Findings of Quality Assessment and Monitoring: An Illustrated Analysis. Ann Arbor, MI, Health Administration Press, 1985.
8. Ellwood P: Shattuck lecture—Outcomes management: A technology of patient experience. N Engl J Med 318:1549–1556, 1988.
9. Franklin G, Haug J, Heyer N, et al: Outcome of lumbar fusion in Washington State Workers' Compensation. Spine 19:1897–1904, 1994.
10. Grumbach K, Luft H, Roos L, Brook R: Regionalization of cardiac surgery in the U.S. and Canada: Geographic access, choice, and outcomes. JAMA 274:1282–1288, 1995.
11. Harris J (ed): Evaluation and management of common health problems and functional recovery in workers: The American College of Occupational and Environmental Medicine Occupational Medicine Practice Guidelines. Boston, OEM Press, 1997.
12. Iezzoni L: Risk Adjustment for Measuring Health Outcomes. Ann Arbor, MI, Health Administration Press, 1994.
13. Institute of Medicine: Access of Health Care in America. Washington, DC, National Academy Press, 1993.
14. Institute of Medicine: America's Health in Transition: Protecting and Improving Quality. Washington, DC, National Academy Press, 1994.
15. Johnson WG, Baldwin ML, Burton JF Jr: Why is the treatment of work-related injuries so costly? New evidence from California. Inquiry 33:53–65, 1996.
16. Karpatkin R, Shearer G: A short-term consumer agenda for health care reform. Am J Public Health 85:1352–1355, 1995.
17. Mardon R, Mitchell G: The Impact of Florida's Low-Back Practice Guideline on Treatment of New Workers' Compensation Injuries. State Center for Health Statistics, Agency for Health Care Administration, 1997.
18. Nadzam D, Turpin R, Hanold L, White R: Data-driven performance improvement in health care: The joint commission's indicator measurement system (IMSystem). Joint Comm J Qual Improve 19:492–500, 1993.
19. National Committee for Quality Assurance: Health Plan Employer Data and Information Set, Version 3.0. Washington, DC, NCQA, 1997.
20. National Committee for Quality Assurance: Medicaid HEDIS. Washington, DC, NCQA, 1996.
21. Office of Technology Assessment: Health Care Reform: Report Cards Are Useful but Significant Issues Need to be Addressed. Washington, DC, U.S. Government Accounting Office, 1994.
22. O'Leary D: Performance measures: How are they developed, validated, and used? Med Care 33(suppl):JS13–JS17, 1995.
23. Palmer RH: Understanding and Choosing Clinical Performance Measures: Development of a Typology. Washington, DC, U.S. Department of Health and Human Services, Agency for Health Care Policy and Research, 1995, publications 95-N001 and 95-N002.
24. Rudolph I, Wiley J, Dervin K, et al: What do injured workers think about their medical care? San Francisco, California Division of Workers' Compensation, 1998.
25. Schauffler H, Rodriguez T: Exercising purchasing power for prevention. In Wilkerson J, Given R (eds): Competitive Managed Care: The Emerging Health Care System. San Francisco, Jossey-Bass, 1997, pp 83–99.
26. Sum J: What Workers Know About the Workers' Compensation System. San Francisco, California Commission on Workers' Compensation and Health and Safety, 1997.
27. Welch WP, Miller ME, Welch HG, et al: Geographic variation in expenditures for physicians' services in the United States. N Engl J Med 328:621–627, 1993.
28. Zaidman B: Industrial Strength Medicine: Report to the Minnesota Legislature. Minnesota Department of Labor and Industry, 1990.

E. LIZA GREENBERG, RN, MPH
RON LEOPOLD, MD, MBA, MPH

PERFORMANCE MEASUREMENT IN WORKERS' COMPENSATION MANAGED CARE ORGANIZATIONS

From American Accreditation
  HealthCare Association/URAC
Washington, DC (ELG)
  and
ManagedComp
Waltham, Massachusetts (RL)

Reprint requests to:
E. Liza Greenberg, RN
American Accreditation HealthCare
  Association/URAC
1275 K Street NW
Suite 1100
Washington, DC 20005

Injured workers are increasingly being treated in managed care settings. Among managed care organizations delivering workers' compensation health care services, a concurrent effort has been underway to increase availability and reliability of information on clinical performance. Both providers and managed care organizations (MCOs) influence clinical outcomes; thus, issues relating to measuring the performance of each are of interest. This chapter describes several major initiatives to develop standard performance measures in group health managed care settings. The implications of these models for workers' compensation are discussed, including challenges to production of workers' compensation clinical performance measures as a result of differences in delivery systems and information systems. Several national initiatives to examine performance issues are described, and the perspective of one national managed care company that has designed and implemented a physician "report card" is presented.

As states have responded to escalating costs in the workers' compensation health care arena, many have implemented workers' compensation reforms based on managing care for injured workers. Currently, 29 states have some type of managed care program for workers' compensation.[2] Largely as a result of variations in state regulations, the form and structure of these managed care programs is quite diverse. MCOs offer tailored services, including medical case management, utilization management, network management, bill review, and claims administration. Managed care functions also may be carried out by indemnity insurance carriers. Managed care processes are often overlaid on a fee-for-service payment structure. Increasingly, workers' compensation MCOs offer a provider network combined with case management as the primary care management approach.[21]

Regardless of the structure of the MCO, there has been increased interest in reporting data on organizational performance affecting clinical outcomes. In managed care systems, the organization affects clinical performance by steering patients to specified networks of providers, identifying clinical guidelines, creating financial and other incentives to encourage use of specific protocols, and measuring and providing feedback on provider performance. Physician interventions also play a critical role in determining outcomes. Physician-level measurement, comparison, and reporting is a concurrent thrust in the field of performance measurement. Report cards and provider profiles are most commonly used among MCOs to assess provider performance.

Standardized performance measures designed to assess clinical performance against benchmark clinical protocols can increase accountability for the delivery of quality care and can create incentives for organizations to ensure more comprehensive management of injuries and illnesses. Clinical performance reporting is viewed as an important consumer protection and as an integral element of quality improvement. From the consumer's perspective, decreased choices for patients through managed care and increased use of clinical practice guidelines necessitate increased organizational accountability for quality of care.

More typically than clinical performance measures, workers' compensation MCOs and purchasers of managed compensation services have demonstrated an appetite for economic performance information. Lost-time rate, average numbers of lost work days and, ultimately, cost per case are fundamental drivers of business decisions in this arena. Unlike group health medical care delivery, an important economic driver in workers' compensation medical care delivery is time. Payors in group health typically do not bear the cost burden of delays in treatment the way that workers' compensation payors do. For instance, an unnecessary 3-week delay in a critical step in the treatment and recovery of a patient may have no impact on the clinical outcome or the medical services that are used. If the patient is receiving wage-replacement payments for a work-related injury, however, unnecessary delays become an important consideration in the delivery of medical care.

NEED FOR STANDARD CLINICAL PERFORMANCE MEASURES

In the workers' compensation arena, no industry-wide clinical performance measures have been adopted for managed care, and the measures that are used are not standard from organization to organization. MCOs frequently measure performance related to utilization, lost days, and referrals, but the clinical inputs and outcomes for these measures often are not assessed. National performance measures that could be used to compare clinical performance of workers' compensation MCOs have not been developed,[13] but experts have noted that standard clinical measures would permit improved monitoring and comparisons of clinical quality in managed care settings.[13,26]

As in group health, the emergence of risk-bearing arrangements and incentive arrangements between carriers and managed care companies has created a new emphasis on understanding variations in clinical treatments of injured workers and more effectively managing care of workers. (Such risk arrangements also have raised concerns about the possibility of providers and payors seeking short-term gains by denying necessary care.) Performance measures not only improve care management processes by benchmarking current practices against known best practices, but they also act as a deterrent to both under- and overutilization. Organizations may be held accountable for issues such as how well they promote access to treatment from appropriate providers, the timeliness of treatment, the appropriateness of treatment, and satisfaction of patients with the treatment.

Performance measurement systems rely heavily on information technology and availability of data. However, data management often is less evolved in workers' compensation than in group health managed care settings,[27] and access to complete clinical data is a challenge given the diversity of organizations involved in managed care arrangements. For example, the entity accountable for payment of medical and/or indemnity claims controls access to data and also determines the data elements and format to be collected. MCOs that pay claims or process data through bill review have enhanced access to data for analytic purposes. Most provider organizations can analyze only the information that is available to them, which is often a subset of the total activity of a claim. Analysis of organizational and provider performance is often confounded by lack of reliable data.

One major impetus for developing measures is the variability of treatment for the same injury within the workers' compensation health setting[3] and even greater variation when injuries occur in a workers' compensation setting versus a nonworkers' compensation setting.[14,25] Medical costs for injuries occurring in a workplace setting are estimated to be up to 1.5 times higher than costs for the same injury in nonworkers' compensation claims.[8] This degree of variability has not been clearly associated with better health outcomes.[25] Although it has been hypothesized that a higher intensity of services (the "sports medicine approach") is appropriate for workers' compensation cases, higher utilization of services also has not been linked to better outcomes. Performance measures may reduce this variability by focusing attention on interventions definitively linked with better outcomes.

APPROACHES TO PERFORMANCE ASSESSMENT: ACCREDITATION AND PERFORMANCE MEASURES

Quality measurement in health care refers to the process of identifying which interventions and activities result in the most desirable outcome. Quality of organizations can be measured in terms of (1) structure: does the organization have the capacity to provide good care, (2) process: is it carrying out appropriate interventions, and (3) outcome: is the patient's health optimized as a result of the intervention? Accreditation has typically focused on assessing structure and processes, while performance measures examine processes and related clinical outcomes.

Quality of individual providers can likewise be measured in terms of (1) structure: is the provider appropriately trained and licensed, and does the provider's office facility have the capacity to provide good care, (2) process: are the clinician and office staff delivering medical care in an appropriate and timely manner, and (3) outcome: is the injured worker returning to normal or optimal functionality?

Standard performance measures recently have been used in the group health setting for the following purposes: to assist purchasers, consumers, and regulators in health care decision-making by providing comparable data and information on health care; to identify patterns of compliance by providers and health plans with accepted standards of care; and to protect consumers by identifying variations in care and improving the effectiveness of treatment. Accreditation is a separate but sometimes complementary process for ensuring quality in health care, and it often assesses structural elements of an organization. Both accreditation and performance measurement are helpful in producing information about quality, which can shift purchasing decisions from a cost-only basis to a combination of cost and quality.

Accreditation as a Method of Assessing Performance

Through accreditation, organizations can be examined and compared to established standards. Accreditation standards provide an objective, external review of quality processes and provide assurances to regulators and purchasers. Accreditation assesses whether the organization is capable of delivering quality care. In health care, accreditation has become intermingled with the regulatory and purchasing processes. For example, a number of states require certain types of organizations to be accredited by the American Accreditation HealthCare Commission/URAC (Commission/URAC) or by the National Committee for Quality Assurance (NCQA) as a condition of doing business. The Health Care Financing Administration (HCFA) requires hospitals to be accredited by the Joint Commission for the Accreditation of Healthcare Organizations (JCAHO) as a condition of doing business with the Medicare program. Increasingly, private purchasers are making accreditation a condition of contracting in group health purchasing decisions.[24] When accreditation standards are rigorous and meaningful, they can spur performance improvements through increased competition on the basis of quality.[6]

The Commission/URAC is the only organization that accredits workers' compensation MCOs. The organization has established standards for workers' compensation utilization management programs and workers' compensation provider networks (Table 1). Particularly in workers' compensation managed care, where there is tremendous product variation resulting from differences in state regulation, national accreditation is valuable in its measurement of consistent standards indicative of health care quality. Four states currently deem or mandate Commission/URAC accreditation for workers' compensation managed care programs;

TABLE 1. Categories of Commission/URAC Workers' Compensation Accreditation Standards

Utilization Management Programs	Provider Networks
Confidentiality of information	Provider selection
Responsibility for initiating utilization review	Provider availability and accessibility
Staff qualifications	Network management and operations
Utilization management program qualifications	Provider contracting
Accessibility and onsite review procedures	Provider disciplinary action
Information on which utilization management is conducted	Worker complaint and grievance process
Procedures for review determinations	Confidentiality
Appeals of determinations not to certify services	Marketing and sales activities
	Quality management plan
	Quality management structure, organization, and staffing
	Quality management program
	Credentialing
	Delegation of credentialing

deemed status indicates that accredited programs are recognized in lieu of state licensure or otherwise deemed to meet state standards of care.

In general, accreditation standards differ from performance measures in the degree of specificity and in the range of reported outcomes. An accreditation standard often focuses on the structure and process of an organization and allows for multiple approaches for meeting that standard. For example, Commission/URAC standards specify that workers' compensation utilization management programs must have a quality improvement program. The elements of form and content of quality assurance programs are not specified as long as companies "maintain and document an ongoing, structured quality management program that promotes objective and systematic monitoring and evaluation of UM [utilization management] processes and services."[1] Managed care companies may meet this requirement with multiple forms of quality initiatives tailored to the needs of the purchasing organization.

Accreditation standards thus capture the diversity of the managed care marketplace but have limited value in promoting direct comparisons between programs and outcomes of programs. Alternatively, performance measurement sets developed at the national level have a high degree of specificity, for the specific purpose of promoting comparisons between organizations.

Performance Measurement of Workers' Compensation MCOs

Recent efforts in performance measurement among workers' compensation MCOs have focused on the production of performance report cards based on provider clinical profiles.[7] Networks with more integrated data systems conduct quality assessment activities that analyze selected utilization data to ascertain how closely the rates for network physicians conform to normative rates for these procedures. Norms are established through the use of commercial guidelines, such as those developed by Milliman and Robertson, or through comparison with local practice.

As noted, many individual managed care workers' compensation organizations have established their own criteria for performance and outcomes. For example, MetraComp, a subsidiary of United HealthCare, is developing a system to produce performance report cards for its participating provider networks. The report cards will contain information on performance relating to economic variables, success at return to work, sustained work return, litigation rates, vocational rehabilitation rates, and employer/employee interactions. The company is developing a relational database to support production of the report cards.[20] MetraComp's efforts target provider accountability rather than MCO-level accountability.

ManagedComp also has developed a report card for its network of primary occupational physicians. ManagedComp's goal was to create an objective way of evaluating physician performance in workers' compensation cases. This report card generates a multidimensional snapshot of the physician's performance with his or her ManagedComp caseload. The dimensions evaluated include adjusted medical costs, productivity, medical quality, customer satisfaction, and patient protection concerns. The information also is used to generate feedback to physicians, counsel them when necessary, identify improvement opportunities, and determine incentive payments.

The Travelers Company implemented a process last year among several managed care companies to identify issues relating to production of uniform outcomes measures. The company convened several meetings throughout the United States and addressed issues such as how to define quality relating to satisfaction, case cost, compliance with practice parameters, and other measures. The work has not yet been published. Travelers tracks return to work, percent impairment, cost, and utilization in its current reporting set.

Review of the occupational health literature reveals numerous relevant studies on the development of comparable performance measures among organizations. These tools would be an important starting point in developing national parameters for measuring clinical performance. Data collection instruments that have been studied include functional status measures,[5] patient satisfaction surveys,[17] and clinical outcomes measures.[11,28] This research will be instructive in moving forward to identify the best available standardized measurement tools for use across organizations.

NEW DIRECTIONS IN MANAGED CARE QUALITY AND PERFORMANCE MEASUREMENT

Quality Measurement Versus Performance Measurement

Performance measurement is the process of measuring how well an individual provider or organization carries out selected activities. The activities that are measured are those that are believed to represent quality health care and may address either the process or outcome of health interventions. Ideally, performance measures are selected from the range of health care interventions that have been scientifically shown to produce the best health outcomes. However, because evidence is not available regarding the effectiveness of many interventions, selection of performance measures in many instances involves expert consensus as to what constitutes quality health care.

Developers of standard performance measures seek the following features in each measure: (1) comparability—activities that can be measured in a similar way from organization to organization, (2) accountability—interventions and patients for which the organization is clearly accountable, and (3) causality—in which a result can be linked to the intervention.

The quality of health care intervention ultimately is measured by the outcome: did the patient get well? In occupational health, an added outcome measure is whether the patient returned to work and whether he or she assumed the same or modified work capacity. For chronically ill or disabled patients, a good outcome may be maximizing function or slowing the progression of the disease. In preventive care, the outcome would be that the disease or injury never occurs.

One significant challenge in developing performance measures in workers' compensation is to design measures that detect true differences in the care as opposed to variations in patient populations or benefits.

HMO Techniques as a Model for Workers' Compensation Organizations

With the emergence of risk-bearing MCOs, incentives have begun to fall into place for organizations to manage care processes to reduce financial risks. Proactive delivery of care for high-risk patients is thought to be effective care management and effective risk reduction. Health maintenance organizations (HMOs) linked patients with primary care providers (PCPs) as a method of holding individual providers accountable for care of individual patients. It was also thought that through leverage gained in employment or contractual arrangements, MCOs could influence the behavior of physicians. The characteristics of some MCOs—integrated delivery and payment structures, increasingly sophisticated information systems, an enrolled population, and accountable PCPs—enabled techniques of standardized performance measurement to progress. Consequently, the focus of performance measures shifted from assessing the quality of care that patients *did* receive to assessing the delivery of care that patients *should* receive.

Several models of performance measurement in the group health setting invite examination for possible adaptation to occupational health managed care. The three most widely used performance measurement sets in group health include the HealthPlan Employer Data and Information Set (HEDIS), developed by the NCQA; ORYX, developed by JCAHO; and FACCT measures, developed by the Foundation for Accountability (FACCT).

In the early 1990s, the HMO Group, a national trade organization representing group and staff model HMOs, initiated a project to produce standardized HMO performance information for employer-purchasers. In 1992, responsibility for the standard performance measurement tool, known as HEDIS 1.0, was transferred to NCQA, an independent national organization that accredits HMOs. Since 1992, HEDIS has gone through three major revisions (HEDIS 2.0, 2.5 and 3.0), each reflecting increasing sophistication of HMO data and information systems and improvements in the science of performance measurement.

HEDIS 3.0 is used voluntarily by more than half the nation's HMOs. Reporting is required by many purchasers, including HCFA. Through comparable, standardized data, health plans can be held accountable for the delivery of quality health care. In the latest version, some outcome measures, including patient satisfaction, have been added to HEDIS[22,23] (Table 2). HEDIS data have resulted in increased attention to quality improvement efforts as health plans seek to measure up to industry benchmarks. Purchasers also have recognized the value of performance measurement in other health insurance products. HCFA is now sponsoring efforts to develop standard performance and accountability measures for fee-for-service health care.

JCAHO, a national accreditation organization for hospitals and some types of MCOs, is also involved in the development of performance measures.[16] Through its ORYX system, released in 1997, JCAHO initiated the first attempt to link performance measurement and accreditation. Measures were analyzed to ensure that the following attributes had been addressed: (1) measures were, in fact, performance measures; (2) data can be generated by existing databases; (3) data to be reported are of high quality; (4) risk adjustment and stratification issues have been considered; (5) feedback is provided to the health care organization for internal quality improvement use; and (6) measures are relevant to accreditation.[15]

FACCT was established to increase availability of reliable and meaningful information to help consumers and purchasers make health care decisions. Unlike

TABLE 2. Categories of HEDIS Measures Contained in the 1996 HEDIS Version 3.0

Effectiveness of care

Access/availability of care

Satisfaction with care

Health plan stability

Use of services

Cost of care

Informed health care choices

Health plan descriptive information

HEDIS = HealthPlan Employer Data and Information Set

NCQA, which develops performance measures and specifications, FACCT compiles existing data and assembles them in categories most useful to consumers. FACCT measures address issues such as functional status, quality of life, and patient satisfaction.[18] Results are reported in a consumer-friendly format based on "steps to good care, experience and satisfaction, and results" of care.[10] FACCT measures have been compiled in the areas of depression, adult asthma, breast cancer, diabetes, health risks, health status, and consumer satisfaction.

Challenges of Performance Measurement in Workers' Compensation MCOs

Examination of how HMO performance measures are produced for HEDIS is worthwhile as a model but also reveals a number of key structural differences between HMOs and workers' compensation MCOs that affect performance measurement. Certain features of HMOs enable these organizations to capture data and information on patients in a more sophisticated manner than occurs in nonmanaged settings. Structural attributes of HMOs that facilitate production of performance measures are described below, and contrasting elements of workers' compensation MCOs are highlighted in italics.

- **Enrolled population**. HMOs typically have a rigorous process for determining who is eligible for benefits. Enrollment information thus defines the population for which the HMO is held accountable. Using the population or selected subsets of the population (e.g., children under the age of 2), the HMO can calculate rates of interventions (e.g., the percentage of children under the age of 2 who received a specific immunization). *Identifying the denominator of injured workers to follow may be a challenge. Not all injured workers file workers' compensation claims. Of those that enter the workers' compensation system, not all injured workers are typically referred to the MCO. A third-party administrator (TPA) or indemnity carrier often will case-manage patients directly, referring the more complicated cases to the MCO. In addition, even the population of injured workers may be difficult to track for the following reasons: inaccurate information from employers on injured workers, underreporting of injuries, and workers' opting out of the managed care system.*

- **Access to patients**. Through the enrollment process, the HMO gains access to contact and demographic information about enrolled patients. This provides a base for outreach, both relating to the need for services and for conducting survey assessments of the HMO's performance. *The MCO may have access only to injured workers and usually has no contractual role in prevention of workplace injuries. A work-related injury or illness triggers a claim, but MCOs typically have limited information on risk factors and potential injuries prior to the claim. As noted, the MCO may not have access even to all injured workers, because some individuals are case-managed through the insurer or opt not to use the managed care system.*

- **Uniform coding**. A HEDIS measure is a health care indicator (e.g., the number of women in the appropriate age range who receive a mammogram) accompanied by specific instructions as to how that indicator will be derived. To produce a valid indicator, each health care organization must use the same claims coding information, must include and exclude the same files, and must use the same data sources for information. *In addition to the challenges faced by HMOs, coding of workers' compensation medical claims may not have the level of specificity needed to track severity or the specific nature of the injury* *or illness.[7] As the workers' compensation claim is processed through medical and indemnity channels, medical data often are not entered into the system. When this is the case, the outcome is not easily linked with specific medical interventions. Even when medical coding is consistent, outcomes generally cannot be determined from medical claims information without additional information such as functional status.*

- **Access to data**. As both the payor of care and the provider of care, the HMO has access to a wide range of data. If the HMO has the capacity to capture and analyze these data, it has access to a rich array of information on use of services and treatment. Administrative data are a key source of information on procedures and, often, diagnoses. Pharmacy and laboratory data provide another method for tracking treatment and diagnosis. Information from patient records, though rarely integrated with electronic information, offers more complete information on interventions and clinical status. Claims may be incomplete or lack information on diagnosis and intervention. Medical records data thus complement information derived from claims data. Chart data is particularly important in determining severity of illness. *A workers' compensation MCO, if it is not also the payor, does not have access to data beyond medical claims data. Insurance carriers or TPAs may process bills for services, but they may not provide the data to the MCO or link it to medical information in a clinically meaningful way. Data linkages will be facilitated by new federal standards for electronic data interchange currently under development as mandated under 1997 Health Insurance Portability and Accountability Act legislation, although use of the new standards is voluntary by workers' compensation MCOs.*

- **Relationships with physicians**. Through contracts with physicians and physician groups, HMOs are able to steer groups of patients to specific providers. Through steerage of patients and financial arrangements, they exert some leverage over the behavior of providers. The influence of HMOs can be used to encourage providers to meet certain targets. *Many workers' compensation MCOs may contract with large numbers of providers to ensure the greatest access to care. This strategy dilutes the expertise of the network and the leverage of the MCO to influence practice patterns of any single provider. Conversely, selective network contracting may allow the MCO to use more experienced providers but may affect access. MCOs have little influence over the care processes of non-network providers, and most states allow patients the option of leaving the network at some point.*

- **Incentives**. HMOs are often at risk for medical losses. They often share risk with providers through capitated or incentive arrangements. The premise of these arrangements is that capitation will encourage providers and plans to intervene with the earliest and most effective clinical services to prevent long-term and expensive complications. *Managed and nonmanaged workers' compensation systems have competing and sometimes contradictory financial incentive systems. Fee-for-service arrangements create no incentives for providers to manage care. Discounted fee-for-service may encourage overutilization by creating a reverse incentive. Capitation, rarely used in workers' compensation, could encourage underutilization. Case rates represent a promising approach to incentive pricing.*

- **Infrastructure Investment**. Although few payors have explicitly agreed to fund performance measurement activities in HMOs, at-risk HMOs have flexibility in use of resources. HMOs have made major investments in information systems as an approach to more cost-effective care management. *Workers' compensation MCOs generally sell their product to a payor, not a patient, and market themselves on the basis of cost. Payors may require some types of performance information (e.g., utilization and cost) but have infrequently demanded performance information on quality of care indicators. Payors only recently have developed an appetite for clinical performance information from workers' compensation MCOs.*

Technical Issues in Developing Reliable Standard Measures

As workers' compensation managed care companies continue to gain prominence, they will be challenged to compare results of clinical interventions. While the field of performance measurements for MCOs has developed tremendously recently, it is by no means an exact science.[19] A number of technical issues, described below, continue to raise challenges in developing reliable data at the provider and MCO levels. Workers' compensation MCOs face these challenges in developing occupational injury-specific performance measures and also face unique challenges related to the regulatory and structural variations in workers' compensation organizations. Skeptics of performance measurement note that it may be unfair to make comparisons between organizations until the following issues are reliably addressed.

- **Time frame for assessing outcomes**. Many outcomes are long-term outcomes that cannot be easily linked to a specific health intervention. A performance measure often must identify intermediate- and shorter-term outcomes to assess the effectiveness of health services. For example, while return to work may be an outcome for most injured workers, for catastrophically injured workers not expected to return to work, intermediate measures of the effectiveness of care must be determined.[4]

- **Defining the desired outcomes**. It is not always simple to determine what the outcome should be or how to measure it in a standard way. Some outcomes are subjective and therefore differ among different people. For example, it is exceedingly difficult to measure pain as an outcome because perceptions vary among individuals.

- **Identifying the "denominator."** To calculate a rate such as the number of workers who received a tetanus shot when they were injured with a laceration and who were not up-to-date on vaccinations, the number of individuals receiving a laceration in the workplace or insurance pool must be known—the denominator. If only the most severe cases are reported, the range of treatments will be skewed. Selective reporting of cases also skews the known frequency of disease, which may affect efforts dedicated to prevention.

- **Managing differences in benefit structure**. Differences in the availability of services such as physical therapy, chiropractic, or preventive services may affect outcomes. This varies regionally across the country as well as within a given state. In workers' compensation, the variations between states in the patient's right to select or change providers affect the ability to measure and influence quality of services.

- **Risk adjustment**. This is one of the most important factors in making fair comparisons between treatments and providers. Data must be adjusted for differences in patient characteristics, availability of facilities, and severity of illness. Case mix, case severity, and geography are important variables that deserve careful consideration. No universal tools are available for making these adjustments.

- **Statistical significance**. A bad outcome could be a random occurrence or could be a pattern of poor care. To detect patterns, a large number of events must take place. "Typical" or "normative" physician behavior is probably more important to determine than clinical response to outlier situations. The actual levels of statistical significance must be calculated for the illness. Until an MCO can track a statistically significant number of events, random variations cannot be distinguished from true variations in care. Because providers often specialize in treating certain illnesses, provider profiles can be useful for examining practice patterns. The drawback to provider profiling is that the provider may only see a few patients for each insurer, again diminishing the conclusions that can be drawn from the limited sample.
- **Need for reliable tools**. Many experts in performance measures are now recognizing that the ability of the patient to function is an important indicator of health. Standard tools such as the SF-36 have been developed to assess function, and some have been adapted to occupational health settings.[5] However, the validity and reliability of functional status tools must be assessed for different populations and the use of the tool for different purposes (such as a return-to-work predictor). Also, many physicians do not have the training or time to administer these tools. Surveys are being used more frequently to augment claims and encounter data. A number of validated tools are in use in group health, which could be validated and standardized for workers' compensation. These tools include the Consumer Assessment of Health Plans Survey, the SF-36, and others. Surveys could be administered to users of services or could be administered at the purchaser level.
- **What to measure**. In some instances, scientific evidence will be available that demonstrates the effectiveness of certain interventions (e.g., immunizations); in others, however, professional debate continues as to what constitutes the most effective and thus the highest quality of care (e.g., treatment of low back injuries). The issue of what to measure continues to present challenges equivalent to the challenge of developing reliable and valid performance data.

In developing performance measures specifically targeting workers' compensation MCOs, a number of additional technical questions will need to be addressed.

- **Accountability**. If standard measures of performance are developed, whose performance is to be the target? In the workers' compensation MCOs, many functions relevant to managing care are carried out by multiple vendors. It will be important to determine how to create incentives to coordinate care between multiple vendors while holding managed care companies accountable for elements over which they exert control.
- **What measures?** What should be the distribution of measures between clinical care, access to care, prevention, or disability that may be relevant indicators of performance? Issues of interest include measures of MCO performance and physician performance. A mix of measures may be appropriate for the tool, which must be adaptable to variations in network design and workers' compensation managed care products. The appropriate balance of process and outcomes measures must be determined.
- **Who is the primary audience for data and information?** HEDIS was designed to provide health plan-level information for purchasers. It has since

been adapted to provide information for consumers and is recognized to be of value to regulators. FACCT was designed for consumers and purchasers from the outset. Most developers of performance measurement sets have struggled with the issue of how to make data meaningful to people before they are in an emergent situation.

- **What data sources should be used, and at what cost?** Workers' compensation MCOs have access to multiple types of data. Some are readily available, such as administrative claims; other types, such as patient records and surveys, are expensive to collect and have reliability problems. Access to data from employers, employees, and insurance carriers may be difficult but must be considered. The cost of data collection must be weighed with the benefit of having tools to evaluate performance.

- **What outcomes should be measured?** Researchers have identified many problems related to defining occupational health outcomes (e.g., the endpoint for a return-to-work outcome could be the date of release, the date of return to limited duty, or the return to full duty). Particularly in workers' compensation, the outcome may be attributable to nonclinical issues such as social issues and benefits, which should be factored into assessments of clinical performance.

- **State regulatory variations**. Managed care alternatives are structured differently in almost every state. MCOs only should be accountable for interventions they have the capacity to influence. This may make state-to-state comparisons more challenging.

- **Variations in MCO structure**. Care management processes may vary by insurer, TPA, or MCO. Services may be carried out in-house or subcontracted to a vendor. Comprehensive performance measures may necessitate analysis of information from multiple sources that do not necessarily have incentives to cooperate.

A PHYSICIAN REPORT CARD IN THE WORKERS' COMPENSATION MANAGED CARE SETTING

Physician-level report cards may be developed to increase accountability of providers in a number of dimensions. They may be used primarily to ensure that providers are performing as expected: an MCO that has invested resources into the development of an occupational physician network would consider ongoing monitoring of the clinical and economic performance of physicians a critical aspect of assuring the long-term viability of the asset. Report cards are also useful in the continuous quality improvement process; most physicians welcome performance feedback based on valid performance evaluation information. Finally, report cards can be useful in making business decisions to improve quality and efficiency of the network. MCOs may use a report card as a factor in ongoing contracting and patient channeling decisions.

Report Card Case Study

Over the past two years, ManagedComp, a Massachusetts-based workers' compensation MCO, has developed a report card for a group of select physicians, primary occupational providers (POPs), as part of its POP program. As part of the contract, POP physicians agree to be held accountable for the outcome of clinical care of work-related injuries and the work situation created by those injuries. ManagedComp's goal was to create an objective way to evaluate POP performance in workers' compensation cases.

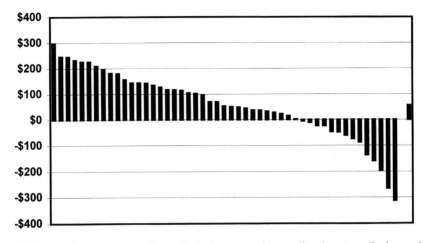

FIGURE 1. Average case saving (adjusted) compared to predicted case medical costs by individual provider (zero dollars represents predicted medical costs).

The Report Card Philosophy

ManagedComp launched its POP program with a report card as an integral component. Starting from the premise that POPs who are enrolled in the program are accountable for the results of care for all of their patients, the company includes all cases seen by the POP during the first week of treatment. Whenever possible, objective data are used. Summary and detailed medical claims information is used for the analysis. Because ManagedComp recognizes that all POPs will likely care for "problem cases," the approach has been to examine patterns of care rather than individual cases. The analysis is performed based on the assumption that most cases are uncomplicated; adjustments are then made for outliers.

Outcome Measures Included in the Report Card

Five major areas were identified for evaluation. Within each of these areas, several distinct measurements were made.

1. **Medical costs**. ManagedComp POPs are asked to serve as care directors for ManagedComp claimants. Therefore, these providers are held accountable for the cost of all medical services rendered on injured workers who are seen in POP offices within the first week of treatment. The report card compares actual costs to predicted costs for each case after adjustments are made for case mix and case severity (Fig. 1).

2. **Productivity protection**. Reducing unnecessary lost productivity and facilitating return-to-work are central priorities for ManagedComp. Because disability is a major cost-driver for workers' compensation, the report card evaluates POPs on rate of disability for a population of cases and duration of disability on a per case basis (Figs. 2 and 3).

3. **Medical quality and efficiency**. ManagedComp believes that efficiency improvements in health care also represent quality improvements. Medical services information is compared with claims data from nationally recognized clinical practice standards in a process that measures medical quality in workers' compensation.

4. **Customer satisfaction**. Recognizing that customer perception is a critically important way for health care companies to gauge how well their provider networks are doing, ManagedComp obtains feedback on POPs from three sets of

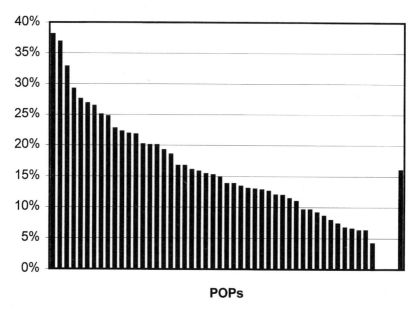

POPs

FIGURE 2.   Lost time (disability) rate for a population of cases. POP = primary occupational provider.

customers: (1) patients, (2) employers (clients), and (3) ManagedComp case managers. An independent firm is employed to collect, tally, and score results for each POP (Fig. 4).

5. **Patient protection concerns**. ManagedComp wants to send a clear signal that patients need to be protected from inadequate or questionable medical care. For

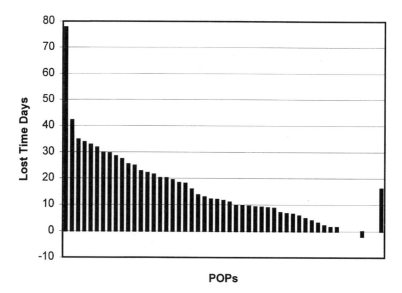

POPs

FIGURE 3.   Average lost days per lost-time case.

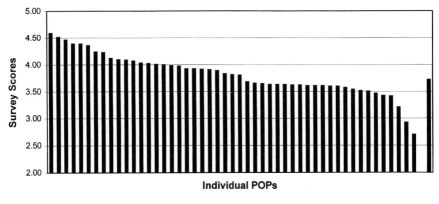

FIGURE 4.   Patient satisfaction.

every POP, five sentinel indicators are monitored for quality problems or adverse events. These indicators include patient perception of quality, employer perception of quality, and utilization of medical services for specified injuries.

Adjustments and Scoring

Each POP is evaluated on cases that have been identified as seen in that provider's office. A report card is performed only if a statistically significant number of observations have occurred. Each POP's caseload is evaluated for case mix and case severity on a comparative basis. Providers who have treated a significantly higher than average case mix, or whose case load has been identified as significantly severe, receive compensatory adjustments throughout the scoring process.

Adjustments for state workers' compensation differences are also made. Other adjustments, such as financial interest in ancillary services and whether the situation was rural versus urban, hospital-based versus free-standing, or contractor-provided versus owner-operated, may be added in the future.

For each attribute that is evaluated, the results of all POPs are compared. The mean of the group and the standard deviation of the distribution are used as guideposts in scoring. In addition, when independently validated measurements can be obtained (i.e., state lost-time rate, nationally recognized recommended utilization rate), they are used as a benchmark for comparison. All scores are based on a 4.0 scale and are appropriately weighted. POPs are given their own score and a summary of the scores of the group as a whole (Table 3). This information is also used to generate feedback information to POPs, to counsel POPs when necessary, and to identify improvement opportunities and determine incentive payments. The scoring

TABLE 3.   Example of Report Card Scores* of ManagedComp Physicians

	Medical Costs	Productivity Protection	Medical Quality	Customer Satisfaction	Patient Protection Concerns	Total
Dr. Smith	3.56	3.37	3.25	3.80	3.50	3.46
Dr. Jones	3.08	2.96	3.30	3.33	2.75	3.10
Average**	3.25	3.16	3.30	3.45	3.20	3.24

* Based on a 4.0 scale; adjusted for case mix   ** For all primary occupational providers

system does not force scores to a curve, i.e., if all providers perform well, it will be acknowledged. In general, clusters receive similar scores, and differences in scoring occur only when a definite distinction between two points can be made (see Fig. 4).

The ManagedComp initiative in provider performance evaluation has been invaluable in assisting the company in maintaining the quality of medical care delivered by network physicians. It has been a useful tool in conducting ongoing continuous quality improvement initiatives in all aspects of the delivery of medical services and disability management.

THE FUTURE OF PERFORMANCE MEASUREMENT IN WORKERS' COMPENSATION

Development of national measures of clinical interventions that are linked with good outcomes is one of the most promising avenues for managed care accountability. A number of national initiatives are underway to examine the overall impact of managed care on workers' compensation costs and the influence of clinical treatment on workers' compensation outcomes. These national efforts to hold MCOs accountable complement the activities of individual companies targeting physician accountability.

National Initiatives

The Workers' Compensation Research Institute (WCRI) has created a database containing information from 30 workers' compensation MCOs. WCRI developed specifications for data to ensure that consistent data were contributed from different MCOs. WCRI is developing analytic methods to examine data to determine performance benchmarks for individual and aggregate companies. The International Association of Industrial Accident Boards and Commissions has a database of medical claims information that possibly may be able to be linked to injury and other related data to identify industry benchmarks. These efforts may provide a framework for assessing the comparability of data provided by different types of organizations and for identifying what other data sources will be needed to develop useful measures of performance, but they do not focus on clinical interventions.

At least two federal agencies are involved in performance issues relating to workers' compensation health care. The National Institute for Occupational Safety and Health (NIOSH) has convened an ad hoc working group to address performance issues. NIOSH's mission is to investigate and research workplace safety and health issues. The Agency for Health Care Policy and Research (AHCPR) has conducted expert workshops on workers' compensation managed care issues targeting state legislators. AHCPR's effort has been directed at educating state policy makers on issues relating to improving the quality of workers' compensation health care. AHCPR has created a database of more than 1,200 performance measures, CONQUEST, which may contain measures of relevance to workers' compensation.

The widespread emergence of practice guidelines and practice parameters provides a foundation upon which to build performance measurement efforts.[12] The American College of Occupational and Environmental Medicine has developed guidelines for numerous occupational injuries, as have Washington, Colorado, Massachusetts, and other states. Several of these guidelines are modeled on guidelines developed initially by AHCPR. In developing national clinical performance measures, recommendations that are common to major guidelines and that are derived from evidence-based guidelines may be an appropriate starting point.

The Robert Wood Johnson Foundation is sponsoring a major grant program, the Workers' Compensation Health Initiative. Grants are awarded for the purpose of developing research and evaluation projects for improving the quality of care in workers' compensation health care. Projects have included efforts to evaluate state-sponsored managed care initiatives and, also, the assessment of tools that could be used to measure functional status, likelihood of injury recurrence, and long-term job retention.[9]

Finally, the Commission/URAC has been awarded a grant from the Workers' Compensation Health Initiative to develop and demonstrate a set of standard performance measures for workers' compensation MCOs. The goal of the Commission/URAC project is to improve the quality of care to injured workers by providing a basis for purchasers, consumers, and policymakers to compare MCO quality through standard data and information reports. Measurements of clinical and other aspects of performance will enable MCOs to compare themselves to industry benchmarks and establish quality goals. This project has national scope and will be guided by a national advisory committee representing MCOs, purchasers, labor, providers, and researchers. The Commission/URAC has commitments from five major MCOs to demonstrate the measures, which will be evaluated for reliability and validity. The final measurement tool will be widely disseminated for voluntary adoption by the managed care industry.

CONCLUSION

In short, clinical performance measurement of MCOs and individual providers has become the standard of practice in group health managed care arrangements. The tools used to assess and report performance are of value as models to workers' compensation MCOs. As managed care arrangements in workers' compensation expand, concomitant responsibilities arise for these organizations to be accountable for the care processes they manage. Still, the diverse structural arrangements between workers' compensation insurance purchasers, MCOs, and other vendors present challenges in developing standard measures of performance that could be used to compare clinical performance among organizations. Data and information systems' infrastructure and integration capacity for medical information analysis lags significantly behind systems in the group health arena. Further, the interweaving of medical and social insurance in workers' compensation raises technical challenges in measuring medical outcomes of workers' compensation health care. MCOs individually are developing systems to measure performance, primarily at the physician level. The Commission/URAC plans to develop measures useful for comparing organizational performance. Success in these endeavors will improve the quality and usefulness of information available on clinical performance and ultimately improve the quality of care delivered to injured workers.

REFERENCES

1. American Accreditation HealthCare Commission/URAC: Workers' Compensation Utilization Management Standards. Washington, DC, AAHC/URAC, 1997.
2. Anderson J: State by State Laws and Regulations on Workers' Compensation Managed Care. 1997 Edition. Alexandria, VA, Capitol Publications, 1997.
3. Atlas S, et al: Application of outcomes research in occupational low back pain: The Maine Lumbar Spine Study. Am J Ind Med 29:584–589, 1996.
4. Baldwin M, Johnson W, Butler R: The error of using returns-to-work to measure the outcomes of health care. Am J Ind Med 29:632–641, 1996.
5. Beaton D, et al: Measuring health in injured workers. A cross-sectional comparison of five generic health status instruments in workers with musculoskeletal injuries. Am J Ind Med 29:618–631, 1996.
6. Christian J: Managing comp care a challenge. Business Insurance, May 24, 1997.

7. Comp provider profiling efforts slow to produce results. Workers' Compensation Managed Care 5(10):1–2, 1997.
8. DeLizio M: Managed care and workers' compensation: Where the system is today. Managed Care Week/Managed Care Perspectives. 1–4, Jan. 6, 1997.
9. Dembe A, Himmelstein J: New directions in workers' compensation medical care. Workers' Compensation Managed Care Sourcebook. New York City, Faulker and Gray, 1997, pp 99–105.
10. Foundation for Accountability: Fact Sheet. Portland, OR, FACCT, 1997.
11. Franklin G, et al: Outcomes research in Washington State workers' compensation. Am J Ind Med 29:642–648, 1996.
12. Harris J: Development, use and evaluation of clinical practice guidelines. J Occup Environ Med 39:23–34, 1997.
13. Himmelstein J, et al: Measuring and improving quality of workers' compensation medical care. John Burton's Workers' Compensation Monitor 4–9, November/December 1995.
14. Johnson W, Baldwin M, Burton J: Why is the treatment of work related injuries so costly? New evidence from California. Inquiry 33:53–65, Spring, 1996.
15. Joint Commission for the Accreditation of Healthcare Organizations: National Library of Healthcare Indicators. JCAHD, Oakbrook Terrace, IL, 1997.
16. Joint Commission for the Accreditation of Healthcare Organizations: Performance measurement systems. Web site information www.jcaho.org. November, 1997.
17. Kyes K, et al: Reliability and validity of medical outcome and patient satisfaction measures among injured workers. In Washington State: A pretest. Am J Ind Med 31:427–434, 1997.
18. Lansky D: Foundation for accountability (FAACT): A consumer voice on health care quality. JCOM 3:54–58, 1996.
19. McGlynn E: Six challenges in measuring the quality of health care. Health Affairs 16(3):7–21, 1997.
20. MetraComp: Provider profiles popular with physicians. Workers' Compensation Managed Care May 1997.
21. Milliman and Robertson: HMO Managed Workers' Compensation Strategies and Products. Milliman and Robertson, 1995.
22. National Committee for Quality Assurance: HEDIS 3.0. Draft. Washington, DC, NCQA, 1996.
23. National Committee for Quality Assurance. HEDIS 3.0 Executive Summary. Web site information www.ncqa.org. November, 1997.
24. O'Kane M: Accreditation standards in managed care. Am J Managed Care 2:1081–1086, 1996.
25. Pransky G, et al: Outcomes research: Implications for occupational health. Am J Ind Med 29:573–583, 1996.
26. Rudolph L: A call for quality. J Occup Environ Health 38:343–344, 1996.
27. Schuckman P: Workers' Comp Meets Managed Care. InfoCare 32–37, January/February, 1998.
28. Stiens S: Rehabilitation intervention for patients with upper extremity dysfunction: Challenges of outcome evaluation. Am J Ind Med 29:590–601, 1996.

KATHRYN L. MUELLER, MD, MPH

MANAGED CARE WORKERS' COMPENSATION OUTCOME MEASUREMENTS: HOW CAN A CLINIC COMPETE?

From the Division of Emergency
  Medicine
University of Colorado Health
  Sciences Center
Denver, Colorado

Reprint requests to:
Kathryn L. Mueller, MD, MPH
Associate Professor of Preventive
  Medicine and Surgery
Division of Emergency Medicine
University of Colorado Health
  Sciences Center
4200 E. 9th Avenue, Box B-215
Denver, CO 80262

Further disease management programs will ideally be cultivated through forging new partnerships within and across health care systems; they will be supported by sophisticated, user-friendly clinical information systems; and they will be informed by rigorous health services research.[15a]

Managed care organizations have become the predominant mode of health care in general health and workers' compensation. Health care spending inflation has decreased from 16% in 1981 to 4.4% in 1996, according to the Health Care Financing Administration, which attributes the decrease to managed care.[2] Workers' compensation legislation regulating or requiring managed care has been enacted in 26 states.[15] Managed care organizations frequently develop financial incentives for physicians who comply with their guidelines or standards. In a national study, 23% of surveyed physicians reported receiving incentives based on patient satisfaction, 18% based on measures of quality such as rates of preventive care services, and 16% on practice profiles assessing their use of medical resources.[22] When a clinic or clinic organization contracts with a managed care organization, the measures for quality of care and service frequently are not well defined, allowing the clinic organizations themselves to create outcome criteria. Performing true outcome studies on a clinic population can be difficult. If clinic organizations plan to market their care to others and show continual improvement, they must evaluate the care and services they provide using measures of patient satisfaction and efficiency.

TABLE 1.   Examples of Process Measures

Waiting time for patients
Patient satisfaction with clinic personnel
Time required for transmission of work release and other workers' compensation papers to insurer and employer
Appropriate indications for treatment ordered
Referral to specialists when indicated
Appropriate initial return-to-work status—full duty, restricted, not returned to work
Early identification of patients not making functional progress
Patient education provided on the first visit
Worksite evaluations performed for appropriate cumulative trauma cases
Percentage of patients treated by one primary physician
Employer satisfaction with service

Structure, process, and outcome affect the quality of medical care that is provided.[14] The managed care organization and the clinic practice model determine structure. Quality improvement programs often monitor process to determine efficiency and customer satisfaction. Outcome is frequently defined as the patient's functional status after treatment. In commercial managed care, many process monitors are considered "outcomes." Examples of process measures and outcome measures are shown in Tables 1 and 2, respectively. This chapter discusses the feasibility and utility of studying both process and patient status outcomes in a clinical setting.

Initially, the clinic organization defines outcomes that reflect quality of care for a specific patient population. Before exploring methods of evaluation and determining whether personnel or money is available to complete a specific evaluation, the organization considers the importance of the defined outcomes to active health care providers in their clinics and to management goals. The following six steps will help create a meaningful, achievable set of outcome measures.

1. Review current managed care contracts and organizational expectations.

The National Committee for Quality Assurance (NCQA) accredits health maintenance organizations based on quality improvement, utilization management, credentialing, and member rights and responsibilities. The HealthPlan Employer Data and Information Set (HEDIS) was developed in association with NCQA. Although this data set is for general health care, some measures could be applied to workers' compensation. The Utilization Review Accreditation Commission (URAC) specifically

TABLE 2.   Examples of Outcome Measures

Total time off work ordered by physician
Length of time from beginning treatment to maximum medical improvement
Long-term job retention
Medical services used per diagnosis or medical cost equivalent
Health status survey—general–SF-36, SF-12, or Health Status Questionnaire-12
Diagnosis-specific functional survey
Other patient report of function or satisfaction with outcome of treatment
Need for ongoing medical care at case closure
Return to work status at case close—return to previous job with no restrictions; return to previous job with restrictions; released to work with restrictions but not employed; permanent total disability

accredits workers' compensation managed care. Comparing a clinics' staff and policies to some of the above criteria can be useful. Examples include the percentage of primary treating physicians who are board-certified (NCQA recommends 75%), annual provider turnover (NCQA suggests less than 5%), and unimpeded access to mental health care in appropriate cases.[29]

Many managed care contracts have service expectations regarding how soon patients must be seen once they arrive in the clinic, how easily patients can access appropriate specialists, whether patients receive adequate follow-up instructions, and whether patients are satisfied with the physical surroundings of the clinic and the service provided by desk personnel. In workers' compensation, the other customer, the employer, also must be satisfied with the quality of return to work information and promptness in transmitting other workers' compensation information as required by state statute. These important issues can be monitored in many ways. If computers include patient check-in and release time, these data can provide a reasonable estimate of the length of time a patient was in the clinic. Similar monitoring may be performed for faxing or telephoning appropriate information to employers simply by comparing the time a fax was sent or comparing the telephone log with the time that the patient was seen.

Many patient surveys are available to measure patient satisfaction with patient-physician interaction, physical surroundings, desk personnel, and timeliness of the visit. Most of the surveys are based on Likert scales and ask patients to what extent they agree or disagree with specific statements (Appendix A). Telephone surveys may best achieve a representative workers' compensation sample.[17] However, phone surveys are personnel-intensive, and patients may be difficult to reach by telephone during the day. A return of at least 60% on written patient surveys is usually necessary to provide a reasonable representation of patient opinion.[12] This may be difficult to obtain by mail in a workers' compensation population, especially when the patient has legal representation. If the patient completes the survey in the office at the end of the case, there is a tendency for the survey to be biased because the patient is aware that the survey is being monitored by the clinic itself. The same problem occurs when clinic personnel perform telephone surveys. Despite these problems, some type of patient satisfaction survey should be performed periodically to evaluate service.

Employer satisfaction also should be monitored, using telephone or written surveys of risk managers and supervisors. Satisfaction with the quality and type of information provided, clarity of work restrictions, and promptness of information provided are all appropriate issues to monitor.

2. Monitor medical treatment outcomes that are limited in scope and of interest to physicians and other health care providers in the clinic.

There may be concern regarding excess spinal fusion, outcome of cumulative trauma cases, or difficulty returning nonsurgical low back pain patients to work. If providers are interested in studying a question, they will be more likely to complete any additional forms necessary to collect the information. Although medical treatment can be reviewed retrospectively using case reviewers and medical records, this implicit technique requires training of case reviewers and retesting to ensure that reviewers are consistent in grading the records and are reliably recording information in the originally defined manner.[18,19] If the investigational question is limited to a simple question that can be evaluated using an explicit technique, such as whether specific indications are present when a spinal fusion is ordered, physicians can complete an additional form for applicable cases. When using physician-reported information, one should recall that providers are more likely to report their own behavior as compliant than case reviewers may be.[19]

In a small clinic setting, many of these measures cannot be studied with any validity. If the question is isolated to the presence or absence of indications for treatment and whether the treatment was ordered, a compliance rate can be determined among the physicians. The number of cases per physician and the severity of cases will affect the result. Merely informing physicians of their performance versus the performance of other physicians in their group can change behavior.[21] One must remember to accommodate for unusual circumstances, such as patients' refusal of treatment, family situations that do not allow patients to continue the treatment, or the interference of work or religious beliefs with treatment. Some case severity information should be included in these surveys. The treatment compliance rate is not likely to provide an outcome measurement that can be compared with those of other local clinics. However, it can provide information as to the compliance of physicians with local or national treatment guidelines.[1,30,31]

Outcome measurements unique to workers' compensation can be used to evaluate treatment outcome, including permanent disability, time off work for a specific diagnosis, and number of cases with litigation.[26] Disability time ordered for a specific diagnosis can be compared with two published sources: *The Medical Disability Advisor*, which is largely based on medical consensus, and *Official Disability Guidelines*, which garners information from several sources, including the Occupational Safety and Health Administration and the National Hospital Data Service.[27,35] In addition, the American College of Occupational and Environmental Medicine's (ACOEM) treatment guidelines and many state medical treatment guidelines recommend time for return to work based on diagnosis and severity.[1,30,31] With these measures, the physicians' ordered time off in the clinic can be compared with several standards. Allowances should be made for severity factors that would increase the disability time or other interfering factors, such as the patient taking a vacation, a family illness that took time away from the usual recovery period, or the employer's inability to accommodate return to work. The latter variable is accounted for in ACOEM's guidelines.

While litigation clearly reflects costly and difficult cases, it is a problematic outcome measure in a small clinic setting. Litigation is relatively uncommon. Therefore, an increase in the rate from two cases to five cases per physician may not be a statistically reliable change. It is also difficult to demonstrate any relationship between litigation and medical treatment. Litigation frequently occurs because the patient is unhappy with the employer rather than the physician. It may be useful to track this factor internally, but it is unlikely to directly reflect medical treatment and is of no external use due to the absence of a standard comparison rate.

3. Consider patient function and return to work as outcome measures.

There are many ways to view long-term outcomes. Although whether the patient returned to full duty at the end of the case is one measurement, investigators have shown that initial return to work does not reveal many workers' long-term income losses, which occur over years.[4] When the patient has permanent physical limitations, return to work is difficult to assess because it depends on the employer's ability to accommodate rather than on the medical treatment.

Using a standardized questionnaire to assess the patient's activities of daily living and function can be a better measure of determining changes in health status, particularly if the patient completes a baseline questionnaire at the initiation of treatment. Pre- and posttreatment surveys can monitor improvement using standard criteria. One can evaluate function using generic quality of life surveys or diagnostic-specific functional surveys. Popular generic surveys include the Medical Outcomes Survey Short Form (SF-36) or its abbreviated version, the SF-12.[33] The 12-item health status questionnaire

(HSQ-12) produced by Stratis Health is an additional short functional questionnaire[28] (Appendix B). All of these forms are easily administered. The difficulty with the quality of life measures is their extremely general measures of health status and lack of sensitivity for specific diagnostic problems such as carpal tunnel syndrome or low back pain.[8,24,32,34] They may not be useful in many workers' compensation populations because the severity of the illness is not high. Useful patient function measures will be sensitive to subtle changes in activities of daily living or function.[20] Multiple disability measurements exist for low back pain, including the commonly used Oswestry Low Back Disability Questionnaire and the Roland-Morris Questionnaire.[6] These measurements have been tested and used in multiple settings and thus may provide a basis for following patients. An upper extremity disorder functional scale recently developed at the University of Massachusetts has been described in the literature.[25]

4. Consider the feasibility of monitoring the most important goals and consider how to use the information that is obtained.

Performing process monitoring for time and efficiency of services rendered and customer satisfaction is necessary in most clinical settings to monitor quality. When improvement is demonstrated, the results can be used to promote the clinic. Usually, no specific local yardsticks are available, but managed care organizations can be consulted to determine if they have required times for waiting and if they have already measured some of their clinics. This will help the clinic determine what information to release, avoid duplication of effort, and obtain already standardized forms.

Medical treatment issues are difficult to study. Initially, only relatively clear issues that are amenable to process monitoring and an explicit technique should be attempted. Because many complex issues impinge on individual cases, some researchers believe that process monitoring should be the main technique for evaluating care in the clinical setting.[3,7,9,11] For instance, if there is concern regarding appropriate narcotic prescribing, which is generally not recommended for workers' compensation injuries and is rarely recommended in ACOEM's guidelines, it can be monitored if a computer system includes a record of prescription drugs.[1] If chart review is required, monitoring narcotics may not be feasible. If indications for surgery or a specific treatment are important, a short checklist might be created that physicians would complete every time the surgical procedure or treatment was ordered to determine compliance with the necessary indications. The results from the latter type of monitoring may not truly reflect the physician's actions prior to the monitoring intervention, because the monitoring sheet itself is likely to encourage appropriate behavior. When choosing outcome measures that reflect patient satisfaction, one must remember that a physician's criteria for correct treatment and good outcome do not necessarily match a patient's preferences or opinions.[10,13] Standardized questionnaires that involve patients in the formulation and grading process can be used.

5. Consider the limitations of the selected evaluation plan.

The initial intent of quality improvement is exactly that—to monitor service and treatment and improve quality.[5,16] The outcome studies discussed in this chapter are unlikely to meet statistical significance and cannot account for all of the variability found within patients in a specific clinic. One should consider these issues when evaluating the results. One can say with certainty how many patients were registered and then dismissed from the clinic within a certain amount of time if the computer system records that information. However, if the data entry for these items is flawed, the study will be wrong. At the other extreme, using a generic quality of life survey to reflect the quality of care at closure of the case presents huge interpretative difficulties because outcome may be highly affected by factors out of the clinic's control, including concurrent disease, age, family resistance to treatment, psychological factors, and lack of sensitivity to less severe disease.[34]

If a specific diagnosis is being studied, the cases that are selected should truly represent the defined diagnostic category. ICD-9 codes garnered from a computerized database are frequently faulty. Better techniques include using provider-entered classifications or chief complaints identified by the patient. Within each diagnostic category one should consider age variations, type of work performed if relevant to the outcome measure being studied, education of the patient, the employer's ability to accommodate the patient's return to restricted duty, the patient's willingness to complete medical treatment, and the severity of the disease process among individuals being studied. The importance of these variables will depend on the outcome measures.

An outcome measurement should not be undertaken if there is no clear measurement goal that corresponds to prior research. Reporting that 60% of the patients did not receive carpal tunnel surgery but did return to work has no real significance unless some other research or quality measure shows that 60% reflects good care. Thus, clear goals of compliance or outcome substantiated by research must exist before any treatment outcome measurements are attempted.

Finally, it is essential to remember that changes in one set of outcome measurements can reflect an untoward effect on other outcomes. For instance, if the goal was to decrease the number of laminectomies and it was possible to demonstrate a decrease in the clinic population compared to the community standard, insurers may prefer the clinic because medical costs would decrease. It is possible, however, that laminectomy is not being provided to patients who would improve significantly with surgery and have a better postoperative functional status. The same patients may be dissatisfied that no laminectomy was provided and may be less likely to return to work than patients who had a laminectomy. Similar issues may occur regarding disability days. Perhaps the time off work for patients with carpal tunnel syndrome has been decreased, but returning the patient to work earlier led to increased pain and decreased function. The same patients may have required surgery more often and may have been less likely to retain their jobs at case closure than patients who were off work for a longer time and gradually returned to work.

6. Choose recipients of final outcome reports carefully.

Consider the effect of releasing the information from the evaluations to consumers of managed care organizations versus providing the information only internally to improve quality of care. When the Health Care Financing Administration originally began recording annual death rates for Medicare patients at community hospitals, officials hoped that the information would serve the public by allowing comparisons between facilities for lower mortality rates. In fact, the public paid little or no attention to this information but did, however, react to occasional dramatic negative occurrences reported by the media.[23] Thus, the public does not process percentages and morbidity information well. Patient satisfaction is important to market to patients and employers and will always be a commodity that consumers understand. Other quality of care information may be better interpreted by professionals.

Well-conceived outcome measurements can improve quality and enhance marketing. Providers and other personnel will benefit when important process measures are regularly tracked. When clear numerical goals are compared with actual performance, quality will improve. More detailed treatment process or outcome measurements are most successful when providers have a sincere interest and curiosity in the outcome that is being studied. Choosing the initial studies carefully will ensure quality improvement, involved personnel, and marketable results.

APPENDIX A

PATIENT SATISFACTION SURVEY

Your health care providers at _____
are interested in knowing if you were satisfied with our medical services.
Please fill out the form below. Thank you.

	Strongly Agree	Agree	No Opinion	Disagree	Strongly Disagree
1. The medical team (doctors, nurses, therapists, social workers, etc.) treated me with RESPECT AND COURTESY.	□	□	□	□	□
2. The medical team LISTENED TO MY CONCERNS AND UNDERSTOOD MY PROBLEM.	□	□	□	□	□
3. The medical team EXPLAINED to me what was going to be done and why.	□	□	□	□	□
4. I had all my QUESTIONS ANSWERED.	□	□	□	□	□
5. The medical team used words that were EASY TO UNDERSTAND.	□	□	□	□	□
6. I was involved in the DECISION MAKING as much as I wanted to be.	□	□	□	□	□
7. The medical team SPENT THE TIME with me that my condition required.	□	□	□	□	□
8. I have CONFIDENCE in the medical team's ability and knowledge.	□	□	□	□	□
9. The members of my medical team (doctors, nurses, therapists, social workers, etc.) TALKED TO EACH OTHER about my care.	□	□	□	□	□
10. I UNDERSTAND what is normal to expect when I get home and how to care for myself.	□	□	□	□	□
11. OVERALL, I was satisfied with the care that was provided.	□	□	□	□	□
12. Please explain any answers that you needed to check "Disagree" or "Strongly Disagree".					
13. Please describe any experiences you really felt good about.					

From University Hospital, Denver, Colorado; with permission.

APPENDIX B

QUALITY OF LIFE QUESTIONNAIRE

Your health care providers at _____
*are interested in knowing the status of your health and recovery. Please fill
out the form below. Thank you.*

1. In general, would you say your health is ...	□ Excellent □ Very Good □ Good □ Fair □ Poor

The following items are about activities you might do during a typical day. Does your health now limit you in these activities? If so, how much?	Yes, limited a lot	Yes, limited a little	No, not limited at all
2. Lifting or carrying groceries?	□	□	□
3. Climbing *several* flights of stairs?	□	□	□
4. Walking *several* blocks?	□	□	□

5. During *the past 4 weeks*, how much difficulty did you have doing your work or other regular daily activities as a result of your physical health?	□ Not at all □ A little bit □ Some □ Quite a bit □ Could not do daily work

6. During *the past 4 weeks*, to what extent have you accomplished less than you would like in your work or other daily activities as a result of emotional problems (such as feeling depressed or anxious)?	□ None at all □ Slightly □ Moderately □ Extremely

7. During *the past 4 weeks*, to what extent has your physical health or emotional problems interfered with your normal social activities with family, friends, neighbors, or groups?	□ None at all □ Slightly □ Moderately □ Extremely

8. How much bodily pain have you had during *the past 4 weeks*?	□ None □ Very mild □ Mild □ Moderate □ Severe □ Very Severe

APPENDIX B (Cont.)

These questions are about how you feel and how things have been with you during the *past 4 weeks*. For each question, please give the one answer that comes closest to the way you have been feeling. How much of the time during the *past 4 weeks*:	All of the time	Most of the time	A good bit of the time	Some of the time	A little of the time	None of the time
9. Have you felt calm and peaceful?						
10. Did you have a lot of energy?						
11. Have you felt downhearted and blue?						
12. Have you been a happy person?						

Who completed this form?	□ I filled it out with no help □ I filled it out with help from family or friends □ I filled it out with help from a health care provider □ Family or friends filled it out □ Health care provider filled it out

HEALTH STATUS QUESTIONNAIRE-12 VERSION 3.0

Terms of Use

Stratis Health hereby grants permission to copy and use the Health Status Questionnaire (HSQ)-12 Version 3.0 in accordance with the following conditions which shall be assumed by all to have been agreed to as a consequence of accepting and using this document:

1. Changes to the HSQ-12 Version 3.0 may be made without the written permission of Stratis Health. However, all such changes shall be clearly identified as having been made by the recipient.

2. The user of the HSQ-12 accepts full responsibility, and agrees to indemnify and hold Stratis Health harmless, for the accuracy of any translations of the HSQ-12 Version 3.0 into another language or format, and for any errors, omissions, misinterpretations, or consequences thereof.

3. The user of the HSQ accepts full responsibility, and agrees to indemnify and hold Stratis Health harmless, for any consequences resulting from the use of the HSQ-12 Version 3.0.

Please note that the Type Specifications are frequently undergoing review and revision. We suggest you contact Stratis Health prior to implementing any of the instruments to insure that all materials are current.

Scoring Rules

HSQ-12 scoring involves two steps: (1) recoding responses, and (2) calculating scale scores.

Step 1: The first step involves recoding the response values from the instrument. It is important to note that the response values on the instrument are not necessarily recoded with equal intervals between the values. See the chart on page 783 for the recoded response values for each HSQ-12 item.

APPENDIX B (Cont.)

Step 2: The second step involves calculating an average of the recoded response values for the multi-item scales (Physical Functioning and Mental Health) to create a summary score. For single-item scales, the recoded response value is the summary score. The summary scores represent the proportion of total possible values obtainable for the scale. For example, if a person scores 50 on the Physical Functioning scale, he/she obtained 50% of the maximum possible score. See the chart on page 784 for the calculation rules and an example.

All scales are scored so that the higher score represents a positive health attribute. For example, a high score for Physical Functioning indicates few or no limitations in activities such as walking, stair climbing, bending, kneeling, or stooping. Bodily Pain is scored so that a high score represents freedom from pain.

Item recoding and scale scoring are most efficiently performed using standard data analysis and database management software (e.g., SAS, SPSS, FoxPro, dBase). Although both steps may be performed using a calculator, it is more efficient and reliable to enter the numbers corresponding to the specific response values into a spreadsheet or data entry package and allow the computer to process the necessary calculations.

Missing Responses

Subjects often will leave one or more items blank on a health survey. For the multi-item scales (Physical Functioning and Mental Health), missing responses may be estimated from responses to other items on the same scale if at least two items have been completed. Several techniques may be used, but the most valid is calculating the average score across completed items on the same scale for the subject. For example, if questions 2 and 3 are answered and 4 is left blank, an average of the scores from 2 and 3 is taken to be the estimated summary score. If more than one item is missing for these scales, the scale score cannot be calculated and should be recorded as missing. For calculating the single-item scales (Role Limitations due to Physical Functioning, Bodily Pain, Health Perception, Energy/Fatigue, Social Functioning, Role Limitations due to Mental Health), if the response is missing, then the scale score is treated as missing.

APPENDIX B (Cont.)

HSQ-12 USER GUIDE

HSQ-12 Scoring Algorithms First Step: Recoding the Response Values		
Item Numbers	**Original Response Category[1]**	**Recoded Value Of:**
1	1 -------------> 2 -------------> 3 -------------> 4 -------------> 5 ------------->	100 85 60 25 0
2, 3, 4	1 -------------> 2 -------------> 3 ------------->	0 50 100
5	1 -------------> 2 -------------> 3 -------------> 4 -------------> 5 ------------->	100 65 25 10 0
6	1 -------------> 2 -------------> 3 -------------> 4 ------------->	100 65 45 0
7	1 -------------> 2 -------------> 3 -------------> 4 -------------> 5 ------------->	100 75 50 25 0
8	1 -------------> 2 -------------> 3 -------------> 4 -------------> 5 -------------> 6 ------------->	100 85 65 45 25 0
9, 10, 12	1 -------------> 2 -------------> 3 -------------> 4 -------------> 5 -------------> 6 ------------->	100 80 60 40 20 0
11	1 -------------> 2 -------------> 3 -------------> 4 -------------> 5 -------------> 6 ------------->	0 20 40 60 80 100

[1] Precoded response choices printed on the questionnaire

APPENDIX B (Cont.)

HSQ-12 USER GUIDE

HSQ-12 Scoring Algorithms Second Step: Computing Scale Scores			
Scale	**Number of Items**	**Scale Items**	**Minimum Number of Items to Compute a Score**
Physical Functioning	3	2, 3, 4	2
Role Limitations Attributable to Physical Health (Role-Physical)	1	5	1
Bodily Pain	1	8	1
Health Perception	1	1	1
Energy/Fatigue	1	10	1
Social Functioning	1	7	1
Role Limitations Attributable to Mental Health (Role-Mental)	1	6	1
Mental Health	3	9, 11, 12	2

Formula:

$$\frac{\text{Sum of Recoded Scale Items}}{\text{Number of Completed Scale Items}} = \text{Scale Score}$$

Example:

The Mental Health score is computed by adding the values for the recoded scale items 9, 11, and 12 then dividing by 3.

$$\frac{\text{HSQ9} + \text{HSQ11} + \text{HSQ12}}{3} = \text{Mental Health Score}$$

If a patient's recoded values for items 9, 11, and 12 are 80, 100, and 60 respectively, then computing the Mental Health scale score would be as follows:

$$\frac{80 + 100 + 60}{3} = 80$$

Revised January 1988. From Stratis Health, 2901 Metro Drive, Suite 400, Bloomington, MN 55425; with permission.

REFERENCES

1. ACOEM Occupational Medicine Practice Guidelines: Evaluation and Management of Common Health Problems and Functional Recovery in Workers, Beverly Farms, MA, OEM Press, 1997.
2. American Medical Association: Managed care cited for slow-down in spending. Am Med News, Feb. 2, 1998.

3. Angell M, Kassirer JP: Quality and the medical marketplace—Following elephants [editorials]. N Engl J Med 335:883–885, 1996.
4. Baldwin ML, Johnson WG, Butter RJ: The error of using returns-to-work to measure the outcomes of health care. Am J Ind Med 29:632–641, 1996.
5. Berwick DM: Continuous improvement as an ideal in healthcare. N Engl J Med 320:53–56, 1989.
6. Beurskens AJ, de Vet HC, Koke AJ, et al: Measuring the functional status of patients with low back pain. Spine 20:1017–1028, 1995.
7. Blumenthal D: Quality of Health Care: Part 1: Quality of care—What is it? N Engl J Med 335:891–894, 1996.
8. Bombardier C, Melfi CA, Paul J, et al: Comparison of a generic and a disease-specific measure of pain and physical function after knee replacement surgery. Med Care 33:AS131–AS144, 1995.
9. Brook RH, McGlynn EA, Cleary PD: Quality of Health Care: Part 2: Measuring quality of care. N Engl J Med 335:966–970, 1996.
10. Calkins DR, Rubenstein LV, Cleary PD, et al: Failure of physicians to recognize functional disability in ambulatory patients. Ann Intern Med 114:451–454, 1991.
11. Chassin MR: Quality of Health Care: Part 3: Improving quality of care. N Engl J Med 335:1060–1063, 1996.
12. Dillman DA: Mail and Telephone Surveys: The Total Design Method. New York, Wiley & Sons, 1978.
13. Dolan JG, Bordley DR, Miller H: Diagnostic strategies in the management of acute upper gastrointestinal bleeding: Patient and physician preferences. J Gen Intern Med 8:525–529, 1993.
14. Donabedian A: The quality of medical care. Science 200:856–864, 1978.
15. Eccleston SM: Managed Care and Medical Cost Containment in Workers' Compensation: A National Inventory 1995–1996. Cambridge, MA, Workers' Compensation Research Institute, 1995.
15a. Ellrodt G, Cook DJ, Lee J, et al: Evidence-based disease management. JAMA 278:1687–1692, 1997.
16. Elwood PM: Outcomes management: A technology of patient experiences. N Engl J Med 318:1549–1556, 1988.
17. Franklin GM, Fulton-Kehoe D: Outcomes research in Washington State workers' compensation. Am J Ind Med 29:642–648, 1996.
18. Gilbert EH, Lowenstein SR, Koziol-McLain J, et al: Chart reviews in emergency medicine research: Where are the methods? Ann Emerg Med 27:305–308, 1996.
19. Grilli R, Lomas J: Evaluating the message: The relationship between compliance rate and the subject of a practice guideline. Med Care 32:202–213, 1994.
20. Guyatt GH, Fenny DH, Patrick DL: Measuring health related quality of life. Ann Intern Med 118:622–629, 1993.
21. Jones FG: Education-based practice pattern analysis: A tool for continuous improvement of patient care quality. Am J Med Quality 7:120–124, 1992.
22. Lake T, Peter RF: Results from Community Tracking Study. Data Bulletin (8):Fall 1997, 1–2.
23. Mennemeyer ST: Death and reputation: How consumers acted upon HCFA mortality information. Inquiry 34:117–128, 1997.
24. Patrick DL, Deyo RA, Atlas SJ, et al: Assessing health-related quality of life in patients with sciatica. Spine 20:1899–1909, 1995.
25. Pransky G, Feuerstein M, Himmelstein J, et al: Measuring functional outcomes in work-related upper extremity disorders: Development and validation of the upper extremity function scale. J Occup Environ Med 39:1195–1202, 1997.
26. Pransky G, Himmelstein J: Evaluating outcomes of workers' compensation. In Kimpan K (ed): Workers' Compensation Medical Care: Effective Management of Outcomes. Cambridge, MA, Workers' Compensation Research Institute, 1996, pp 11–32.
27. Presley R (ed): Medical Disability Advisor: Workplace Guidelines for Disability Duration, 2nd ed. Horsham, PA, LRP Publications, 1994.
28. Radosevich D, Pruitt M: Twelve-Item Health Status Questionnaire. Stratis Health, 1998.
29. Seltzer J, Nash D: Models for Measuring Quality in Managed Care: Analysis and Import. New York, Faulkner & Gray, 1997.
30. State of Colorado, Department of Labor and Employment, Division of Workers' Compensation: Low Back Pain Treatment Guidelines. Colorado Dept. of Labor and Employment, 1995.
31. State of Colorado, Department of Labor and Employment, Division of Workers' Compensation: Upper Extremity Guidelines. Colorado Dept. of Labor and Employment, 1995.
32. Testa MA, Nackley JF: Methods for quality-of-life studies. Annu Rev Public Health 15:535–559, 1994.

33. Ware JE, Kosinski M, Keller SD: A 12-item short-form health survey: Construction of scales and preliminary tests of reliability and validity. Med Care 34:220–233, 1996.
34. Wilson IB, Cleary PD: Linking clinical variables with health-related quality of life. JAMA 273:59–65, 1995.
35. Work-Loss Data Institute: Official Disability Guidelines: Length of Disability Data by ICD-9 CM from CDC and OSHA plus NHDS Hospital Length of Stay. Riverside, CT, Work-Loss Data Institute, 1996.

STACEY M. ECCLESTON
RICHARD A. VICTOR, JD

REGULATORY TRENDS IN WORKERS' COMPENSATION MANAGED CARE

From the Workers' Compensation
    Research Institute
Cambridge, Massachusetts

Reprint requests to:
Stacey M. Eccleston
Workers' Compensation Research
    Institute
101 Main Street
Cambridge, MA 02142

Rapidly increasing medical expenditures coupled with evidence pointing to poor health outcomes and inappropriate or ineffective treatment became a primary focus of the national health care and workers' compensation communities beginning in the late 1980s. National health care costs grew at an average annual rate of about 10% from 1985–1992, and workers' compensation costs grew at an average annual rate of nearly 15%, peaking in 1992. Even when adjusting for the level of employment, workers' compensation medical costs grew at an annual average rate of almost 13% (Table 1). This period of rapid growth drew much attention from those attempting to curb escalating costs and is perhaps the catalyst for many of the medical cost containment initiatives currently in place in workers' compensation. At the same time, evidence in the group health environment that treatment plans vary substantially for the same injuries and that managed care techniques may reduce both inappropriate and appropriate hospitalization[8] began to surface. Other studies on treatment patterns and patient outcomes raised questions regarding the appropriateness and quality of care being provided under such plans.[1,4,9]

In workers' compensation several medical care regulatory initiatives surfaced to address the cost and quality of health care. At the same time, efforts by employers and insurers were implemented in the private sector. These initiatives took the form of price controls and utilization controls initially and, more recently, implementation of managed care and treatment guidelines.

TABLE 1.   Workers' Compensation and Total U.S. Medical Expenditures, 1985–1995

Year	Aggregate Medical Expenditures		Medical Expenditures per Person	
	All Payors, U.S. (billions)	Workers' Compensation (millions)	All Payors per Capita, U.S. (dollars)	Workers' Compensation per Worker (dollars)
1985	$428.2	$7,080	$1,523	$73
1990	$697.5	$14,309	$2,364	$131
1991	$791.7	$16,009	$2,577	$148
1992	$834.2	$18,252	$2,792	$168
1993	$892.1	$17,521	$2,938	$158
1994	$937.1	$17,200	$3,061	$151
1995	$988.5	$16,700	$3,219	$142
Annual average percentage change, 1985–1992	10.0	14.5	9.0	12.6
Annual average percentage change, 1992–1995	5.8	–2.9	4.9	–5.2
Annual average percentage change, all years 1980–1995	9.7	10.5	8.7	8.7

SOURCES: "All payors" data (both aggregate and per capita figures) come from *Health Care Financing Review*, Fall 1996, Vol. 18, No. 1, p. 199. Workers' compensation aggregate data for 1980–1993 are from *Social Security Bulletin*, Vol. 58, No. 2, Summer 1995, p. 52. The 1994–1995 aggregate data come from an as-yet-unpublished article, "Workers' Compensation: Benefits, Coverage, and Costs, 1994–1995," by Jack Schmulowitz. Employment data for all years used to calculate "per worker" figures come from *Employment and Earnings*, the U.S. Department of Labor, Bureau of Labor Statistics.

From Workers' Compensation Research Institute: Managed Care and Medical Cost Containment in Workers' Compensation: A National Inventory, 1997–1998. Cambridge, Massachusetts, WCRI, 1997; with permission.

Table 2 indicates that workers' compensation price controls in the form of provider and hospital fee schedules are common regulatory strategies and that limited provider choice and change are also common among the states in an effort to improve disability management and reduce costs. Among the more recent regulatory trends was the addition of managed care regulation and mandates and the introduction of treatment guidelines for use in workers' compensation. Managed care regulations were generally added to workers' compensation statutes in 1992–1995. Although the policies that were implemented are generally adaptations of strategies that have been implemented by nonworkers' compensation insurance programs, the unique nature of workers' compensation medical care dictates some variation. The medical care component of workers' compensation differs from medical care delivered in the nonoccupational arena in several important ways, as follows:

1. Reducing workers' compensation medical costs is not an end in itself. Disputes over workers' compensation nonhealth benefits (income or indemnity benefits) may have a substantial impact on the quantity, quality, and cost of workers' compensation medical care. Workers' compensation medical cost-containment programs must therefore place greater emphasis on disability management and the effectiveness and quality of medical care and its ability to return individuals to work.

2. The ability to direct care within provider networks in workers' compensation is governed by statutory provider choice and change rules in each state. Although managed care regulation has increased the ability of employers and insurers

to direct the initial treatment for the most part, the use of exclusive networks cannot be enforced in workers' compensation.

3. Litigation and disputes over compensability, the extent of disability, and other nonmedical service delivery issues change the role of the health care provider. The treating provider in the workers' compensation environment not only controls treatment plans and direct medical costs but also plays a major role in determining the patient's ability to return to work and the amount of indemnity benefits.

4. In the workers' compensation environment, attorneys can become involved in choosing the provider and the level of services. In disputed cases, incentives for the use of health care change in a way that may increase costs and affect health outcomes. Also, distrust among workers, providers, employers, and others makes it difficult to implement medical cost-containment strategies.

5. Workers' compensation medical costs amount to only about 3% of the nation's total health care costs, and they are spread across many workers' compensation payors, which makes it difficult for workers' compensation payors to negotiate favorable rates or influence medical practice patterns in many areas of practice.

6. Workers' compensation is an entitlement program governed by complex legislation and influenced by diverse political constituencies. Employee cost-sharing or copayments are generally prohibited in workers' compensation, and limits are often placed on the use of restricted provider networks such as managed care organizations.

The goals of managed care in workers' compensation include not only the delivery of cost-effective, quality care but also a focus on disability management and enabling injured workers to return to productive employment as soon as they are ready. This chapter defines managed care as it is used in workers' compensation, and it summarizes the managed care policies of each state and the District of Columbia and links those policies to the regulatory environment by qualifying the ability to use such arrangements. This chapter also describes the components of regulated managed care policies, including certification requirements, the minimum number and types of providers, utilization review, case management, treatment guidelines, internal dispute resolution, and other requirements. Finally, this chapter addresses the new innovations in outcomes measurement as defined by patients' well-being and daily functioning as a way of evaluating the impact of managed care techniques on quality of care.

DEFINITIONS

Managed care in workers' compensation is defined here as an organization, most often referred to as a managed care organization (MCO), that seeks to deliver cost-effective and quality care. These organizations generally maintain an administrative function and provider network, and they often offer services including case management, utilization review, bill review, practice guidelines, and quality assurance programs. The definition used here revolves around the provider network concept. The states credited with mandating or regulating managed care all include a provision for a provider group to which employees may be directed for some or all of their treatment. Where a jurisdiction mandates or regulates use of preferred provider organizations (PPOs) or case management techniques in lieu of an MCO or health care organization, they are included in this category; however, they are appropriately identified as such.

Mandated managed care as referred to here includes any jurisdiction in which the provision of workers' compensation health care services under a managed care

TABLE 2. Common Regulatory Cost-Containment and Disability Management Strategies in Workers' Compensation, 1997*

Jurisdiction	Limited Initial Provider Choice	Limited Initial Provider Choice (via MCO only)	Limited Provider Change	Limited Provider Change (via MCO only)	Medical Fee Schedule	Hospital Payment Regulation	Mandated Managed Care†	Mandated Utilization Review	Mandated Bill Review	Treatment Guidelines
Alabama	X		X		X	X				
Alaska			‡		X	X				X◊
Arizona	X◊		X		X					
Arkansas	X		X		X	X		X	X	§
California	X◊		X		X					X
Colorado	X		X		X		X◊	X	X	X
Connecticut	X		‡	X	X	X		X	X	X
Delaware										
District of Columbia			X							
Florida	X		X		X	X	X◊	X	X	X
Georgia	X		X		X	X				
Hawaii			‡		X	X				X◊
Idaho	X		X							
Illinois			‡							
Indiana	X		X							
Iowa	X		X							
Kansas	X		X							
Kentucky		X	‡	X	X	X		X	◊	X
Louisiana			X		X	X		X	X	
Maine	X		‡		X	X		X		X
Maryland					X	X				
Massachusetts		X◊	X		X	X		X		X
Michigan	X		‡		X	X		X	X	
Minnesota		X	X		X	X			X	
Mississippi			X		X			X	X	X
Missouri	X		X							
Montana		X	X		X	X		X		
Nebraska	X◊		X		X	X				§

(Table continued next page.)

TABLE 2 (Cont). Common Regulatory Cost-Containment and Disability Management Strategies in Workers' Compensation, 1997*

Jurisdiction	Limited Initial Provider Choice	Limited Initial Provider Choice (via MCO only)	Limited Provider Change	Limited Provider Change (via MCO only)	Medical Fee Schedule	Hospital Payment Regulation	Mandated Managed Care†	Mandated Utilization Review	Mandated Bill Review	Treatment Guidelines
Nevada		X	‡		X	X	X◊	X	X	X
New Hampshire		X		X	§◊	§◊	◊			
New Jersey	X		X			X				
New Mexico	X◊		X		X	X		X		
New York		X			X	X				
North Carolina	X		X		X	X			X	X◊
North Dakota		X◊	X		X	X	X◊	X	X	
Ohio		X		X	X	X	X	X	X	X
Oklahoma		X	X		X	X				X
Oregon		X	X◊		X	X			X	X
Pennsylvania	X		X		X	X				X
Rhode Island				X	X	X		◊		
South Carolina	X		X		X	X			X	
South Dakota		X	X		X	X	X◊			X◊
Tennessee	X		X					X		
Texas	X		X		X	X		X	X	X
Utah	X		‡		X			X		X
Vermont	X				X	X	◊			
Virginia	X		X							
Washington			X◊		X	X		X	X	X
West Virginia				X	X	X		X	X	X
Wisconsin			‡		X	X				
Wyoming			X		X			X	X	X
TOTALS**	25	12	33	6	40	36	6	20	16	21

* Policies presented are as of January 1997, although implementation dates may be later. Notes and references include known policies through July 1997.
† This column shows states where payors are required to provide managed care. In addition, 19 other states have managed care regulations.
‡ These states all allow an unrestricted one-time change (sometimes after an initial treatment time period), but subsequent changes are restricted.
§ Guidelines are being developed.   ** Excludes ‡ and §.   ◊ See NOTES for more details.

(Table continued next page.)

TABLE 2 (Cont).   Common Regulatory Cost-Containment and Disability Management Strategies in Workers' Compensation, 1997*

◊ NOTES

Alaska:	Treatment guidelines limit the number of physical therapy and chiropractic treatments.
Arizona:	Initial provider choice is divided between the employer and the employee.
California:	Initial provider choice is divided between the employer and the employee.
Colorado:	Employers/insurers in several designated counties must offer provision of medical services through a recognized MCO as regulated under the health insurance code. Employers/insurers not offering full managed care must offer medical case management services.
Florida:	Effective January 1, 1997, treatment must be provided through managed care arrangements.
Hawaii:	Guidelines stipulate the maximum level of utilization.
Kansas:	The DWC no longer contracts with a bill review vendor.
Massachusetts:	The limitation is via PPO, where employees may be directed for their initial visit.
Nebraska:	Employer may select provider unless employee selects a provider with whom he or she has obtained treatment in the past.
Nevada:	All employers covered by the state industrial insurance system are under managed care contract. Additionally, self-insured employers may either contract with the state system, make PPO arrangements, or contract with other managed care organizations, if they choose to.
New Hampshire:	New Hampshire mandates the use of managed care for residual markets and allows voluntary managed care participation in other circumstances. A new schedule was set to take effect in July 1997. However, legislation repealed that fee schedule in 1998.
New Mexico:	The employer or insurer can control provider choice and change during the 60 days following the injury or after that period.
North Carolina:	Guidelines limit the amount of rehabilitation, chiropractic, and physical therapy visits.
North Dakota:	The limitation is via risk management plans. Mandatory managed care includes case management, bill review, and utilization review. The state fund contracts with a third-party administrator to provide these services. Employees retain the right to choose their own physician and are not directed to provider networks. As of August 1, 1995, employers may use a Bureau-approved risk management program. In those situations the employer has initial choice unless the worker opts out prior to suffering a work injury.
Oregon:	Employee is unrestricted for two changes; any further changes must have insurer or agency approval. MCOs may apply their own rules to govern change of provider.
Rhode Island:	Surgical preauthorization is the only specific requirement.
South Dakota:	Mandatory for insurers as of January 1995 and for self-insurers as of January 1996. Although mandatory, employees may obtain treatment with providers outside of the plan if the providers agree to abide by the terms of the agreement. Treatment guidelines set durational limits and return-to-work targets.
Vermont:	Required only for assigned risk pool; otherwise it is simply allowed. Employees may opt out of the plan after initial treatment upon written notice.
Washington:	By statute a self-insurer or the state fund must approve a change in provider. However, in practice the employee almost always changes provider without first getting approval.

From Workers' Compensation Research Institute: Managed Care and Medical Cost Containment in Workers' Compensation: A National Inventory, 1997–1998. Cambridge, Massachusetts, WCRI, 1997; with permission.

arrangement is required on the part of the insurer or employer. In this context, the existence of a managed care arrangement does not imply that patients must obtain treatment within that arrangement. In fact, even in states with mandated managed care, an employee may be able to obtain treatment outside of the plan in some cases.

Regulated managed care as referred to here includes jurisdictions in which the use of managed care arrangements in workers' compensation has been regulated by statute or rule. The regulation often includes certification requirements that define the minimum number and type of providers to be included, as well as rules about ownership of organizations. Regulations also often define whether employees must seek treatment within the organizations once they are established, but this is often a function of existing provider choice laws in the state. Regulations also may define required elements in an MCO such as utilization management services, internal dispute resolution processes, and quality assurance requirements. In jurisdictions that have regulated managed care use, employers/insurers are not required to provide services under a managed care arrangement. However, if they do provide such services, any arrangement they make must conform to the stated regulations.

MANAGED CARE AND PROVIDER CHOICE IN WORKERS' COMPENSATION

The extent to which a managed care plan can successfully control costs and improve quality of care may be related to its ability to control the choice of treating and subsequent providers. States that allow employees to opt out of plans at their discretion may compromise the ability of payors to effectively apply managed care arrangements. On the other hand, if networks do not contain physicians that provide quality care, requiring care within those networks would be detrimental. An effective managed care arrangement is one that can best meet the patient's needs and that allows the continued direction of care within a provider network that comprises physicians with the best patient outcomes. Being able to measure and maintain these favorable outcomes is paramount to maintaining effective networks. In all cases of managed care, employees may choose physicians outside of plans in emergency situations or if a particular type of specialist is not available within the plan. Beyond that, however, the ability of a workers' compensation patient to obtain treatment outside of the MCO varies.

Managed care arrangements in workers' compensation fall into two major categories: (1) those in which employees can be directed for all their medical care treatment and (2) those in which participation is basically voluntary on the part of the employee. This may simply be the result of existing provider choice rules in the state or may be a function of managed care "opt out" provisions in the regulations. Of the 51 jurisdictions in the United States, 19 require employees to seek treatment within networks if networks are offered, and 31 states allow employees to choose their own provider either initially or after a specified time. One state, Arizona, allows the employer/insurer or employee to direct the care depending on whether the employer is self-insured for workers' compensation or purchases insurance from a third party.

Before the advent of managed care regulations in workers' compensation, statutes provided for either the employee or the employer/insurer to choose the employee's health care provider. The introduction of managed care regulations into workers' compensation truly impacted the existing provider choice rules in only a few states. In Connecticut, Kentucky, Nevada, and New Hampshire, the introduction of managed care regulation allowed existing choice and change of provider rules to change depending on whether a managed care arrangement exists. These four states allow the employer/insurer to direct the care if a managed care arrangement exists in an otherwise employee choice state. In other states, the initial choice or subsequent change of provider may be affected by the existence of managed care arrangements. However, the employer/insurer's ultimate ability to direct ongoing care in these states does not change.

States that have not mandated or regulated managed care and have employee choice of physician may find it difficult to benefit from managed care arrangements, particularly if an adversarial, distrustful relationship exists between the employee and employer. Additionally, states that have mandated or regulated the use of managed care in workers' compensation, but have retained the employee's right to direct his or her own treatment, have succeeded in making managed care arrangements potentially useful only in situations in which employee/employer relationships are most likely already positive—in other words, where an employee will not opt out for reasons other than those relating to the quality of care. The best way to maintain a patient's treatment within an established network is to provide quality care through networks that encourage employees to retain those physician services. States in which the employer/insurer has the authority to direct the employee's care throughout the life of a claim may realize greater benefits through implementation of a managed care program, provided that care is taken to fill networks with qualified physicians with positive patient outcomes.

WORKERS' COMPENSATION MANAGED CARE REGULATIONS

A total of 26 jurisdictions currently have some sort of explicit managed care policy regulating or mandating the use of managed care organizations or plans. Six of these states have mandated the use of managed care arrangements for treating most of their injured workers, and two of the states have mandated its use for the states' residual markets only. The other 18 of the 26 states have specifically authorized and regulated the use of managed care organizations and plans. Among these jurisdictions are several different scenarios:

- Mandated provision of services by which payors must furnish health care through managed care arrangements and employees can be required to seek treatment within the plans;
- Mandated provision of services by which payors must furnish health care through managed care arrangements, but employees may obtain treatment within the plan or opt out to "any willing provider" or to any nonplan provider of their choice;
- Regulated, but not mandated, managed care by which payors may choose to furnish health care through managed care arrangements, and if a managed care arrangement exists, employees may be required to obtain treatment within the plan;
- Regulated, but not mandated, managed care in which payors may choose to furnish health care through managed care arrangements, and employees may obtain treatment within such arrangements or may opt out of the plan and/or obtain treatment with nonplan providers.

The remaining jurisdictions do not have explicit policies, but managed care is allowed and is actively being pursued to the extent practical in light of provider choice rules, collective bargaining agreements, and other workers' compensation rules or statutes. Table 3 lists the categories and the states that fall within each.

TABLE 3. Workers' Compensation Managed Care and Provider Choice Policies, 1997*

Ability to Require Patient to Seek Medical Care Within Exclusive Networks for Treatment Duration			Inability to Require Patient to Seek Medical Care Within Exclusive Networks for Treatment Duration		
Mandated (Employees Must Treat Within Plans)	*Regulated But Not Mandated (Employees Must Treat Within Plans)*	*Allowed But Not Regulated (Employer/ Insurer Directs Care)*	*Mandated (Employees May Opt Out of Plans)*	*Regulated But Not Mandated (Employees May Opt Out of Plans)*	*Allowed But Not Regulated (Employee Directs Care)*
Colorado†	Arkansas	Alabama	North Dakota	California	Alaska
Florida	Connecticut	Arizona‡	Ohio	Massachusetts	Arizona§
Nevada	Georgia	Idaho	South Dakota	Minnesota	Delaware
	Kentucky	Indiana	Vermont**	Montana	District of Columbia
	Missouri	Iowa		Nebraska	Hawaii
	New Hampshire††	Kansas		New York	Illinois
	New Jersey	South Carolina		Oklahoma	Louisiana
	North Carolina	Tennessee		Oregon	Maine
		Virginia		Pennsylvania	Maryland
				Rhode Island	Michigan
				Utah	Mississippi
					New Mexico
					Texas
					Vermont‡‡
					Washington
					West Virginia
					Wisconsin
					Wyoming

* Mandated or regulated managed care here refers to a managed care organization providing services including, but not limited to, utilization review services and case management services. It does not include jurisdictions where utilization review or other individual components alone are mandated in isolation from MCO arrangements. Policies presented are as of July, 1997.

† Employers/insurers not offering full managed care must offer medical case management services.

‡ Arizona has employer choice of physician for self-insured employers and has employee choice otherwise.

§ Arizona has employer choice of physician for self-insured employers and has employee choice otherwise.

** Mandated for residual market only.

†† Mandated for residual market only, otherwise it is regulated.

‡‡ Mandated for residual market only.

Adapted from Workers' Compensation Research Institute: Managed Care and Medical Cost Containment in Workers' Compensation: A National Inventory, 1997–1998. Cambridge, Massachusetts, WCRI, 1997.

Certification Requirements for Managed Care Organizations

Most managed care laws require certification of MCOs. The certification requirements generally govern the required components of each of the managed care arrangements. The certifying agency is often the workers' compensation agency in the state, but it may be the commissioner of health, commissioner of insurance, another state agency, or a combination of several agencies.

Typically, certification requirements include a specification of the minimum number of providers or types of providers that must be made available within the plan, an established utilization review program, case management services, internal dispute resolution mechanisms, and requirements for reporting data to the certifying agency. A description of how the MCO meets the above goals is an important part of the application process. Many jurisdictions require the establishment of specific return to work, rehabilitation and, also, safety services within their MCOs. These are specialized services that are important in workers' compensation and different from those typically found in other health care service arrangements. Other regulatory requirements may include implementation of established treatment guidelines or development of plan-specific treatment guidelines, staff training mechanisms, peer review, quality assurance programs, and fraud detection units. Many of the required elements exist as part of functioning MCOs regardless of whether they are required for workers' compensation certification. They are generally seen as part of the entire managed care package that seeks to provide cost-effective, quality care.

Most workers' compensation managed care regulations give the employer/insurer the flexibility to furnish services through a single or multiple plans, and most place no restrictions on whether an employer/insurer can have a financial ownership interest in the plan. For example, California employers must offer choice between at least two plans, and if the health care organizations are owned or controlled by the workers' compensation insurer, a third choice must be offered. New York's PPO program has a similar requirement but carriers cannot have a financial interest in any of the choices. Minnesota and Oregon also do not allow the employer or insurer to have a financial interest in any managed care program offered, but in Minnesota the plan can be owned by the insurer's parent corporation.

Providers in Plans

Typically, the managed care certification process requires that "plans must have a sufficient number of providers in a sufficient number of specialties so as ensure prompt, convenient access to care." Geographic access is often an important element. A total of 15 of the 26 states with workers' compensation managed care regulations use similar broadly defined language. The other 11 states specify the actual number or types of providers that must be available before certification can occur. As noted earlier, some statutes maintain that "any willing provider" may be a participant in an MCO. This is accomplished directly, through a requirement to include all providers, or indirectly, through the ability of employees to opt out of a plan to seek a provider who is willing to abide by plan terms. These policies have an impact on the "exclusivity" of a provider network.

MEASURING THE OUTCOMES OF MEDICAL CARE AND DISABILITY MANAGEMENT

A quality assurance program is paramount if a managed care arrangement is to meet its goals of providing high-quality care. Outcomes measures are also critical to demonstrate to policymakers the impact on workers of various managed care programs.

As a result, some states mandate a quality assurance program as part of the MCO's certification requirements. Without a quality assurance mechanism, it would be difficult to justify requiring individuals to obtain treatment within plans. Most quality assurance programs focus on processes as opposed to results. Sometimes, as in Florida, regulations require that specific outcomes data be collected and submitted for analysis. It is unclear, however, if this effort is successful in assessing quality. Quality assurance standards, often developed by committees composed of agency officials and providers within organizations, usually measure accessibility, availability, adequacy, appropriateness, effectiveness, and timeliness of care. Often, the utilization review mechanisms, dispute resolution, and case management process are part of the quality assurance program.

The outcomes of interest in workers' compensation are broader than in nonoccupational medical care. Key outcomes to be measured include the following:

- Costs of medical care and disability income benefits
- Speed and sustainability of return to work
- Earnings recovery upon return to work
- Worker general health and work functioning
- Worker satisfaction with the medical care and disability management processes.

This information is generally not part of a patient's medical record and has generally been unavailable for analysis. However, the Workers' Compensation Research Institute (WCRI) is developing an outcomes measurement system that collects the above information. It relies on detailed claim record data and supplements it with standardized worker surveys. Such surveys have been and continue to be used to measure the quality of nonoccupational medical care. Studies performed as part of the Rand Health Insurance Study[11] and the Medical Outcomes Study[10,13] have succeeded in improving such patient surveys by allowing comparisons to be made of patients with chronic health problems to patients sampled from the general population. WCRI and other investigators are continuing research to adapt these measures to the workers' compensation setting and to develop new measures that are appropriate for evaluating the impact of disability management.

The increased use of such worker survey-based outcomes measures offers the opportunity to monitor health and disability management outcomes from the patient's point of view and to track those outcomes over time. With such tools, analysts and policymakers can measure outcomes of workers' compensation patients being treated within different types of managed care or case management arrangements versus other arrangements. Outcomes studies can be used by policymakers and analysts to evaluate the balance between cost and quality of care and to compare the costs and benefits of different ways of structuring and financing health care services. MCOs can use outcomes studies to provide treatment that results in the best patient outcomes—outcomes that lead to the best patient functionality and afford the best opportunity to return to productive employment.

REFERENCES

1. Brook RH, Ware JE, Rogers WH, et al: Does free care improve adults' health? Results from a randomized controlled trial. N Engl J Med 309:1429–1434, 1983.
2. Eccleston S, Yeager C: Managed Care and Medical Cost Containment in Workers' Compensation, A National Inventory, 1997–1998. Cambridge, MA, Workers' Compensation Research Institute, 1997.
3. Health Care Financing Administration: Health Care Financing Review. Vol 18, No 1. Baltimore, U.S. Dept. of Health and Human Services, 1996.
4. Lohr KN, Brook R, Kamberg C, et al: Use of medical care in the RAND health insurance experiment: Diagnosis of service specific analyses in a randomized controlled trial. Med Care 24(suppl): S1–S87, 1986.
5. National Council on Compensation Insurance: Compendium of Workers' Compensation Managed Care Statutes and Regulations. New York, NCCI, 1995.
6. Nelson B: Workers' compensation benefits: Coverage and costs. Social Security Bull Vol 58, 1995.
7. Schmulowitz J: Workers' Compensation Benefits, Coverage, and Costs, 1994–1995 [manuscript].
8. Siu AL, Sonnenberg FA, Manning WG, et al: Inappropriate use of hospitals in a randomized trial of health insurance plans. N Engl J Med 315:1259–1266, 1986.
9. Sloss EM, Keeler EB, Brook RH, et al: Effect of a health maintenance organization on physiologic health: Results from a randomized trial. Ann Intern Med 106:130–138, 1987.

10. Stewart AL, Ware JE: Measuring Functioning and Well-Being. Santa Monica, CA, Rand Corporation, 1992.
11. Stewart AL, Ware JE, Brook RH, et al: Conceptualization and Measurement of Health for Adults in the Health Insurance. Santa Monica, CA, Rand Corporation, 1978–1980.
12. U.S. Department of Labor: Employment and Earnings. Washington, DC, Bureau of Labor Statistics, 1997.
13. Ware JE Jr, Sherbourne CD: The MOS 36-item Short Form Health Survey (SF-36). Conceptual framework and item selection. Med Care 30:473–483, 1992.
14. Ware JE Jr, Snow K, Kosinski M, Grandek B: SF-36 Health Survey, Manual Interpretation Guide. Boston, The Health Institute, New England Medical Center, 1993.
15. Workers' Compensation Research Institute: WCRI Research Brief. Vol 13, No 10. Cambridge, MA, WCRI, 1997.

ALLARD E. DEMBE, ScD

EVALUATING THE IMPACT OF MANAGED HEALTH CARE IN WORKERS' COMPENSATION

From the Occupational and
  Environmental Health Program
Department of Family and
  Community Medicine
University of Massachusetts
  Medical Center
Worcester, Massachusetts

Reprint requests to:
Allard E. Dembe, ScD
Assistant Professor
Occupational and Environmental
  Health Program
Department of Family and
  Community Medicine
University of Massachusetts
  Medical Center
55 Lake Avenue North
Worcester, MA 01655

Soaring medical expenditures contributed to the dramatic cost increases in workers' compensation insurance that occurred during the 1980s and early 1990s.[6] As costs escalated, employers, insurers, and state government officials looked to managed health care approaches as a promising strategy for curbing medical expenses. Many states enacted new legislation or regulations permitting the use of restricted physician networks, utilization management, discounted fee schedules, and other managed care techniques.[10] Private vendors and health care systems moved to exploit the resulting market opportunities.

Several research efforts have been undertaken to assess the impact of managed health care in the workers' compensation system. Policymakers want to know whether the introduction of managed care into workers' compensation has been effective in constraining costs and which techniques are most efficacious. Questions are being asked about the influence of managed care on the type and quality of medical service provided to injured workers and whether it actually leads to better outcomes or jeopardizes workers' ability to obtain appropriate care.

Although many workers' compensation managed care methods have been adapted from those used in the general health care sector, evaluating their impact on costs and quality of care for occupational conditions poses special research challenges due to the unique nature of medical services in the workers' compensation system. For example, in workers' compensation medical care, a direct connection usually exists between the health care provider's findings and the patient's eligibility for wage replacement (indemnity) benefits available through workers' compensation insurance. In addition to routine diagnosis and treatment, medical care for workers' compensation cases often includes impairment determinations and judgments about the patient's readiness for return to work. Coordination and communication between primary medical care and ancillary rehabilitation activities is especially critical. Because of its focus on eligibility for compensation benefits and return to work, the medical care provided in workers' compensation cases has significant implications for labor relations and employment litigation. Disputes are common, and there are substantial administrative requirements. Many employees are particularly sensitive about the selection of clinician and the potential for diminished choice in managed care arrangements.

All of these factors can potentially affect the utilization and performance of managed care techniques. Researchers attempting to evaluate the influence of managed health care in workers' compensation must consider these forces in their study design. One of the greatest challenges confronting researchers is the need to isolate the effects of managed care approaches from concurrent changes taking place in the workers' compensation system. For example, in several states the initial authorization for establishing managed care plans coincided with the passage of comprehensive workers' compensation reform legislation that changed benefit levels, modified eligibility criteria for considering disorders to be work-related, introduced tougher measures to detect fraud, established requirements for employer loss prevention and safety programs, and revamped dispute adjudication procedures.[9] Disentangling the relative impact of a health care system's managed care features from these other changes is methodologically quite difficult.

CONSIDERATIONS FOR THE DESIGN AND CONDUCT OF EVALUATION STUDIES

In formulating an effective strategy for evaluating the impact of managed care in workers' compensation, investigators must consider several key issues, as described below.

Clearly Defining the Intervention to Be Studied

Because so many approaches exist for managing medical care, cost, and health services utilization, researchers must precisely specify the nature of the managed care arrangement to be studied in a particular setting. Classifying and defining the features of managed care is particularly difficult in situations involving multiple care systems, employers, insurers, or states. The managed care techniques applied by health plans, providers, insurers, employers, and independent vendors must be clearly distinguished.

Decisions need to be made about what constitutes a legitimate managed care approach. Some researchers might exclude techniques that are focused narrowly on containing costs, such as bill repricing or negotiated discounts from prevailing fee schedules, while others would consider these to be a critical element of managed care. Some authorities define managed care arrangements as those having provider risk-sharing through capitation or some other incentive-based provider payment plan. To some people, managed care implies the existence of a restricted provider network or panel of physicians. Many workers' compensation managed care plans employ so-called case management, but even this concept is potentially ambiguous: it could refer to medical case management performed by nurses or other health care professionals, management of medical claims as performed by insurance company personnel, communications and coordination programs initiated by employers, and disability management efforts orchestrated by physical therapists or rehabilitation specialists. Similarly, researchers need to precisely define and describe other potential managed care techniques, such as treatment guidelines, practice protocols, utilization review procedures, educational programs, and workplace accident prevention measures.

Identifying the Important Research Questions

A study's design will depend on the nature of the questions to be examined. Selection of the appropriate research questions is important and may be quite complicated. For example, will the investigation focus exclusively on measuring outcomes, or will it also try to describe and critique the experiences of providers, employers, and workers in adopting and using the managed care system? Is it important to consider the applicability of the approach to other settings or states? Will the study only examine the impact of the intervention on workers' compensation outcomes, or will it also explore its significance for general health care, unemployment, social security, or other health and welfare systems?

It is vital that investigators state their hypotheses explicitly. What is the presumed effect of the various managed care approaches? What is the supposed mechanism by which cost savings are achieved? Specifying these assumptions at the beginning of a study helps guide its conduct and plans for data acquisition. For example, if an investigator wants to determine the attitudes of clinicians, workers, or employers toward managed care, some type of direct survey of those individuals will be needed. Specifying research assumptions explicitly and describing the investigators' orientation toward managed care also can help reveal potential sources of bias. Because of the significant implications of workers' compensation medical care for workplace industrial relations, very different assumptions concerning the effects of managed care may be offered by researchers aligned more toward the labor or management perspective. Of course, sources of research funding should be identified and any potential conflicts of interest disclosed.

Defining the Study Period

Because managed care interventions can have many different components, it is often difficult to specify the time periods to be covered in a study. It is not unusual for portions of a managed care program to be implemented in stages or for it to apply to some members of a work population before being adopted by the entire group. For these reasons, it can be challenging for investigators to determine when an intervention began and what dates to use for characterizing the study period. A detailed description of the intervention and a timeline portraying its development and implementation can help sort out these issues.

Case Definition and Recruitment

Various approaches can be taken to determine which individuals or cases to include in the managed care population to be studied. The investigator might decide that the study group will comprise all incident injuries occurring during a particular period. Alternatively, the study group could be defined by all claims filed during a specific period, by all medical care provided, or all workers' compensation payments made during a specific time. The differences between these ways of formulating the study group might be significant. Many workers' compensation claims remain open for many weeks, months, or even years. During that time, an individual might receive care from a variety of providers representing various managed care and traditional health delivery models. The way in which different episodes of care are differentiated and analyzed can have a profound impact on the study's findings. In some managed care arrangements, enrollees are permitted to receive care from outside the plan or to opt out of the arrangement after a prescribed time. Dealing with such subtleties in the definition of the study population and data collection effort can be extremely complex. Likewise, an individual health care provider might be a member of numerous managed care networks or health systems; the same provider also might be offering traditional fee-for-service treatment unrelated to any managed care plan. In some instances, the clinician might even be unaware of which, if any, managed care plan is covering services for a particular patient delivered on a particular occasion.

Choosing Appropriate Control and Comparison Groups

Most studies attempt to compare the experiences of injured workers receiving managed care to others receiving customary or traditional care. The selection of the comparison group will depend, in large part, on the overall study design. Studies that take great care in assuring that the study and control groups are as similar as possible, except for the managed care intervention, are generally considered to be the most rigorous and well designed (Fig. 1).

Before-and-after studies comparing the experiences of a group following introduction of a managed care initiative to experiences of the same group before the intervention are the least powerful and persuasive because they cannot account for the relative contribution of other significant changes that may have transpired during the same period, such as shifts in business and employment conditions and state workers' compensation legislation. Therefore, it is often necessary to identify contemporaneous control groups whose experiences can be compared to those of the study population during the equivalent time frame.

For the comparison to be convincing, the control group needs to be just like the study population in all relevant respects except for the latter's inclusion in the managed care plan. This typically is accomplished by matching the members of the control group to the study population according to characteristics such as age, gender, occupation, past medical history, and type of injury. On a more macroscopic level, participating employers also can be matched to nonparticipating control firms according to size, location, industry grouping, workers' compensation premium and insurance arrangement, experience modification, union status, and other features.

However, even the most comprehensive matching process can fail to produce a truly ideal comparison group that controls for all extraneous variables. Systematic

FIGURE 1. The relative rigorousness of four types of study designs. Adapted from Washington Department of Labor and Industries and the University of Washington Department of Health Services: Workers' Compensation Managed Care Pilot Project: Final Report to the Legislature. Olympia, WA, 1997.

differences may remain between the study and comparison populations that potentially affect the outcomes of interest and thereby distort the apparent impact of the managed care intervention. For example, because enrollment into many managed care programs is left to the discretion of individual workers or employers, those volunteering for these programs may be more health conscious or have a more receptive attitude toward managed care than those who do not enroll. Studies from the general health arena have confirmed that persons voluntarily selecting managed care plans are usually healthier than others.[15] Controlling for this sort of selection bias and other potential confounding factors is often difficult, even in the most well-matched comparison studies.

In light of these considerations, many authorities consider the most rigorous study design to be a randomized trial, in which members of the study population are randomly assigned into groups that do or do not receive the intervention. In this way, differences between the study and comparison group can be minimized. From a practical standpoint, though, establishing a randomized trial for workers' compensation medical care is rarely feasible for a variety of reasons, including legal restrictions in many states over the employer's ability to direct specific workers into managed care arrangements and, also, complexities that would result in claims administration and pricing of insurance policies. Most studies of workers' compensation medical care have concerned natural experiments wherein employers and workers choose to participate in various managed care plans; consequently, identifying a perfectly matched comparison group has been a formidable challenge.

Ensuring Adequate Sample Sizes

Medical care is only one factor affecting an injured worker's ability to recover from an injury and resume work. For example, the employer's ability to offer transitional or light duty is known to affect this outcome, and numerous studies have shown that psychosocial factors, such as the worker's satisfaction with the job, also are important.[11,13,16] Because medical care is only one determinant of an injured worker's recovery, differences between outcomes in the managed care study population and the comparison groups may be small. To observe such subtle differences, it is necessary to ensure that the sample sizes are sufficiently large to detect the variations in a statistically significant manner.

Assuring sufficiently large study and comparison groups can be quite challenging. Annual occupational injury incidence rates typically are 8–12%, and most injuries generally require medical treatment only and do not involve compensable lost time. The compensable lost-time (indemnity) cases might have a much lower annual rate, typically 1–5% of the workforce.[21] Fewer than 20% of lost-time cases normally account for most workers' compensation costs. Therefore, in a study assessing workers' compensation costs, it will generally be necessary to capture information on a small proportion of cases drawn from a limited number of claimants from the original population. For example, among a population of 10,000 workers, only about 40 serious cases ($0.20 \times 0.02 \times 10,000$) might be expected to occur during a year. Statistically significant variations between study and comparison groups could be quite difficult to observe given such a small number of cases. The problem is further complicated by the fact that incidence rates vary considerably by industry, so that a study covering a comparatively low-hazard occupational group such as office workers or teachers would need even larger sample sizes to be credible.

Another complexity in the determination of sample sizes involves the multiplicity of outcomes being evaluated in any particular study and the variety of data sources usually needed to assess these domains. Ideally, separate power calculations should be performed for each domain under investigation based on its expected variability and the type of data to be used in its assessment. Determining the necessary sample sizes is further complicated by the paucity of available information on outcome variability in workers' compensation medical care and the resulting uncertainty about expected standard deviations on which to base the calculations of statistical power.

Data Acquisition

Many workers' compensation insurance carriers, third-party administrators of self-insurance programs, health care provider organizations, and state government agencies have developed administrative databases to collect and analyze information concerning claims handling, payment, medical utilization, and costs. These systems can provide a convenient and useful source of information upon which to base a research study.

However, there are important limitations inherent in the use of such administrative databases. Some of the limitations are practical, e.g., the ability of researchers to gain access to proprietary data and confidential information. Because uniform data standards have not been widely adopted in the workers' compensation arena, the type of information and its formatting can vary considerably between databases. This can be especially troublesome if multiple employers or insurers are involved in the study.

More importantly, substantial variation can exist in the quality, completeness, and accuracy of information contained in these administrative databases. Many were developed as transactional systems that were designed to process bills or claims. As such, they may have limited scope and contain little qualitative detail, particularly regarding outcomes, utilization, and the process of care. Substantial time lags may occur between an event and its entry into the system. Some data in administrative systems have notoriously poor validity, e.g., the veracity of recorded ICD-9 codes as an indicator of the type of injury actually sustained by a claimant.

Some important domains, particularly patient-centered perspectives about process of care, functional status, satisfaction, and vocational ability, will rarely be available through existing administrative databases. For this reason, direct questioning of injured workers, employers, providers, and other key participants is often necessary. A variety of standardized survey instruments have been developed for these purposes, and special adaptations of widely used functional assessment questionnaires, such as the Medical Outcomes Study SF-36 form, have been devised for use in workers' compensation settings.[19,26] However, even if a particular survey tool has been validated and used successfully in one environment, there is no assurance that it will perform well in another. Researchers need to pretest its performance and psychometric properties in the specific population and context of a particular study.

The timing of outcomes assessment and data acquisition can be crucial to the success of a study. Methodologic decisions need to be made about when to conduct the measurement and whether to stagger it to follow a particular event, such as the filing of a claim, the initiation of treatment, the end of treatment, the payment of benefits, or the resumption of work. Typically, multiple measurements will be made at intervals such as 3, 6, and 12 months after treatment to measure changes in outcome and the retention of improvement. Since a small proportion of cases with long-term disability usually accounts for a large share of workers' compensation costs, extended follow-up assessments at 18, 24, or even 36 months could be required.

Outcomes Measurement

The identification of research questions will dictate the selection of outcome variables. Researchers need to consider the interests of affected groups in determining what to measure, because employers, workers, health care systems, insurers, and policymakers will likely be interested in different outcomes. At the least, researchers will want to determine the impact of the managed care intervention on costs and injured employees' return to work.

A precise and complete estimation of costs can be difficult to obtain. The total cost of a workers' compensation case is a function of various cost elements, including payments for medical services, pharmacy charges, indemnity benefits for lost wages, administrative and legal expenses, and associated costs covering rehabilitation, permanent impairment, and death benefits. It is unlikely that any single database will contain reliable information on all these components. Benefits sometimes may be paid out in the form of lump-sum settlements, especially for litigated and serious cases, thereby further complicating the collection of accurate cost data.

Besides the direct costs of a workers' compensation claim, there are associated indirect costs that are difficult to estimate, including costs related to diminished work productivity, workplace job accommodations, unreimbursed administrative expenses, and intensified economic burdens on injured workers and their families.

Insurance indemnity payments are often used as a surrogate for determining the duration of disability and estimating the date of the injured employee's return to work. However, using indemnity payments in this way can be misleading for several reasons. Studies have shown that injured workers' actual return to employment frequently does not correspond with the authorized release date indicated in the insurer's records or the termination of insurance indemnity payments.[4,25] Many workers initially return to a job with reduced hours or lower pay, information that is seldom contained in administrative records. Some previously injured employees subsequently leave their jobs or the original injury recurs. All of these factors must be considered when determining the true return to work date and its impact on outcome.

Along with determining the impact of the medical intervention on costs and return to work, it is important to consider its effect on the patient's recovery from symptoms and restoration of the patient's physical, vocational, and social functioning. Objective tests and instrumentation are being devised to gauge patients' physical capabilities.[20] Results of such tests, along with self-reported responses to questionnaires, can be used to collect and assess information on functional status. Questionnaires and surveys are used extensively to assess participants' satisfaction with care and their perception about the handling of their case. Most investigators of workers' compensation managed care measure outcomes by using a combination of insurance administrative data, medical data, and primary data derived directly from claimants, employers, and health care providers.

In addition to measuring costs, outcomes, and satisfaction, some investigators will want to examine the process of care and utilization of medical services. Various domains can be explored, including the type of medical professional providing care, the mix of hospital and outpatient services, provider payment and reimbursement methods, extent of care provided outside the plan, the use of modified and light duty, and prevention efforts. Some studies contain qualitative analyses, relying on focus groups, interviews, and written records to describe the process of care and participants' experiences (Table 1).

TABLE 1.   Potential Outcome Measures for Studies of Workers' Compensation Managed Care

Direct Costs	Indirect Cost Measures	Medical and Functional Outcomes	Process of Care	Satisfaction
Medical	Claims incidence rate	Functional capacity	Service utilization	Employee
Indemnity	Lost days rate	Physical impairment	Number/type of visits	Employer
Administrative	OSHA recordable rate	Symptoms	Number/type of treatments	Provider
Legal	Return to work status	Injury recurrence		Insurer
Pharmacy	Duration of disability	Mental health status	Hospital/outpatient utilization	
Disability benefits	Modified/transitional work status	Role/social functioning	Type of provider utilization	
	Job accommodation expenses	Clinical test results: range of motion pulmonary function sensory testing	Geographic access	
	Decreased earning capacity		Timeliness of access	
	Duplicate payments		Referral patterns	
	Unnecessary/redundant treatments		Prescription drug utilization	
	Decreased work productivity		Guideline adherence	
	Recurrences		Case management services	
	Delays		Disputes/litigation patterns	
	Fines/penalties			
	Retraining, rehiring expenses			
	Cost-shifting			
	Case-shifting			
	Misreporting			
	Accident prevention expenses			
	Effects on worker's family			
	Litigation-related costs			

SUMMARY OF RESEARCH FINDINGS

Only a few credible large-scale studies have been conducted evaluating the impact of managed care in workers' compensation, sponsored mostly by state government agencies overseeing managed care pilot programs. Several other prominent research projects have been launched in response to funding initiatives introduced during 1996 and 1997 by the National Institute for Occupational Safety and Health and The Robert Wood Johnson Foundation.[8] In addition, numerous employers and health plans have issued reports regarding the impact of managed care in particular workers' compensation settings, but those studies generally have not been conducted by independent researchers and lack methodologic rigor. Consequently, their results must be interpreted with caution. The Appendix summarizes the most prominent studies. Highlights are presented below.

Washington State Managed Care Pilot Program

In many ways, the study of Washington's managed care pilot program[12,29,30] can be considered the benchmark for a well-designed and well-documented evaluation of managed health care in workers' compensation. An experienced team of health services researchers from the Washington State Department of Labor and Industry and the University of Washington examined the pilot program, which was established in 1994 and involved occupational medicine networks paid on a capitated basis. The study benefited from Washington's status as an exclusive-fund state, in which the state government fund serves as the sole insurance payor for workers' compensation cases. This permitted the researchers to have especially good access to employer's insurance and employment records. The study design was a prospective matched-control group comparison, with control firms matched to participants by location, industry, size, wage rate, and insurance status. The study featured an especially broad array of outcomes measures and extensive follow-up 6 weeks, 6 months, and 18 months after the injury. In light of the capitated payment system, the investigators relied on surrogate "shadow" bills to estimate actual medical expenditures and make comparisons to traditional treatment costs.

Medical costs were reduced by 27% in the managed care group but patient satisfaction among that group was diminished compared to those receiving traditional care. Few significant differences were observed in medical or functional outcomes between the study and comparison groups. Although average indemnity costs per claim were 37% lower in the managed care group, the difference was not statistically significant. The results of this study need to be interpreted carefully in light of the unique circumstances existing in Washington, its exclusive-fund insurance status, and the use of a relatively unusual managed care model based on capitated networks of providers specially trained in occupational medicine.

Florida Managed Care Pilot Program

The study of this program was the first examination of a state-sponsored managed care pilot.[1,3] Study results have been influential in prompting other states to adopt similar workers' compensation managed care programs. The Florida Department of Insurance engaged researchers from Milliman & Robertson, Inc. to evaluate two authorized pilot projects, one involving CAC-Ramsey, a large closed-panel health maintenance organization, and a preferred provider organization established by the Travelers Insurance Company. In the Ramsey study, claimants were randomly assigned to the managed care intervention or a traditional-care control group. The Travelers study was a prospective matched-control group comparison. Results among the controls in the latter study were adjusted to account for regional differences in medical utilization.

Average total claim costs were reduced by 23–54% among the managed care participants, but patient satisfaction with care was diminished. A decomposition analysis indicated that most of the cost savings could be attributed to the lower cost of hospital services, a lower incidence of indemnity claims among study participants, and fewer and less costly use of physician services. About 15% of the savings were attributable to discounts of Florida's prevailing fee schedule, which was considered to be high relative to other states. It was not clear why there was a significantly reduced incidence of indemnity claims in the study group. It might have been a reflection of earlier, more intensive, and more effective medical care and disability management. Alternatively, it could be an artifact of expedited (and possibly premature) release for return to employment unrelated to actual medical improvement or a result of more restrictive initial medical determination of compensable work-relatedness in disability cases. A risk-sharing arrangement between Ramsey and the state of Florida whereby Ramsey received half of any cost savings from the project might have introduced some bias in this regard. Results of the claimant survey covering satisfaction and postinjury health status were based on a relatively low response rate of 21.9%.

New Hampshire Assigned Risk Pool Managed Care Project

Due to soaring costs within New Hampshire's assigned risk pool, all insurance policies after April 1, 1993, were assigned to a joint program conducted by Liberty Mutual Insurance Company and Healthsource JobCare, under which injured workers received medical care within the JobCare managed care network. Conducted by Milliman & Robertson, Inc., the study of the New Hampshire Assigned Risk Pool Managed Care Project[31] used a retrospective claims analysis comparing the experiences among the program participants with two nonmatched control groups. The study concentrated primarily on evaluating costs; it did not assess medical or functional outcomes, satisfaction, or process of care.

Overall workers' compensation costs were approximately 9–22% less in the managed care study group. The incidence of indemnity claims and the magnitude of indemnity benefits was significantly less among the managed care patients. Because no evaluation was made of postinjury physical health, functional status, or satisfaction, it was not possible to determine if the managed care arrangement compromised the quality of care. The results are somewhat limited by the absence of a contemporaneous control group, which makes it difficult to discern whether external environmental or economic factors affected the outcome.

Oregon Managed Care Program

Since 1990, Oregon has authorized the use of state-certified managed care organizations (MCOs) for treatment of occupational injuries and illness covered under workers' compensation insurance. All certified MCOs in Oregon feature a designated network of providers, case management, utilization review, and treatment guidelines. In 1995, a retrospective analysis of claims with medical payments made during the first 6 months of 1994 was performed by researchers from the Oregon Department of Consumer and Business Services to compare experiences of claimants receiving care within an MCO to those receiving traditional care from providers not affiliated with an MCO.[23,24,32] A subset of the study population consisted of patients from firms having workers' compensation insurance through SAIF, the state's largest insurance carrier.

The average medical cost per claim was virtually the same in both the study and comparison groups. However, among the subset of patients covered by SAIF, there was a 27% reduction of medical costs among those treated within an MCO. Patient satisfaction with medical care was lower in the managed care group. Indemnity costs were not evaluated. A survey of injured workers uncovered the intriguing finding that workers are generally not aware of whether they are receiving treatment within an MCO. Only 33% of MCO-treated respondents correctly reported that they received care within an MCO. Because assignment for treatment to an MCO in Oregon can be made by an insurer only after it receives and accepts a claim (so that medical care outside of an MCO may have already begun), there is a considerable potential in this study for misclassification between study and comparison groups that could dilute the observed results.

Other Studies

No other large-scale controlled studies have evaluated the impact of managed health care in workers' compensation. However, various case studies and descriptive accounts have been reported in the literature. Bernacki and Tsai describe 3 years' experience under a managed care arrangement put into place at Johns Hopkins University for its own employees.[2] This managed care plan, consisting of a preferred provider network, case management team, return to work program, and prevention efforts, produced a reduction in total cost per claim of 23%, and average medical costs per claim decreased by 22% from 1992–1995. Indemnity and administrative expenditures also fell. However, this was a pre/post comparison with no independent control groups. Moreover, because the managed care plan was run by the employer itself (Johns Hopkins), it is difficult to isolate the relative impact of changes in health care delivery from employer-based management changes, which also can be expected to significantly affect outcomes and return to work.

The National Council on Compensation Insurance (NCCI), an information services organization funded primarily by the insurance industry, used actuarial and econometric analyses to estimate that Florida employers participating in managed care arrangements during 1993–1995 achieved total workers' compensation cost savings averaging about 11.6%.[22] Another interstate study conducted by NCCI for Intracorp, a national managed care company, found that total average workers' compensation claims costs fell 23% when managed care techniques are used within the first 3 months after injury.[17,18] The NCCI attributed most of the cost savings to decreased duration of serious indemnity cases.

No controlled studies have been conducted of California's decision to allow managed health care for injured workers to be delivered through certified health care organizations (CHCOs). However, several private companies participating in the program have reported significant cost savings. For example, FHP/Great States Insurance reported in 1997 that loss ratios in its California certified health care organization averaged 41%, versus 55% for nonparticipants.[14] MetraComp, another CHCO, reported workers' compensation cost savings of about 50%, attributable mainly to reducing the length of work disability.[14] A different California managed care plan, the Kaiser/State Fund Alliance, has reported total cost savings of 34% and reductions in the duration of temporary disability averaging 32%.[27]

Similar anecdotal reports have been forthcoming from various employers. For example, use of a preferred provider network and onsite medical case management was credited with producing a 25% workers' compensation cost savings at Chicago's police department.[7] Stanford University ascribed $240,000 in annual cost savings and a 40% reduction in legal costs to the use of a managed care provider network and bill review procedures.[7] Owens-Corning Fiberglass Co. in Toledo, Ohio, reported more than $1 million in annual cost savings as a result of implementing its managed health care plan.[5] Reports such as these, which lack independent empiric validation, must be interpreted with caution, particularly because total workers' compensation costs and claims filings have declined in most states since 1993 as a result of benefits reductions, accident prevention initiatives, and other legislative, regulatory, and economic developments. Only a methodologically sound study with suitable control groups could clarify whether some or all of the observed cost savings were actually due to the use of managed health care.

Additional studies are being undertaken and should soon be producing results. Cornell University has been retained to evaluate the New York State Managed Care Pilot Program.[28] Researchers from Ohio University will be assessing the impact of managed care arrangements in Ohio. Other research on the impact of managed health care in workers' compensation is planned or underway in Pennsylvania, Minnesota, Arkansas, Colorado, California, and Florida.

CONCLUSION

The available empiric evidence consistently indicates that the use of managed health care techniques in workers' compensation can result in cost savings, but that patient satisfaction with medical care is diminished. The existing evidence is inconclusive as to whether the use of managed care in workers' compensation affects medical and functional outcomes.

The studies suggest that, on average, total workers' compensation claims costs can be reduced by 20–30%, with savings on both medical and indemnity benefit payments. The observed cost savings have resulted mostly from the introduction of discounted fee arrangements, decreased utilization of medical services, and a lower incidence and duration of indemnity claims. The effect of discounted fee schedules can be expected to have the greatest impact in states such as Florida, which had relatively high prevailing provider fees prior to establishment of the managed care program. In such an environment, establishing a lower fee structure can be expected to result in an immediate one-time cost savings that may not be sustainable in subsequent years. Likewise, changes in utilization patterns to eliminate unnecessary or inappropriate services can produce a rapid cost decline compared to previous unmanaged fee-for-service contexts. However, once the new utilization norms have been established, future additional cost reductions may be difficult to achieve.

Most studies have observed that cost savings are realized, in part, from a reduction in the incidence and duration of indemnity claims, but few have investigated this phenomenon closely to determine if it is solely the result of managed health care. Proponents of managed care speculate that the improved access to care, early medical interventions, and aggressive case management featured in many managed care plans are effective in reducing disability spells and improving patients' conditions before income replacement benefits are needed. Skeptics wonder whether the decline in disability cases is produced by more restrictive diagnostic criteria for determining the work-relatedness of disorders, premature release for return to work prior to full recovery, more conservative rating of patients' impairment level, or greater scrutiny and refusals in the claims-handling process. Adding to the uncertainty is the fact that the incidence and length of indemnity claims has declined throughout the United States since 1993, especially in states that have introduced reform legislation lowering benefit levels. Further research is needed to help clarify the differential effects of these factors.

Studies have demonstrated consistently that workers' compensation patients treated in managed care plans are less satisfied with their medical care. Claimant surveys have revealed several key factors adversely affecting satisfaction, including restrictions on patient choice of clinician, reduced geographic convenience in accessing care, and patients' perception that the quality of care is inferior in managed care plans. In at least eight states since 1993, the enactment of new regulations authorizing the use of managed care organizations in workers' compensation created the initial legal opportunity for employers and insurers to limit employees' choice of provider. Many workers, labor representatives, and public health advocates are suspicious that the introduction of managed care into workers' compensation may actually reflect a broader employer-driven campaign to erode benefits, tighten eligibility criteria, and weaken employees' control over health care and compensation issues.

Little difference has been observed in medical or functional outcomes between workers' compensation patients treated under managed care arrangements and those receiving traditional medical care. However, few studies have evaluated patients longer than 6 months after injury, which may not be long enough to accurately assess the ultimate impact of care on physical and functional status. Additionally, nonmedical factors involving labor-management relations, worker demographics, and psychosocial forces may play an important role in long-term functional recovery, thereby diluting the observed effect of managed medical care interventions.

Research now underway should help shed light on many of the unanswered questions regarding the impact of managed health care in workers' compensation. As managed care arrangements and research techniques are refined, additional data should become available to help clarify the relative contribution of specific managed care techniques, the advantages and disadvantages of particular network structures and provider payment plans, and the long-term consequences for total system costs and the quality of care.

ACKNOWLEDGMENT

This chapter has been written with the support of a grant from The Robert Wood Johnson Foundation. The author would also like to thank Kate Kimpan for her helpful comments on an earlier version of this article.

APPENDIX. Studies Assessing the Impacts of Managed Health Care in Workers' Compensation

Study	Nature of Intervention	Research Design	Study Group	Comparison Group(s)	Outcome Measure(s)
Washington State Managed Care Pilot Program[12,29,30]	**Delivery of Care:** Restricted network of providers with special training in occupational medicine. Patient was allowed to choose a primary care physician but was required to stay in the network for the first 9 months of treatment. Two health plans participated: Providence Health Plan and Kaiser Foundation Health Plan of the Northwest. **Payment:** Experience-rated capitation **Care Management:** Changes in claims handling by state insurance fund were made, including handling by specially trained claims managers, suspension of normal utilization review procedures, use of treatment protocols, extensive case management, and streamlining of claims processing, dispute resolution, and communications.	Prospective matched-control group comparison. Data were obtained from the state's administrative database, along with employer and employee telephone surveys. Assessment was made at 6 weeks after injury and 6 months after injury. Extended follow-up at 18 months after injury is planned. Study also included a qualitative process evaluation.	120 employer firms with 177 worksites and 7,041 employees. 1,354 incident injuries and 274 compensable claims (at least 4 lost work days) between April 1, 1995, and Dec. 31, 1996. The pilot's authorizing legislation stipulated that a firm's participation was contingent on their employees' approval as evidence by a majority vote or approval by the workers' authorized labor representative.	392 employer firms matched to study firms representing 12,296 employees. 1,707 incident injuries and 335 compensable claims (at least 4 lost work days) between July 1, 1995, and June 30, 1996. Control firms were matched to those in the study group by location, industry, size, wage rate, and insurance status.	**Costs:** Total average medical cost per claim Time lost duration Time lost payment **Utilization:** Visits, hospitalizations, inpatient days, surgeries, and procedures per claim **Medical and Functional Outcomes:** General health Mental health Physical functioning Role functioning Pain Mobility Vocational status Job modifications Quality of work **Satisfaction:** Employee Employer

(Appendix continued next page.)

APPENDIX (Cont). Studies Assessing the Impacts of Managed Health Care in Workers' Compensation

Washington State Managed Care Pilot Program Findings

Costs	Physical and Functional Status	Satisfaction	Process of Care	Study Limitations	Conclusions and Comments
The average medical cost per claim was 27.2% lower in the study group. Medical savings were derived principally from reducing outpatient surgery and other outpatient and ancillary services.

Lower indemnity costs and shorter length of work disability was found among the study group, but the results were not statistically significant. | No major differences were observed between study and control groups with regard to pain, physical functioning and mental health.

After 6 months (but not 6 weeks), the study group reported somewhat lower "role functioning" scores than did the controls.

After 6 weeks, more patients in the study group reported that their recovery was going poorly (12% vs. 6%) and a greater proportion assessed their overall outcomes as poor (25% vs. 20%).

After 6 months, both groups tended to be less positive about their treatment than at 6 weeks. | Employee satisfaction was consistently lower in the study group at both 6 weeks and 6 months. At 6 weeks, patients in the study group were more dissatisfied with treatment (27% vs. 17%), the attending physician (21% vs. 13%), and access to care (38% vs. 21%). After 6 months, these relative differences remained, and both study and control groups reported greater overall dissatisfaction with treatment (36% in the study group vs. 28% among the controls).

Employer satisfaction was consistently greater in the study group firms than the controls, especially with regard to the quality and frequency of information received about cases. | No major differences in utilization of services were observed. Outpatient utilization was slightly lower among the study group. | **Generalizability:** This form of managed care, relying on capitated occupational medicine networks, is relatively unique and may not be representative of other managed care plans. Also, Washington is an "exclusive fund" state (there are no commercial workers' compensation insurers).

Analysis: The study design did not permit disaggregating the impact of the different managed care elements such as the network, capitation, case management, streamlined dispute resolution, etc.

Data: Data from third-party administrators of self-insured employers were deemed to be "unreliable" and excluded from the study.

Out-of-Network Care: 36% of patients in the study group, formally restricted to the managed care plan, nevertheless chose to get care out-of-network. | Overall, medical costs were found to be about 27% lower in the managed care group, but patient satisfaction with care was diminished. Employer satisfaction, by contrast, was enhanced, principally because of improved claims administration and communication about cases. Few significant differences were observed in medical or functional outcomes.

Patients' overall satisfaction with care in both the study and the control groups was low, with only 40–41% of employees indicating satisfaction with the treatment they received, as assessed 6 months after the injury. |

(Appendix continued next page.)

APPENDIX (Cont). Studies Assessing the Impacts of Managed Health Care in Workers' Compensation

Study	Nature of Intervention	Research Design	Study Group	Comparison Group(s)	Outcome Measure(s)
Florida Managed Care Pilot Program[1,3]	Care was directed by employers into one of two managed care organizations, CAC-Ramsey, a large closed-panel health maintenance organization (HMO) or a preferred provider organization (PPO) network established by the Travelers Insurance Co. In the Ramsey study group, each injured worker could designate a primary care practitioner and was assigned a case manager. Payments for medical services were discounted 15% off the prevailing state fee schedule.	Randomized experimental trial and prospective matched-control group comparison. Data were obtained from insurance claims forms, employer and insurer administrative data sets, and mailed employee surveys.	There were two separate study groups: a) Approximately 17,000 state government employees in South Florida receiving care through CAC-Ramsey. Data were drawn from 1,240 claimants with incident injuries between June 15, 1991, and March 15, 1993. b) 7,500 privately employed workers in the Tampa Bay area receiving care through the Travelers PPO network. Data were drawn from 1,433 claimants with incident injuries between Oct. 1, 1991 and Sept. 30, 1993.	For evaluation of the care delivered through CAC-Ramsey, members of the state employee cohort were randomly assigned into two equal groups, with half receiving care from Ramsey and the other half (producing 1,460 control group claimants) receiving medical care under the traditional fee-for-service arrangement. For evaluation of the care delivered through the Travelers PPO, two control groups were used: one was a set of 1,164 claimants from the same control group of state employees used to evaluate the Ramsey project, matched with the study cohort for injury type and utilization of medical services; the other control group comprised 1,395 claimants from firms covered under a large self-insurance fund in the Tampa Bay area, also matched with the study cohort by type of injury.	**Costs:** Total average medical cost per claim Time lost duration Time lost payment **Medical and Functional Outcomes:** General health Mental health Social functioning **Utilization:** Visits, hospitalizations, inpatient days, surgeries, and procedures per claim **Satisfaction:** Employee

(Appendix continued next page.)

APPENDIX (Cont). Studies Assessing the Impacts of Managed Health Care in Workers' Compensation

Florida Managed Care Pilot Program Findings

Costs	Physical and Functional Status	Satisfaction	Process of Care	Study Limitations	Conclusions and Comments
Ramsey Group: the average total cost per claim was 54% lower in the study group, average medical costs were 58% lower, and indemnity costs 64% less. These savings were attributed to a lower incidence and duration of indemnity benefits (6–7% of savings), less frequent use of hospital services (8–12%), fewer medical treatments (<5%), a discounted fee schedule (15%), and other aspects of Ramsey's managed care program (11–25%). Travelers Group: the average total cost per claim was 23–29% lower in the study group, average medical costs were 28–35% lower and indemnity costs 29% less. These savings were attributed to a lower incidence of indemnity benefits (7–8% of savings), less frequent use of hospital services (11–13%), and fewer medical treatments (<7%).	No significant differences were observed between the study and control groups in self-reporting of postinjury physical health, mental health, or interference with social activities.	Claimants in the Ramsey participant group were less satisfied with the quality of care than claimants in the control group. (65.7% in the study group vs. 82.5% among the controls). Participants in the Travelers PPO arrangement were more satisfied than were those in the Ramsey HMO (80.4% vs. 65.7%). Results were based on 907 responses from 4,150 mail questionnaires (21.9% response rate).	The Ramsey claimants received a lower proportion of hospital treatments compared to the controls (39% vs. 53%). There were also comparatively fewer emergency room visits (36% vs. 41%). The average number of visits and treatments per claim was less in the study group than among the controls. Among the Travelers study group, 25% fewer claimants had hospital treatments compared to the controls. The average number of visits and treatments per claim was also lower in the Travelers study group compared to the controls.	Outcomes data were captured 3 months after the end of the study period, which would not be long enough for costs or medical outcomes to have fully developed. Under the terms of a risk-sharing arrangement with the State of Florida for participating in the pilot, Ramsey received half of any demonstrated cost savings. This may have influenced Ramsey to exert unusually aggressive cost-containment measures and return to work practices. Results of the claimant survey were based on a relatively low response rate of 21.9%. Differences between respondents and nonrespondents were not accessed to gauge possible reporting bias.	Overall average total claim costs were found to be between 23–54% lower in the managed care group, but patient satisfaction with care was diminished. The reduction in claims costs was attributed to lower costs of hospital services, lower incidence of indemnity claims, and fewer and less costly use of physician services. In the Ramsey program, 13–20% of the total cost savings were attributed to the discounted fee schedule used by Ramsey. These savings, in part, reflect the relatively high fee schedule prevailing in Florida at the time of the study and thus might not be generalizable to other areas.

(Appendix continued next page.)

APPENDIX (Cont). Studies Assessing the Impacts of Managed Health Care in Workers' Compensation

Study	Nature of Intervention	Research Design	Study Group	Comparison Group(s)	Outcome Measure(s)
New Hampshire Assigned Risk Pool[31]	Beginning with workers' compensation insurance policies issued after April 1, 1993, all employers in New Hampshire "assigned-risk" plan were covered by Liberty Mutual Insurance Company and had medical care supplied by Healthsource JobCare, a managed care organization. The Liberty Mutual/Healthsource partnership incorporated a PPO provider network, a discounted provider fee schedule, worksite accident prevention consultation, intensive nurse case management, treatment protocols, streamlined claims handling, and other managed care features.	Retrospective descriptive claims analysis comparing the experience among the study group to two nonmatched comparison data sets. Comparisons were made retrospectively from data supplied on April 25, 1995. For comparisons with the second comparison group (Liberty Mutual insured nonparticipants in the Healthsource plan), claims had to be at least 8 months old and thus claims filed after Aug. 31, 1994 were excluded from the analysis.	The study group consisted of all firms covered after April 1, 1993, under New Hampshire's assigned-risk plan serviced by a partnership between Liberty Mutual Insurance Company and Health-source New Hampshire, a managed care provider organization. Data were drawn from 8,542 claims in the study group covered by workers' compensation insurance policies with inception dates between April 1, 1993, and March 31, 1995.	Although there were no independent comparison groups per se, actual experience among the study group was compared to two comparison data sets. One comparison data set was based on a hypothetical aggregate estimate of expected loss experience based on actuarial projections from historical data from study firms, adjusting for wage trends, claim cost trends, benefit changes, and other factors. The other comparison set was derived from 1,280 claims among study firms covered by Liberty Mutual between April 1, 1993, and Dec. 31, 1993, but not participating in the Healthsource managed care plan because their policy inception dates occurred prior to program initiation on April 1, 1993.	**Costs:** Total average claims cost (including medical, indemnity and administrative elements) Claims frequency % of claims with lost-time medical expenditures Wage loss (indemnity) payments No assessment was made of medical or functional outcomes, satisfaction, or process or care.

(Appendix continued next page.)

APPENDIX (Cont). Studies Assessing the Impacts of Managed Health Care in Workers' Compensation

New Hampshire Assigned Risk Pool Findings

Costs	Physical and Functional Status	Satisfaction	Process of Care	Study Limitations	Conclusions and Comments
Compared to "expected values" for April 1, 1993, to March 31, 1995, total claim costs were 21–22% lower among the study group, average medical costs per claim were 11% lower, and average indemnity costs per claim were 21.5% lower. Compared to "expected values" for April 1, 1994, to March 31, 1995, total claim costs were 9–12% lower among the study group, average medical costs per claim were 2% lower, and average indemnity costs per claim were 7% lower. Compared to the "non-Healthsource" Liberty Mutual controls, total claim costs and medical costs were about 9–10% lower among the study group.	Not assessed.	Not assessed.	The incidence of indemnity claims and duration of indemnity benefits was significantly lower among the study group. Fewer hospital services were used.	There were no contemporaneous control groups in this study and, thus, little control over external environmental and economic factors that may have affected outcomes. Only costs were evaluated. There was no assessment of medical or functional outcomes, satisfaction, or quality of care. Thus, it is not possible to tell if the modified medical care arrangement altered or compromised quality. The study was confined to a single insurer and managed care organization and involved only "assigned-risk" employers who could not obtain traditional commercial workers' compensation insurance. The study design did not permit isolating the effects of particular managed care and insurance features, such as the discounted fee schedule, case management, treatment protocols, prevention efforts, and modified claims handling.	Overall workers' compensation claims costs were found to be approximately 9–22% less in the managed care study group. This was attributable to the discounted fee schedule and other managed care "technologies." The incidence of indemnity claims and the magnitude of indemnity benefits was significantly lower in the study group. No assessment of medical or functional outcomes, satisfaction, or quality of care was made.

(Appendix continued next page.)

APPENDIX (Cont). Studies Assessing the Impacts of Managed Health Care in Workers' Compensation

Study	Nature of Intervention	Research Design	Study Group	Comparison Group(s)	Outcome Measure(s)
Oregon Managed Care Program[23,24,32]	In 1990, legislation was enacted authorizing the use of managed care organizations (MCOs) for workers' compensation, and regulations were adopted for their certification. MCOs in Oregon may direct care to a preselected panel of providers, so long as an injured worker can choose from among at least 3 providers in each of various provider categories. An injured worker may initially receive treatment from outside the panel until the insurer accepts the claim. Certified MCOs must offer case management and utilization review and establish treatment guidelines.	Retrospective claims analysis comparing experiences of claims involving MCO enrollees receiving treatment through the MCO compared to two unmatched control groups: those enrolled in MCOs but receiving care outside the plan and those not enrolled in MCOs (i.e., receiving traditional care). Data were obtained from the Oregon state claims database, supplemented by an employee survey.	A sample of 4,697 claims was randomly selected from a total of 85,287 claims with medical payments made between Jan. 1994 and June 1994. The study group consisted of 10.2% of this sample (approx. 479 claims) for which the claimant was covered by and received treatment within a certified MCO. A subgroup of the study population consisted in those covered through SAIF, the state's largest insurer, representing 59.4% of workers.	There were two unmatched comparison groups: 21.1% of the random sample of claims (approx. 991 claims) from employees covered by a certified MCO, but receiving treatment elsewhere, and 68.8% of the sample (approx. 3,231 claims) not covered by a certified MCO.	**Costs:** Total average medical cost per claim Distribution of total costs by medical provider type **Utilization:** Treatments by type of provider **Medical and Functional Outcomes:** General health status **Satisfaction:** Employee **Perceived Value of Services:** MCO Insurer

(Appendix continued next page.)

APPENDIX (Cont). Studies Assessing the Impacts of Managed Health Care in Workers' Compensation

Oregon Managed Care Program Findings

Costs	Physical and Functional Status	Satisfaction	Process of Care	Study Limitations	Conclusions and Comments
The average medical cost per claim was virtually identical between the study and comparison groups ($939 per claim for each group). Within the subset of the study group covered by SAIF, the state's largest WC insurance carrier, the average medical cost was 27.4% less among those treated in MCOs than in the non-MCO controls ($995 vs. $1,362). However, SAIF's average medical payment per claim ($1,060) was considerably (13%) higher than the mean for the entire study group ($939).	58% of the MCO-treated group reported that their postinjury physical health was worse than their preinjury physical health, compared to about 50% among those not treated in an MCO. 10% of the MCO-treated group reported their postinjury health was better, compared to 15% of those treated outside of MCOs. Results were based on responses to a mail questionnaire (see next column for details of the survey).	A significantly greater proportion of those treated in an MCO were dissatisfied with their medical care compared to those treated outside an MCO (20% vs. 35%). Dissatisfaction was attributed to low quality of treatment, inadequate choice of provider, and poor communication. Results were based on 729 responses from 1,398 mail questionnaires, a response rate of 52.1%. In a separate perception survey, respondents from MCOs ranked their utilization review services as having greatest value, followed by panel management services, dispute resolution services, and return to work assistance. Insurers ranked MCO's panel management activities as most important to them, followed by return to work programs and utilization review services.	Workers were generally unaware of whether they were being treated through an MCO. In response to a question in the mail survey, 34% of claimants reported that they did not know whether they had been treated in an MCO and another 34% indicated that they had not been treated in an MCO even though records indicated that they had. Only 33% of workers actually treated in an MCO responded that they received treatment through an MCO. Hospital utilization and use of physical therapists was lower among those treated in MCOs.	There was potential for misclassification between study and comparison groups due to the complex nature of MCO assignment, whereby an insurer can only elect to assign an injured worker to an MCO after a claim has been received and accepted, by which time medical treatment may have already begun. There were statistically significant differences between the study and comparison groups with respect to the industry groupings in which claims occurred, reflecting variations between the major insurer's book of business. There were also variations in the rural/urban mix between groups. These potential confounding variables were not adjusted for in the analysis. The study looked only at medical costs. The impact of MCO status on indemnity costs was not evaluated.	Overall, the average medical cost per claim was found to be about the same in both study and comparison groups. However, among the subset insured by SAIF, the state's largest insurer, there was a 27.4% medical cost saving among the MCO participants. Satisfaction with medical care was lower among those treated in MCOs. Patients treated in MCOs reported that their postinjury health status was slightly worse than those in the comparison groups. No analysis of the impact of managed care on indemnity costs was made.

REFERENCES

1. Appel D, Borba PS: The impact of managed care on workers' compensation claim costs. In Grannemann TW (ed): Review, Regulate, or Reform? What Works to Control Workers' Compensation Medical Costs. Cambridge, MA, Workers' Compensation Research Institute, 1994, pp 166–184.
2. Bernacki EJ, Tsai SP: Managed care for workers' compensation: Three years of experience in an "employee choice" state. J Occup Environ Med 39:1091–1097, 1996.
3. Borba PS, Appel D, Fung M: Florida Managed Care Pilot Program: July 1994 Final Report. Tallahassee, FL, Florida Department of Insurance, 1994.
4. Borba PS: Developing a workers' compensation data collection system. Proceedings of the Agency for Health Care Policy and Research Conference: Workers' Compensation and Managed Care—Challenges and Opportunities in a Changing Health Care System, Chicago, July 30–August 1, 1997.
5. Browne MJ, Anderson DR: Managed care in workers' compensation. In Segre G (ed): 1997–1998 Workers' Compensation Managed Care Sourcebook. New York, Faulkner & Gray, 1997, pp 5–21.
6. Burton JF Jr: Workers' compensation benefits and costs: Significant developments in the early 1990s. Workers' Compensation Monitor 8(3):1–11, 1995.
7. Caldwell B: Proper management cuts companies' workers' comp costs. In Segre G (ed): 1997–1998 Workers' Compensation Managed Care Sourcebook. New York, Faulkner & Gray, 1997, pp 73–75.
8. Dembe AE, Himmelstein JS, Stevens BA, Beachler MP: Improving workers' compensation health care. Health Affairs 16:253–257, 1997.
9. Dembe AE: Preserving workers' benefits in a managed health care environment. J Public Health Policy 19(2):182–200, 1998.
10. Eccleston SM: Managed Care and Medical Cost Containment in Workers' Compensation: A National Inventory, 1995–1996. Cambridge, MA, Workers' Compensation Research Institute, 1995.
11. Feuerstein M, Thebarge RW: Perceptions of disability and occupational stress as discriminators of work disability in patients with chronic pain. J Occup Rehabil 1:185–195, 1995.
12. Franklin G: A closer look at workers' compensation managed care initiatives in several states. Presented at the Agency for Health Care Policy and Research Conference: Workers' Compensation and Managed Care—Challenges and Opportunities in a Changing Health Care System, Chicago, July 30–August 1, 1997.
13. Gatchel RJ, Polatin PB, Mayer TG: The dominant role of psychosocial risk factors in the development of chronic low back pain disability. Spine 20:2702–2709, 1995.
14. HCOs appear to reduce lost time, litigation. Workers' Comp Managed Care 5(2):4, 1997.
15. Hellinger FJ: Selection bias in HMOs and PPOs: A review of the evidence. Inquiry 32:135–142, 1995.
16. Himmelstein JS, Feuerstein M, Stanek EJ III, et al: Work-related upper-extremity disorders and work disability: Clinical and psychosocial presentation. J Occup Environ Med 37:1278–1286, 1995.
17. Intracorp, NCCI use new method to document savings. Workers' Comp Managed Care 3(14):9–10, 1995.
18. Intracorp/NCCI Methodology for Measuring Financial Impact of Workers' Compensation Managed Care Techniques. Philadelphia, Intracorp, 1995.
19. Katz JN: Worker self-report in assessing the quality and outcome of work-associated musculoskeletal disease [white paper prepared for The Robert Wood Johnson Foundation's Workers' Compensation Health Initiative]. Worcester, MA, 1997.
20. Matheson L, Mooney V, Grant J, et al: Standardized evaluation of work capacity. J Back Musculoskel Rehabil 6:249–264, 1996.
21. National Academy of Social Insurance: Workers' Compensation: Benefits, Coverage, and Costs 1994–95, New Estimates. Washington, DC, National Academy of Social Insurance, 1997.
22. NCCI estimates employers will save 11.6 percent under managed care. BNA's Workers' Compensation Report 8:112, 1997.
23. Oregon Workers' Compensation Division: Managed Care in the Oregon Workers' Compensation System. Salem, OR, Oregon Department of Consumer and Business Services, 1995.
24. Oregon: Little change in outcomes between patients in and out of MCOs. Workers' Comp Managed Care 5(11):1–2, 1997.
25. Pransky G, Benjamin K, Hill-Fotouhi C, et al: Outcomes on work-related upper extremity and low back injuries: Results of a retrospective study [manuscript].
26. Stock SR, Cole DC, Tugwell P, Streiner D: Review of applicability of existing functional status measures to the study of workers with musculoskeletal disorders of the neck and upper limb. Am J Ind Med 29:679–688, 1996.

27. Study: Kaiser-state fund program savings "significant." Workers' Comp Managed Care 5(8):12, 1997.
28. Texas Research and Oversight Council on Workers' Compensation: Managed care and workers' compensation: A review of research. In Segre G (ed): 1997–1998 Workers' Compensation Managed Care Sourcebook. New York, Faulkner & Gray, 1997, pp 35–59.
29. Washington Department of Labor and Industries and the University of Washington Department of Health Services: Workers' Compensation Managed Care Pilot Project: Final Report to the Legislature. Olympia, WA, 1997.
30. Wickizer T: Washington State's managed care pilot program: Preliminary findings. Presented at the Workers' Compensation Research Institute's annual conference. Cambridge, MA, March 6, 1997.
31. Witcraft SE, Appel D: An Evaluation of Changes to the New Hampshire Workers' Compensation Assigned Risk Plan as of March 31, 1995. New York, Milliman & Robertson, 1995.
32. Workers express little difference in satisfaction between MCOs, non-MCOs. BNA's Workers' Compensation Report 8:537–538, 1997.

MARCIA L. COMSTOCK, MD, MPH

A STRATEGIC APPROACH TO OCCUPATIONAL INJURIES

From the Consolidated Rail
    Corporation
Philadelphia, Pennsylvania

Reprint requests to:
Marcia L. Comstock, MD, MPH
1157 Lafayette Road
Wayne, PA 19087-2110

Risk management can be defined as a series of tasks and functions methodically undertaken to reduce unexpected financial loss to an organization.[14] In health-related services, it is important to direct primary efforts toward improving patient care with a secondary goal of decreasing financial impact. Successful risk management programs begin with support of the chief executive officer and require accountability on the part of line managers and effective cross-functional collaboration. Although quality assurance and risk management historically were perceived to be at odds rather than complementary, continuous quality improvement (CQI) programs have helped smooth interfaces between the two.[14]

This chapter describes Conrail's development and implementation of an integrated risk management approach to occupational injuries. Focus on the injury risk continuum successfully enhanced primary and secondary prevention. Personal injury risk management (PIRM) resulted in a 75% reduction in lost work days and contributed significantly to a 59% decrease in occupational injuries since implementation during the first half of 1995. The economic impact on the corporate bottom line has been enormous.

The PIRM project had other significant consequences that were unanticipated during the redesign effort. Senior management recognized how fragmentation created inefficiency and cost. A risk management department that included all groups responsible for elements of the total cost of risk was created in late 1994. While initial PIRM efforts focused specifically on addressing events from the point of injury onward, the organizational integration that was achieved allowed the company to take a much broader view of the risk continuum of identification, assessment, and control and to shift resources from "failure" to "prevention."

Our success is particularly noteworthy given the unique obstacles the rail industry faces in managing occupational injuries. The cross-functional approach and managed care techniques we employed should be even more effective in other businesses.

BACKGROUND

Many companies initially focus disability management on group health programs. We first tackled work-related injuries for specific reasons. Rail industry employees are provided a form of 24-hour coverage under a national contract negotiated between class I railroads and the many unions representing our employees. We are experience-rated not as a company but as a part of the industry. Although medical claim costs are high, the impact cannot be directly influenced.

On the other hand, the financial impact of work-related injuries in the railroad is direct and significant. Personal injury claims account for the single largest percentage of the company's cost of risk, which in 1996 was $250 million. The claims are so costly because railroad employees are not covered by workers' compensation but by the fault-based Federal Employer's Liability Act (FELA), a tort-based system of law that governs railroads alone in handling employee disputes involving injury or death. This 1908 act permits employees to sue employers for compensatory damages. Because the system provides no guarantee of financial support, many employees feel no recourse but to seek monetary compensation through the courts.

FELA has no liability limits. The requirement that fault be proven clearly represented a significant advantage to the industry in 1908. However, changing societal perceptions and the increasingly litigious environment has more than turned the tables. In terms of personal injury, there are strong employee attitudes supporting entitlement to certain benefits. This attitude is fueled by union runners and FELA attorneys. Physicians who operate within the FELA system are quick to provide the most aggressive forms of treatment. Jury trials can result in tremendous awards for relatively minor injuries without objective evidence of impairment or disability.[2] The average low back injury settlement is more than three times that of the most generous workers' compensation schedule. According to the Association of American Railroads, the estimated average claim for a low back strain under FELA was more than $105,000 in 1993. Injury claim payments for class I railroads in 1994 were nearly $1 billion; indirect costs, including claims administration, litigation expenses, medical costs, investigation costs, insurance costs, and labor replacement, are estimated to be triple direct payout. However, some injuries go totally uncompensated. Thus, incentives to abuse the system abound.[2]

Complexities related to labor issues are particularly acute when 88% of the workforce is represented by one of 14 separate collective bargaining agreements. Conrail's first goal, "to be the safest carrier," requires cooperative labor-management initiatives. Divisional joint safety teams have existed since 1989. In 1991 the company embarked on a corporate-wide CQI program. While change is difficult for everyone, in the railroad it created a cultural revolution for both management and agreement employees. Clearly, tenets of CQI such as a focus on teamwork run counter to the autocratic, hierarchical, and militaristic culture that characterized the industry and counter to well-entrenched labor principles such as the supremacy of seniority.

Many factors other than the intrinsically adversarial system made development of an effective process for decreasing the impact of occupational injuries on the railroad and its employees exceedingly challenging.

Many functional groups within the company shared responsibility for management of some part of the process, but no one was accountable for the overall risk management effort. In fact, the six most critical groups involved in various aspects of worker safety and injury response reported to four different senior officers. Each organization focused on their own measures of success, which tended to be task- rather than outcome-driven and organizationally rather than process-defined.

There was considerable redundancy and overlap of effort, creating inefficiency and confusion. Roles were sometimes inappropriate and accountabilities not always clear. Historical "turf" issues resulted in poor communication between such key organizations as health services, safety, claims, and operations. While incremental changes in various subprocesses had resulted in some overall improvement, lack of coordination and integration meant less significant bottom line impact.

Health services staff members who were accountable for injury management frequently found themselves caught between conflicting information and interests. They were faced with the difficult task of sorting out facts and making decisions that rarely pleased all parties.

The geographic dispersion and mobility of more than 65% of the population, such as train crews and engineering production gangs, made it extremely difficult to effectively and efficiently provide medical services. Identification of knowledgeable and credible medical consultants, communication, and coordination of effort were extremely time-consuming. When no provider treats large numbers of cases, there is less leverage to control quality and service.

There were also job security issues. At Conrail's creation in 1976, there were more than 100,000 employees. By 1993, there were less than 25,000.

Perhaps the greatest hurdle, however, was cultural. For 150 years relationships between management and labor have been adversarial and punitive. Classic railroad management style characterized by an intimidating approach exacerbated the problems. Historically, bureaucracy and micromanagement were the norm. Supervision focused on numbers, not process. Incentives were counterproductive to the desired change.

Despite the efforts of divisional safety teams, improved equipment, an increasing focus on training, and the CQI program, the winter of 1993 reversed a positive trend in work-related injuries, resulting in a significant financial impact on the company. An increased incidence of illness and injury claims, coupled with rising medical costs and claim settlements, highlighted the impact of this perplexing problem to senior management.

Given the company's situation, as well as ongoing cultural changes, we were able to gain support for a proposal to develop and implement an optimal, integrated process to minimize the human and economic impact associated with work-related injuries. It was recognized that assumptions had to be challenged, preconceived notions discarded, and the injury management process viewed from the eyes of the primary customer: the injured employee.[10] Our decision to use a reengineering approach stemmed from the perception that the processes were too fragmented for repair. Reengineering's focus on redesign of fundamental business processes rather than organizational units seemed more appropriate, especially since the existing process had been designed to work in a different environment.[10]

PIRM was undertaken in two phases. Phase 1 included an analysis of the existing approach, identification of an ideal process, data collection, and identification of discrepancies between the two. Phase 2 focused on development and implementation of action plans to address critical success factors.

PHASE 1

Mapping the Existing Process

Because the first step in risk management is to identify potential risks in an exposure area, we undertook a high-level flow-mapping of the existing complex process. There were 264 "boxes" on the map, representing action steps. This exercise was critically important to increase interorganizational understanding and empathy as well as to identify significant overlap, key bottlenecks, and barriers.

Qualitative Analysis

Our qualitative data collection focused on validating our impression of the issues and potential solutions. A total of 280 individuals were interviewed at all levels of management, union leadership, and employees. We used an outside consultant to conduct field focus groups to help ensure that employees were comfortable expressing their opinions. There were few surprises. Interestingly, interviewees tended to agree on the problems but had different opinions regarding causes and solutions.

Although we recognized the risk of narrowly defining the scope of the problem,[10] it was determined that initial team efforts would focus on addressing events from the point of injury onward and on corrective measures to prevent incidents. However, after proper control measures were identified and implemented, we planned to evaluate and redesign the entire process, including preplacement screening, training, yard and shop standards, and other factors.

Quantitative Analysis

From a risk management perspective, analysis of funds expended on personal injury demonstrated that nearly $140 million was spent on "failure." Little was being spent on prevention. Our quantitative analysis, using 3 years of closed claim data, was conducted by the same outside consultant. It demonstrated predictive associations between geographic location, union affiliation, and crafts, and incidence of injury and claim costs.

Our system does not permit accurate tracking of total medical costs because care for injured employees may have been paid for by employees' "24-hour care" plan and through submission of bills to claim agents. Unlike under workers' compensation, however, the medical component is a relatively modest proportion of the total claim cost. The key driver of the ultimate cost of the FELA claim settlement proved to be lost work days and not diagnosis. Our train and engine service employees had the highest incidence of injury and lost the most days for a given diagnosis; however, overall, the jobs are less physically demanding than many other crafts. Clearly, issues other than medical factors were operative. Thus, lost work days became a key short-term measure of success.

Information from the quantitative analysis was used to develop preliminary predictive models to ensure that resources were not wasted. The models were intended to maximize outcomes by matching the intensity of resource allocation to perceived risk of the individual case, based on past experience.

Benchmarking

Benchmarking of best business practices in key areas was carried out with other railroads and different industries. Conrail employees, on average, tended to lose more than twice as much work time as predicted based on diagnosis and physical requirements of the job.

Redesign

Based on this information and process analysis, we identified three separate but interrelated processes: intervention (medical and disability management), accident investigation, and resolution (claims/financial management).

During the project, three teams redesigned the subprocesses, which were then merged into a single integrated process. A fourth team worked on information technology issues; the nonlinked and incomplete data-systems made communication difficult and analysis cumbersome. We were data-rich yet information-poor.

The teams defined several principles that are critical to an ideal risk management model for personal injuries (Table 1). Most are relevant to integrated disability programs for both on-duty injuries and nonoccupational illness.

Create a Common Goal. First, a common "supraordinate" goal was clearly needed because goals and associated incentives drive behavior. The organizations involved in the injury process had objectives that were relevant to their core areas, but sometimes at odds with another area's goal. For example, claim agents were measured on the number of cases they held direct. Understandably, they were inclined to approve any treatment the patient requested. Health services wanted to eliminate inappropriate treatment and focus on rapid rehabilitation and return to work. However, supervisors were reluctant to take the employee back until he or she completely recovered and even then the supervisors resisted, focusing on the possibility of reinjury, which would result in another negative tally in the Federal Railroad Administration (FRA) statistics.

Focus on Employee Care and Support. The need for demonstrable management commitment to injury prevention and employee care and support was obvious. Fragmentation and disconnects in care that delayed recovery needed to be eliminated. We believed that properly managed quality care could be cost-effective, and savings would come in the form of reduction of lost work time.

Delineate Clear Roles and Accountabilities. Roles needed to be appropriate to functional expertise and integrated to enhance management, and each organization needed to be held accountable for results.

Ensure Real-time Communication. Real-time communication with appropriate decision-makers at the time of injury would allow for early analysis and channeling to the best level of care and would ensure accurate flow of information.

Support the Supervisor. To help maintain a positive relationship between employees and supervisors, we needed to get the supervisor back to the job of running the railroad as soon as possible. The process needed to relieve him of the responsibility for decision-making, avoid wasted hours in the emergency room, and minimize time-consuming paperwork associated with the injury.

TABLE 1. Principles of an Ideal Model

Create a common goal
Focus on employee care and support
Delineate clear roles and accountabilities
Ensure real-time communication
Support the supervisor
Perform a single investigation with root cause analysis
Shift the focus toward prevention
Integrate process and data
Ensure incentives support desired behavior

Perform a Single Unbiased Investigation with Root Cause Analysis. Our qualitative analysis had revealed that in many cases three or more investigations were being conducted into the cause of an injury, but the conclusions were frequently at odds, most likely related to the significant ramifications of determining blame. Our process recommended a single, unbiased investigation with careful root cause analysis that was used to drive prevention efforts.

Shift the Focus Toward Prevention. We recognized that pervasive overreaction to injuries from a numbers perspective was counterproductive. Safety personnel needed to focus less on postinjury activities and more on timely preventive actions.

Integrate Process and Data. Process integration is key to eliminating infrastructure fragmentation and inefficiency and to enhancing management. Integration of information systems helps streamline data analysis.

Ensure That Incentives Support Desired Behavior. Most importantly, an ideal model ensures that performance measures and incentives are aligned across organizations and supportive of the ideal process. Managing numbers alone countermands the broader focus on a risk continuum necessary to long-term success.

PHASE 2

Disability and Medical Management: Strategies

While all three of the redesigned subprocesses were critical to success, this chapter addresses only the medical and disability management elements of PIRM. Several strategies for effective disability management were identified (Table 2).

Manage Care from Time of Injury. Many employees with minor injuries lost time after being treated in emergency rooms and referred to their personal physician. We felt that many of these employees could continue to work if there was communication of accurate job-related information at the time of initial treatment.

Emphasize Work Continuity or Resumption. An emphasis on work continuation, if possible, is critical to decreasing lost work days, getting control of the care from the beginning, and avoiding unnecessary "disability syndromes." It is also therapeutic from the physical and psychological perspectives.[19]

Use Aggressive Case Management Techniques. Considerable support for the value of aggressive case management in both occupational and nonoccupational disability exists. Due to liability concerns, physicians tend to be conservative and are reluctant to push an individual back to work. The case manager can serve as an interface among the employee, treating physician, and the workplace, ensuring that disability management and clinical issues are addressed.[20]

Ensure Employee Participation in Decision-making. Education of employees in conjunction with advocacy is essential in any lost-time management effort. We needed to help our employees understand the complex health care system and make wise choices. It was crucial for the employees to appreciate the risks of excessive testing and treatment, which are much more common than undertreatment in the

TABLE 2.   Disability and Medical Management: Strategies

Manage care from the time of injury
Emphasize work continuity
Utilize aggressive case management techniques
Ensure employee participation in decision-making
Facilitate employee cooperation with program

railroad system. Active participation by the injured worker in making medical decisions that affect him is critical in countermanding "learned helplessness" and in returning a sense of control.[9] Further, we needed to gain trust and buy-in to the new process.

Facilitate Employee Cooperation with Program.   Under FELA, as in workers' compensation employee choice states, employees have complete control over provider selection. We needed to give employees some incentive to use the providers we chose but also ensure that we had the ability to facilitate and oversee care provided by the patient's choice of provider. A temporary wage continuation program had been administered by claims for several years but needed to be managed in concert with the disability management program.

Disability and Medical Management: Tools

To achieve the desired improvement, we developed or modified a number of program elements (Table 3).

First Report of Injury.   We established a toll-free number to respond to calls 24 hours a day for the first report of injury. Such a reporting system enhances efficiency and establishes consistency in any absence-control program. An intake and assessment function is performed, and the injured employee is taken to the nearest appropriate provider. The facility is notified that the employee is en route, the type of injury is described, and the employees' job description is faxed to the facility. A follow-up call is made after the evaluation to determine if the employee is able to return to work in his own or a modified job or to make arrangements for follow-up care. The claim agent is also notified to activate the claims process and accident investigation.

Preferred Provider Network.   A network of primary care providers, occupational physicians, internists, and family physicians was identified and credentialed in close proximity to large population bases so that resources familiar with problems related to railroad injury were available for most cases. Given our dispersed and mobile population, however, Conrail operates in many communities that have few medical providers, fewer who understand the industrial operation and workplace, and sometimes none particularly interested in injury care. We attempted to gain leverage by contracting with existing networks that were serving other industries.

Providers need a hospital affiliation for out-of-hours care, with an understanding regarding arrangements for follow-up care. We also wanted providers who were focused on aggressive rehabilitation and return to work and who would partner with health services and other risk management staff. Recognizing that workers would only stay in the network if it met their needs and was shown to be of good quality,[22] we took particular care to orient providers to special occupational needs, cultural issues, and legal requirements.

TABLE 3.   Disability and Medical Management: Tools

24-hour first report of injury
Preferred Provider Network
Functional job analyses
Disability duration guidelines/treatment protocols
Intrateam referral process
Temporary wage continuation
Early return to work program
Vocational rehabilitation
Information system support

Functional Job Analyses.   To enhance real-time communication and understanding of railroad jobs, specifically functional requirements, accurate analyses of essential functions and their requisite physical abilities are critical. To this end, analyses of key railroad crafts were conducted by the managers of vocational rehabilitation and ergonomics, with input from operations supervisors and job incumbents. In addition, craft-specific videotapes of employees performing essential functions of jobs were developed with measurements of weight, force, distance, and frequency. The videotapes help our preferred providers in their decision-making on work ability.

Disability Duration Guidelines.   Today, guidelines and protocols are rapidly becoming a cornerstone of good quality care. Our employees, more often than those in other industries, seek treatment or are referred to numerous specialist physicians, frequently for relatively minor soft tissue injury. Given the amount of excessive care and time lost for an injury that we documented through our quantitative analysis, the need for these tools to help us manage care seemed obvious. We selected methodically developed and updated disability guidelines and clinical protocols that were based both on reviews and expert opinion with a stringent quality assurance process.

Intrateam Referral Process.   Recognizing the importance of psychosocial and lifestyle issues in susceptibility to injury and in prolonging recovery, we use an intrateam referral process to ensure that all relevant resources are brought to bear on each case. The contentiousness that tends to characterize supervisor-employee relations can be a significant barrier to effective disability management. Anger and resentment toward the company is common and needs to be actively addressed. Many of our injured workers also have socioeconomic concerns.[4] Behavioral health and health promotion expertise is readily available through the divisional health services teams. Early identification of "red flags" helps to ensure that the correct strategy is used to manage all aspects of the disability, as opposed to using a narrow medical focus.[19]

Temporary Wage Continuation.   While our employees have complete choice of provider for injury care under FELA, they do not receive temporary disability benefits as under workers' compensation. To financially support employees actively cooperating with medical management, we provide temporary wage continuation payments at the employee's vacation rate, which acts as an incentive to enhance cooperation.

Early Return to Work Program.   For the program to be successful, we needed to develop a formal early return to work program and educate employees and supervisors regarding its importance to rehabilitation and compliance with the Americans with Disabilities Act (ADA). This represented a major challenge because it required overcoming significant resistance to accepting less than full physical capabilities. Also, the ability to accommodate is limited by issues related to seniority. Current case law supports the precedence of existing labor agreements over ADA requirements.

The preferred option was to accommodate the injured employee's restrictions in his usual position. This was sometimes difficult given the physical demands of railroad work. Another option was to allow bidding on a less physically demanding job for which the worker had required craft seniority.

We decided that a third option was necessary and, collaborating with a vendor experienced with multiunion environments, created transitional work assignments. Working with unions and management, assignments within craft that were compatible with labor agreements were identified. Tasks are progressively performed by employees with a variety of functional limitations. As shown in Figure 1, jobs with increasing levels of physical demands were identified depending on the body

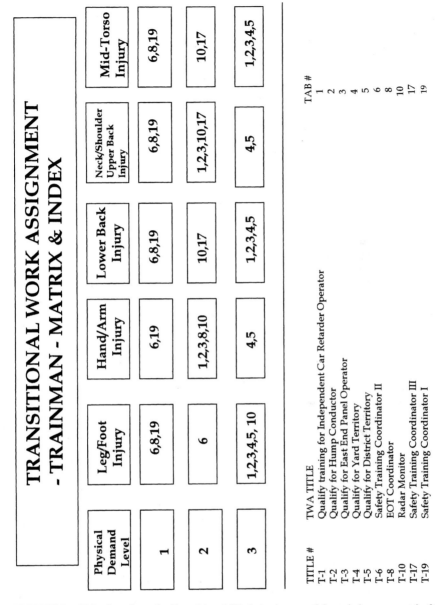

TRANSITIONAL WORK ASSIGNMENT - TRAINMAN - MATRIX & INDEX

Physical Demand Level	Leg/Foot Injury	Hand/Arm Injury	Lower Back Injury	Neck/Shoulder Upper Back Injury	Mid-Torso Injury
1	6,8,19	6,19	6,8,19	6,8,19	6,8,19
2	6	1,2,3,8,10	10,17	1,2,3,10,17	10,17
3	1,2,3,4,5, 10	4,5	1,2,3,4,5	4,5	1,2,3,4,5

TITLE #	TWA TITLE	TAB #
T-1	Qualify training for Independent Car Retarder Operator	1
T-2	Qualify for Hump Conductor	2
T-3	Qualify for East End Panel Operator	3
T-4	Qualify for Yard Territory	4
T-5	Qualify for District Territory	5
T-6	Safety Training Coordinator II	6
T-8	EOT Coordinator	8
T-10	Radar Monitor	10
T-17	Safety Training Coordinator III	17
T-19	Safety Training Coordinator I	19

FIGURE 1. This chart from the Transitional Work Assignment Manual shows a matrix for the trainman craft. For example, a trainman with a lower back injury would generally be returned to one of the three jobs under level 1: 6—Safety Training Coordinator II; 8—End of Train (EOT) Coordinator; or 19—Safety Training Coordinator III. After 2 weeks he or she should progress to level 10 or 17, and so on until able to perform at the physical level required by the original job. The tab number refers to the location of the work assignment description in the manual.

part that was injured. Employees remain in an assignment no more than 2 weeks before being advanced to the next level of physical demand, with their physician's concurrence.

Vocational Rehabilitation.   Given the physical nature of many railroad jobs, some injured employees reach maximal medical improvement and are not able to perform the essential functions of any railroad job for which they have seniority. For these employees, rehabilitative efforts may include placement in jobs outside the industry, including provision of job retraining or education. Timely establishment and aggressive pursuit of the appropriate vocational goal helps to mitigate disability syndromes that are costly to the individual and the employer.

Information Systems Support.   Finally, to make disability management efficient, we needed ready access to all relevant information through integrated data systems. Case managers require systems support with regard to duration guidelines, clinical protocols, and cost tracking to be maximally effective. This was achieved by using a Windows-based case management system. Injury data are downloaded from the mainframe, and pertinent narrative information is uploaded to the claims management system. The system can incorporate selected disability duration guidelines and functional job analyses.

Roles and Responsibilities

With strategies defined and tactics identified, we needed to clarify the process, i.e., specifically define roles and responsibilities.

The **medical care coordinators**, contracted nurse case managers, provide the day-to-day disability management services. They monitor medical treatment against guidelines, coordinate care, and work with treating providers to develop return to work plans. In consultation with the Conrail medical director, they certify eligibility for wage continuation and payment for approved tests or treatment.

The responsibility of the medical case coordinators is to provide ongoing education and support of the employee and assess the need for psychosocial or wellness services. These individuals are closely aligned with the workplace, working with the rest of the health services team. Our experience has shown that "generic" contracted disability managers are generally unaware of cultural realities and unable to identify and address nonmedical issues prolonging recovery. As the key point of contact with the injured employee, the medical case coordinator must convey a sense of concern and advocacy for the patient. Identification of the presence or lack of support systems can be important in effective case management. The coordinators actively seek to give the patient a sense of control to countermand feelings of helplessness and help the injured employee to understand his or her responsibilities and ability to influence treatment outcome. The success of the disability management program directly depends on the skill and effectiveness of these case managers.[4,23]

The **health services managers** are field-based divisional health services team leaders who facilitate intrateam referral to ensure that all appropriate resources are brought to bear on each case. They serve as the "point person" on the PIRM teams, coordinating internal communication and problem resolution.[6] They also drive decision-making on return to work options and monitor employees working in transitional or accommodated positions to ensure they progress safely.

The **PIRM team** is composed of key members of risk management, such as health services, safety and claims, and division management, and it meets weekly to review lost-time cases. Members are accountable for working together to promote safety and decrease lost work days through adherence to the PIRM process. The final decision on when an employee will return to work is made with input from the team and not merely the treating physician.[4] Goals for the team related to lost-time injuries and lost work days are tied to incentive compensation, promoting cooperation.

The role of the **medical director** is critical. In addition to providing support and guidance to the medical care coordinators and health services managers, the medical director must intervene directly in many cases. For example, there may be a lack of cooperation on the part of the employee or treating physician, lack of adequate medical information, multiple or changing diagnoses, or a discrepancy between guidelines and planned treatment without explanation. The medical director attempts to resolve conflict by communicating directly with the treating provider. Because the treating physician by nature of his or her relationship with the patient is not impartial, it may be necessary to arrange for a second opinion or decertify treatment.[19]

In any compensation system, a relatively small percentage of injured workers account for a disproportionate percentage of costs.[17] In these cases, the disability behavior or "illness" is out of proportion to the injury or "disease," and administrative or litigation matters typically overshadow the medical issue.[17] Nonmedical issues cannot be successfully managed with medical strategies. We created the **risk management strategy team** to address complex cases associated with noncompliance or lack of objective evidence of disability. The senior health services manager coordinates the assessment through collaboration with corporate labor relations officers, senior claims directors, the corporate medical director, and the appropriate level of line management. All aspects of the case are evaluated from a total risk perspective and the best overall corporate strategy developed. Inclusion of claims managers in discussions and decision-making is key.[22] The goal of the risk management strategy team is a consistent, defensible process to mitigate liability on high-impact cases.

IMPLEMENTATION AND RESULTS

PIRM was rolled out over 6 months by geographic division, beginning in January 1995. Prior to implementation in each division, intensive supervisory training was conducted in the field, employee communication materials were developed, and providers were selected. We recognized the importance of communicating expectations and describing program benefits at the beginning, because many individuals seek attorneys to advocate for them because they lack information. PIRM implementation teams, with representatives of all key organizations, were formed and charged with tracking the process and outcomes.

The results of PIRM have been extremely positive. The toll-free number for first report of injury is effective, significantly reduces supervisory time, and generally results in appropriate channeling with much less use of emergency rooms for nonemergent problems. Claims is notified in a timely manner to begin the accident investigation. Return to work decision-making, particularly after relatively minor injuries, is improved. The incidence of lost time from minor injuries has been reduced by taking workers to preferred providers and ensuring accurate and timely communication of job requirements and modified duty.

Table 4 summarizes results in terms of FRA frequency rate, lost-time injuries, lost work days, and average days lost per case in 1994–mid 1998. Since implementation, lost-time injuries have decreased more than 67% and lost days have decreased by more than 75%. From the perspective of customer satisfaction, acceptance of the early return to work program by both employees and supervisors has steadily increased. We have saved nearly 12,000 lost work days for 465 injured employees through the voluntary transitional work program and through

TABLE 4. Personal Injury Risk Management Results

	FRA Frequency Rate	No. of Lost Time Injuries	Lost Work Days	Avg. Lost Time per Case
1994	5.11	994	112,936	114 days
1995	3.86	645	61,989	96 days
1996	3.19	524	51,053	97 days
1997	2.54	404	27,967	69 days
1998 (Jan–June)	1.92	164	NA	NA

FRA = Federal Railroad Administration, NA = not available

accommodations within craft. This has translated into increased productivity and direct cost savings.

Aside from savings related to the reduction in injuries and number of lost work days, we have realized significantly greater financial impact on claim settlements. The 2- to 3-year average lag between injury occurrence and settlement of the claim, however, makes quantification imprecise. Biannual actuarial studies performed for Conrail demonstrate a lower per-claim payout since PIRM was implemented. Projections for 1996 and 1997 costs of injury are substantially lower than historical trends would predict.

The 1997 claims numbers are the first to reflect the full impact of PIRM, and the results are outstanding. An 11% reduction in the average cost per lost day occurred in 1997, a statistic we believe reflects better management of the injury once it occurs. We believe the exceptional financial results can be attributed to the wholistic approach that PIRM incorporates.

PIRM evolved considerably over its first two years. While the overall design has maintained its integrity, we have found it necessary to rethink internal versus vendored roles and to refine the management of high-risk cases. As with any change process occurring in the context of a complex business, we faced new challenges even while making headway against old barriers.

However, the integration of risk management and loss control achieved through the "system approach" that the department was able to take resulted in focused and cohesive prevention efforts that affected other elements of cost of risk.

Behavioral-based safety training has been implemented in conjunction with ergonomic modifications, hazard identification and control, and injury prevention programs.

A formalized "indexing" process to define standards and evaluate facilities, operations, and individual safety and health practices was established.

Health services' successful health promotion program, HealthLink, was a catalyst in improving the level of employee trust. As a result, we were able to transition the program to one more focused on high-risk case management and occupational health promotion, such as back care and injury prevention programs.

Finally, decreasing the "cost of risk" became a critical measure in bonus opportunities. In 1996, a divisional premium allocation process was implemented whereby divisional general managers had the potential to recoup for local use some of the money saved by lowering the cost of risk.

In October 1996, it was announced that Conrail would merge with CSX Transportation. In March 1997, after an intense bidding war, it was determined that Conrail would be acquired and split between CSX Transportation and Norfolk Southern Railroad. In June 1998, the Surface Transportation Board voted to approve

TABLE 5. Critical Success Factors

Develop an accurate baseline
Ensure stakeholder buy-in
Match intervention strategy with identified risk
Ensure alignment of goals and incentives
Consider the risk continuum

the planned acquisition. Change of control is scheduled to occur August 23, 1998. Such corporate turmoil and the attendant uncertainty for employees made it difficult to stay focused on safety efforts. Incentive alignment with regard to cost of risk helped ensure that 1997 safety performance continued our trend, with continued reduction in lost-time injuries and lost days for the first half of 1998 (see Table 4).

CRITICAL SUCCESS FACTORS

A strategic approach to occupational injury reduction and management requires several critical factors for success (Table 5).

Develop an Accurate Baseline. Understanding the "as is" before defining the "should be" ensures that controllable and noncontrollable factors are consciously identified. Creation of a detailed work flow map can help eliminate role overlap in a complex program in which both vendor and internal groups play key roles. Clarify expectations with vendors in advance, and make sure that the definitions of *key processes*, *tasks*, and *functions* are compatible.

Evaluate the potential impact of intrinsic constraints such as labor agreements in advance, and incorporate requirements into the process. While correctly designed to support the employee and ensure fair treatment, labor agreements sometimes hinder efforts to ensure appropriateness of care by permitting "doctor shopping" and impede the ability to make employees accountable for their actions. Managed care models that have proved effective in one environment may not be easily adaptable to another that has different constraints.

Careful collection and analysis of baseline data demonstrates the major cost-drivers and, thus, outcome measures.

Ensure Stakeholder Buy-in. The communication strategy is critical to building trust and gaining support. Corporate "silos" that exist at all companies seriously impede communication, and conscious efforts are needed to break down the barriers. All cultures are resistant to change, and anxiety over changing roles and responsibilities is normal. It is worth spending the necessary time to identify champions in all key groups to actively support the redesign. In an environment with little intrinsic trust, enthusiastic support from all groups is desirable. If embarking on a major change process, it would be wise to dedicate staff to training, implementing, and especially monitoring, because it is human nature to revert to old behavior when the new method proves difficult.

Match Intervention Strategy with Identified Risk. The quality (type) and quantity of resource that is used should be determined by risk analysis using predictive models based on past experience. The ability to effectively tailor interventions requires seasoned case managers, an effective primary care network, and effective use of the medical director. In a system without regulatory control over medical care, the ability of case managers to persuade injured patients to participate in managed care can mean the difference between success or failure. The principal of matching strategy with risk also requires use of behavioral health and lifestyle interventions as deemed necessary for a holistic approach.

Ensure Alignment of Goals and Incentives.   This is probably the most important point. Incentives drive behavior. Intraorganizationally, groups with potential impact on the program's effectiveness must have a stake in the program. Success or failure needs to affect each individual directly. Effective programs clearly define accountabilities and align incentives. Vendor incentives also need to be aligned. Vendors will not be truly invested in the organization's success unless given adequate reason to do so through bonus opportunities or penalties.

Consider the Risk Continuum.   For the program to be maximally effective, it must be comprehensive and take a systemic approach to the problem of disability, addressing variables at all points in the continuum. Environmental, organizational, cultural, and physical issues need to be examined to determine their contribution to real illness and injury and to "attitude claims." Any company can derive considerable benefit from aggressive application of an integrated strategy that includes the elements identified in Figure 2.

DISCUSSION

The Problem of Separatist Systems

Hashimoto points out that systems for compensating the injured worker have been developed largely along "separatist" lines. That is, the science of occupational and environmental medicine has not been integrated into the legal and administrative systems. While the medical aspects of the system are relegated to community physicians, few have the requisite expertise or incentives to ensure that the continuum of risk is addressed, including appropriate prevention strategies such as return to work and safety programs.[13]

Inside the corporation, the administration of the injury benefit may proceed without the necessary access to appropriate medical and safety expertise and focus only on reducing the cost of treatment. Implementing managed care in injury compensation systems by limiting treatment may have a detrimental effect on the injured worker's rehabilitation and ultimately increase cost by failing to consider indemnity and further costs of injury. High-quality, timely, and intensive but conservative treatment is better than less costly but ineffective treatment.[13]

Investment in safety and other prevention programs not only reduces injuries, it improves morale and productivity. Yet, incentive to invest is undermined by lack of shared goals and adequate data on the relative cost-benefit ratio of accidents and prevention. A reduction in overall costs of workplace injury requires that the separation of health care delivery from corporate administration and safety programs be addressed.[13]

Managed Care and Occupational Injuries

Managed care can be defined in many ways. One definition is "a mechanism that assures that the health care delivered to a defined group will meet the health care needs of the group."[22] At the time of our redesign process, there was little experience using a managed care approach to occupational injuries. If we can make managed care work in this setting, quality of life, productivity, and corporate competitiveness can be enhanced while total injury costs decline.[22]

Studies have been published describing the use of managed care to help control medical and indemnity losses under workers' compensation.[3,23] Successful outcomes have been attributed to some of the same critical success factors we identified: active employer involvement and accountability, a "system perspective," and an integrated approach that addresses the entire risk spectrum.[3,20] Studies also validate the use of

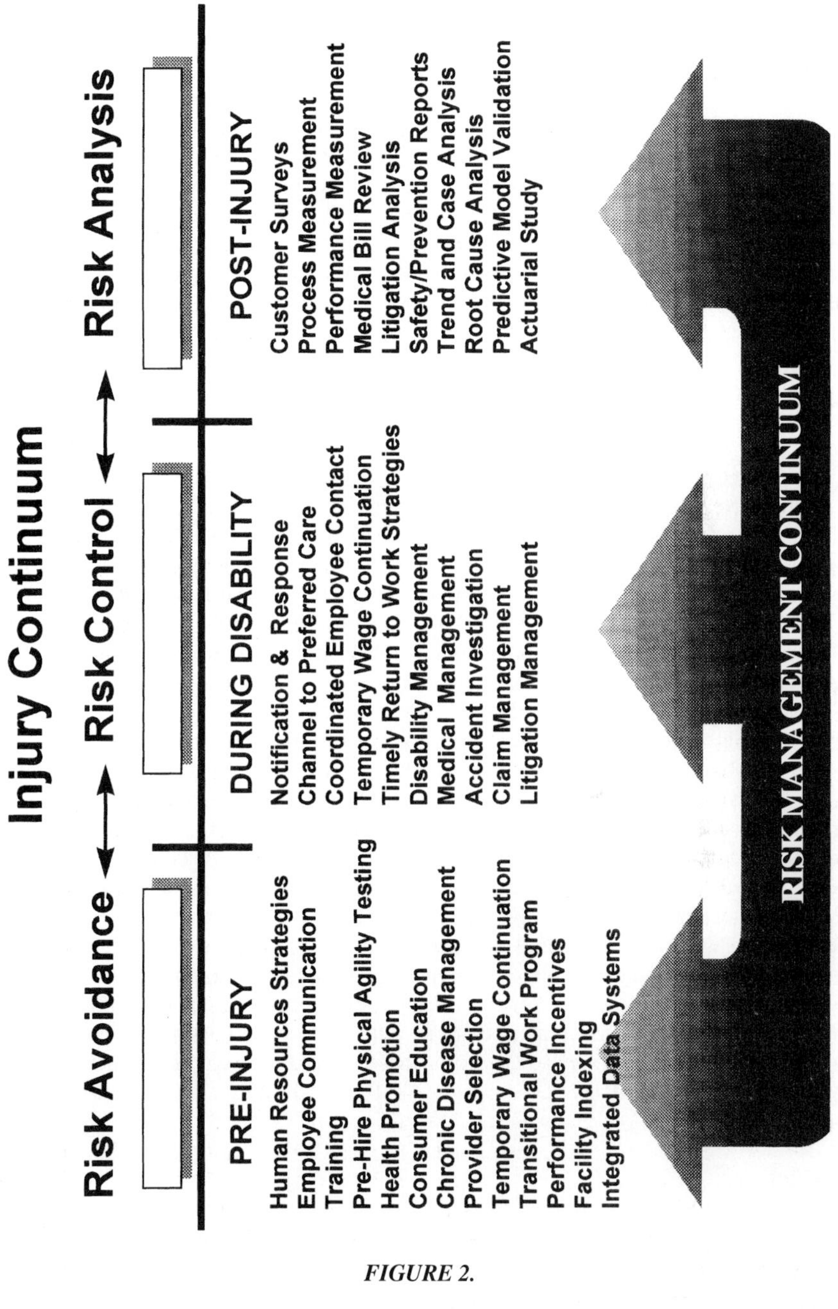

Injury Continuum

Risk Avoidance ←→ Risk Control ←→ Risk Analysis

PRE-INJURY

Human Resources Strategies
Employee Communication
Training
Pre-Hire Physical Agility Testing
Health Promotion
Consumer Education
Chronic Disease Management
Provider Selection
Temporary Wage Continuation
Transitional Work Program
Performance Incentives
Facility Indexing
Integrated Data Systems

DURING DISABILITY

Notification & Response
Channel to Preferred Care
Coordinated Employee Contact
Temporary Wage Continuation
Timely Return to Work Strategies
Disability Management
Medical Management
Accident Investigation
Claim Management
Litigation Management

POST-INJURY

Customer Surveys
Process Measurement
Performance Measurement
Medical Bill Review
Litigation Analysis
Safety/Prevention Reports
Trend and Case Analysis
Root Cause Analysis
Predictive Model Validation
Actuarial Study

RISK MANAGEMENT CONTINUUM

FIGURE 2.

an occupational physician/nurse case management team to coordinate the entire process—from prevention through management of the continuum of care. A workers' compensation managed care pilot project experimenting with capitation as a form of payment in an occupational medicine-based delivery model showed reduction in medical costs, less lost time, equivalent functional outcomes, and improvement in employer satisfaction, especially with communication from providers.[23]

Studies also have confirmed our findings that overall managed care techniques can be used without negative impact if there is an "opt out" provision.[3] Although the no-fault workers' compensation system guarantees financing of health care and the tort-based FELA has no such requirements, both systems support the "rights" or "entitlement" paradigm. As a result, injured employees may view imposition of managed care as an infringement on their rights and attempt to engage in "doctor shopping" to support their legal claim. Permitting a degree of autonomy with regard to provider choice enhances cooperation.[13] When the managed care system is the only option, workers tend to be less satisfied with care.[23]

The Provider Community

To have maximum impact, studies suggest the model requires the coordination of occupational health specialists or primary care physicians who have a solid foundation in preventive medicine techniques. A traditional managed care model may fail due to a lack of appreciation of one or more of the critical elements of risk management and control: recognition and prevention of workplace hazards, evaluation of impairment and disability, fitness for duty determinations, functional job requirements, and the legal and regulatory framework.[23]

Brain reports that health care providers in the community are not well organized or do not have the motivation to coordinate the unique needs of injured workers.[4] There is a tendency to treat every patient encounter as a transactional event and not part of the spectrum of recovery. The treating provider plays a key role in the recovery process and significantly influences the patient's attitude and the ability and willingness to return to work. Thus, an understanding of the importance of a focus on return to work is crucial from a humanistic as well as economic perspective. Delaying return to work does not serve the psychosocial needs of the employee or the economic interests of the employer.[20] The need for ongoing and effective communication among all involved parties cannot be overemphasized, and the initial patient-physician encounter sets the tone.[4] For this reason, development of a specialized network of providers, for initial assessment of work-related injuries, who appreciate work-related issues and complexities and share a focus on rapid recovery is an essential step.[7] When "red flags" for delayed recovery arise, the rehabilitative focus needs to be on function and planning of goals directed toward return to work.[19]

Guidelines

The use of practice guidelines in all health care settings has been slowly gaining acceptance. The significant variation in practice patterns for like injuries cannot be readily explained on the basis of biology or physiology, and such differences can be extremely costly from an economic and humanistic perspective. Variation implies some degree of inefficiency or ineffectiveness. Variation is particularly common with poorly defined pathology, such as the soft tissue sprains and strains that characterize most railroad injuries.[11]

Such tools, however, can never take the place of good medical judgment. To achieve rapid return to work, maximizing outcomes in a work-injured population may require more intensive conservative interventions than suggested by most clinical guidelines. Guidelines are not mandatory; the right approach requires careful analysis of all factors in individual cases.[18] For example, data from health risk assessments voluntarily completed by 65% of eligible Conrail employees during 1993–1995 found that 33% were smokers, 49% overweight, 38% hypertensive, 76% inactive, and 49% at high coronary risk. Given hereditary and lifestyle factors, recovery times exceeding average disability guidelines would be expected. We have used our guidelines in conjunction with internally developed predictors to help case managers determine their expectations of injured employees and to identify when input is required from a medical director.

The Future

If the broad perspective inherent in total population health management is adopted with regard to occupational injuries, managed care may present an opportunity to shift to a public health paradigm, emphasizing the risk continuum: injury, disease prevention, and rehabilitation. A dual focus on humanistic concerns and cost-containment would decrease total costs by preventing injuries while enhancing the quality of medical care and increasing productivity through rapid return to work.[13] Implementing occupational health principles through advanced managed care techniques is consistent with this public health paradigm.[13]

REFERENCES

1. Ackerman RB, Coleman RJ, Leger E, MacDorman JC: Process Quality Management and Improvement Guidelines. AT&T Bell Laboratories, 1987.
2. American Association of Railroads: The Facts about FELA. Alexandria, VA, Loving Associates, Ltd., 1989.
3. Bernacki EJ, Tsai SP: Managed care for workers' compensation: Three years of experience in an "employee choice" state. J Occup Environ Med 38:1091–1097, 1996.
4. Brain GF, Conlon MF: The case management approach to work-related injuries. Orthop Clin North Am 27:831–839, 1996.
5. Reference deleted.
6. Burns J (ed): The Advantages of Managed Disability. Business and Health (Special Report) 1993.
7. Christian J: Managed care: Managed cost or managed quality? Occup Environ Med Rep 11:57–63, 1997.
8. Egdahl RH, Walsh DC: Industry and Health Care, Corporate Medical Departments: A Changing Agenda. Cambridge, MA, Ballinger Publishing Company, 1993.
9. Felton JS: The injured worker and learned helplessness. Occup Environ Med Rep 8:45–48, 1994.
10. Hammer M, Champy J: Reengineering the Corporation: A Manifesto for Business Revolution. New York, Harper Business, 1993.
11. Harris JS: Development, use, and evaluation of clinical practice guidelines. J Occup Environ Med 39:23–34, 1997.
12. Harris JS, Belk HD, Wood LW (eds): Managing Employee Health Care Costs—Assuring Quality and Value. Beverly Farms, MA, OEM Press, 1992.
13. Hashimoto DM: The future role of managed care and capitation in workers' compensation. Am J Law Med 22:233–261, 1996.
14. Kraus G: Health Care Risk Management: Organization and Administration. Owings Mill, MD, National Health Publishing, 1986.
15. Lukes E, Wachs JE: Keys to disability management. AAOHN J 44:141–146, 1996.
16. Marszalek-Gaucher E, Coffey RJ: Transforming Health Care Organizations: How to Achieve and Sustain Organizational Excellence. San Francisco, Jossey Bass, 1990.
17. Menard M: Comparison of disability behavior after different sites and types of injury in a workers' compensation population. J Occup Environ Med 38:1161–1170, 1996.
18. Perry GF: Occupational medicine forum: Return to work policies. J Occup Med 34:102–103, 1992.
19. Rondinelli RD, Robinson JP, Scheer SJ, Weinstein SM: Industrial rehabilitation medicine. 4. Strategies for disability management. Arch Phys Med Rehabil 78:S21–S28, 1997.

20. Shrey DE: Disability management in industry: The new paradigm in injured worker rehabilitation. Disabil Rehabil 18:408–414, 1996.
21. Shrey DE, Lacerte M (eds): Principles and Practices of Disability Management in Industry. Winter Park, FL, GR Press, 1995.
22. Simons RL, Smith JC: Workers' Compensation Health Care Cost Containment. Horsham, PA, CRP Publications, 1992.
23. Sparks PJ, Feldstein A: The success of the Washington Department of Labor and Industries Managed Care Pilot Project: The occupational medicine based delivery model. J Occup Environ Med 39:1068–1073, 1997.

ADRIANNE FELDSTEIN, MD
VICTOR BREEN, MD, MPH
NHU DANA

PREVENTION OF WORK-RELATED DISABILITY

From Kaiser Permanente
Portland, Oregon

Reprint requests to:
Adrianne Feldstein, MD
Kaiser Works
2701 NW Vaughn Street, Suite 150
Portland, OR 97210

This chapter is reprinted in a
slightly modified form from
American Journal of Preventive
Medicine 15(supplement):33–39,
1998; with permission.

Introduction

The cost of work-related injury is large and is rising in many states. Managed care providers are being asked to assist with solutions, particularly in the area of facilitating return to work. Kaiser Permanente of the Northwest responded by developing the Kaiser *on-the-job* program, which includes processes to facilitate the primary and secondary prevention of work-related disability.

The methods utilized here to prevent work-related disability appear effective. They are relevant to many managed care program models and their efforts to improve workplace health and productivity. The results demonstrate statistically significant decreases in physician-authorized average time loss for low-back cases from 1991–1995 (17.8 disability days per case in 1991 and 15 per case in 1995, $p = 0.01$).

According to Oregon State Accident Insurance Fund data, the Kaiser *on-the-job* average total claims cost is reduced 33% for disabling cases as compared to two other health care organizations ($p = 0.002$).

This chapter describes how a managed care provider can work toward both the primary and secondary prevention of work-related disability and presents strategies undertaken by Kaiser Permanente of the Northwest to prevent workplace injury and to minimize disability after injury. The discussion covers key program elements that can change worker, employer, and provider contributions to disability and explains how data collection and feedback methodologies can be used to improve disability performance over time.

Background

Managed health care systems are in a unique position to implement and encourage the use of strategies to prevent workplace injury and illness. They have achieved significant increases in the use of preventive services for nonwork-related injury and illness as compared to nonmanaged health systems. There is no reason that similar methods could not be applied to occupational health.[9] Successful strategies for partnering with worksites in prevention and health promotion can and will be extended to the prevention of work-related injury and illness. Ideally this will come from a process of joint goal-setting for prevention of both work-related and nonwork-related disease and disability. Kaiser Permanente of the Northwest assessed its internal needs and those of its group health workers' compensation customers and responded by developing Kaiser *on-the-job*. Kaiser *on-the-job* is a state-certified managed care organization (MCO) created to deliver managed occupational health and workers' compensation services.

Primary Prevention

The most effective strategy for preventing work-related disability is a primary prevention approach, i.e., preventing the work-related injury or illness entirely. The economic and social costs of workplace injuries are enormous. The costs not only include medical expenses but also lost productivity and wages, the cost of training substitutes, insurance and administrative costs, and equipment damage. The National Safety Council estimated the total cost of workplace injuries in 1987 to be $42 billion, with 35 million work days lost by workers injured on the job.[1] The increasing prevalence of managed care and enrollment of workers in managed care plans will make this cost more visible to managed care. Managed care programs will not only see the injuries and their resulting disability but will also come to understand that there is really no rational separation of a person into work-related and nonwork-related components. If someone is injured on the job, the health care outcomes and disability on the work-related side will affect the health care utilization and ability to get well on the nonwork-related side. Thus, the psychosocial benefits of being in a working as opposed to a disabled role should not be underestimated in describing a program. In particular, disabled workers have general negative perceptions of their health status and are more likely to need medical attention for anxiety, depression, hypochondriasis, and neuroticism.[11]

MCOs will come to understand that work-related injury and illness not only affect overall health care utilization and cost, but this is of significant concern to one of their primary customers, the employers. As noted by Wise in "The Promise and Peril of Managing Workers' Compensation," the nonmedical care cost in work-related injury can equal or exceed the medical care cost.[13] These nonmedical costs are borne by the employer but not the health care provider. Even if the provider strives to make medical care and rehabilitation of the injured employee as cost-efficient as possible, these nonmedical costs will still plague the employer. The nonmedical costs can be eliminated only by preventing work-related disability, and this is accomplished by controlling the causative hazards. The main challenge for managed care involvement in the primary prevention of work-related injury is, "Who pays?" Workers' compensation insurers feel they are providing the service; many employers do not have the money to pay for preventive services; and, with most injury care occurring on a fee-for-service basis, health care providers have no incentives to invest in prevention. Our strategy is to view the employer and the patient as long-term customers whose health and happiness are in our best interest and therefore worthy of investment.

An effective approach to this dilemma is to share injury prevention data and trends with employer partners. In this way, MCOs can help employers to determine the need for and implement primary preventive strategies such as protective equipment programs, hazard information, communication and right-to-know training, industrial hygiene, hazard and safety consultation, fitness-for-duty examinations such as respirator certification, ergonomic consultation, stress management, and employee assistance. We have worked in multiple ways with existing company medical staffs. We have provided standing orders and medical advice for onsite nurses or had our nurses work side by side to increase support for a company physician, e.g., during an immunization program. For example, Kaiser Permanente of the Northwest extended the systems and processes developed for an influenza vaccine program (to prevent a nonwork-related condition) to the worksite for prevention of hepatitis B through a hepatitis B vaccine program. We were able to use existing business processes and contacts to determine high-risk industries and workers and administer 3,000 vaccines at 86 worksites to prevent the occupational transmission of hepatitis B, in addition to the several thousand hepatitis B vaccines administered in our clinics through this program. A flexible approach allows the worksite to capitalize on the resources and skills of two organizations.

Secondary Prevention

Managed care providers can also be effective in secondary prevention (i.e., screening for early health effects from hazardous exposures) for work-related conditions. Managed care providers can help with periodic examinations such as biologic and biologic effects monitoring (e.g., lead screen exposed workers for blood lead levels or organ damage), early onsite screening and treatment by protocol, hearing conservation, and education for workers on self-care.

A key is having appropriately trained staff to do these things. MCOs generally lack staff with the expertise to understand when special testing requirements apply to meet Occupational Safety and Health Administration (OSHA) requirements and when hazards not addressed by OSHA regulations should be monitored, e.g., ergonomic risks.

MCOs also have experience in offering a wide range of models of care delivery that can provide convenience and cost-effectiveness for both workers and employers. These services can be provided through offsite clinics, onsite clinics, telephone or televideo conferencing, or mobile treatment units.

Kaiser Permanente of the Northwest has experience with all but the last of these approaches. In our experience, onsite clinics have improved workers' convenience, participation, and productivity. Televideo conferencing may ultimately obviate the need to have an onsite physician in one company we work with. As employer demand for outsourcing of medical treatment increases, it will be imperative for health delivery systems to develop creative strategies to deliver the care. Industrial hygiene is devoted to the evaluation and control of environmental factors arising from the workplace that can cause impaired health or well being.

MCOs can increase cost-effectiveness for routine employer-directed examinations by integrating some of their health maintenance functions into examinations with worksite focused elements. For example, it makes sense to address smoking cessation, mammography, and other health maintenance functions during a Department of Transportation or other routine occupational examination. Managed care plans will carefully need to assess physicians' skills and credentials for doing this work.

Kaiser Permanente of the Northwest has addressed this need by creating medicine clinics staffed with board-certified occupational medicine physicians as well as a training program for primary care. In addition, as managed care gets involved in the provision of preplacement and surveillance examinations, it will likely generate increasing interest in scientifically evaluating the cost-effectiveness of some popular strategies, an area sorely in need of attention.[7]

Case Management Approach

The strategy that we have found most effective in preventing workplace injuries is to assign a nurse/physician case-management team to every contracted employer. Employers with as few as 25 and as many as 9,000 workers have participated. The standard industrial classification codes of new visits for participating industries are shown in Table 1.

This feature is a part of our standard contract for managed care services and has been welcomed by employers. The physician and nurse work full-time in a Kaiser Permanente occupational health clinic, are trained in worksite assessment, and are expected to follow a standardized approach. The case-management teams are assigned based on a combination of customer preference, major diagnoses of patients seen in the worksite, physician expertise, and geographic considerations. The team visits the assigned site at the time of contract initiation to develop a relationship and open channels of communication with risk management, safety, or, in some cases, human resource personnel; review roles and contacts; go over communication guidelines and confidentiality issues; review time loss and modified work policies; communicate Kaiser *on-the-job* goals and services; and recognize and encourage opportunities for prevention. In addition, the team completes a high-level safety hazard review, including at least high-risk areas, and collects job descriptions for regular and modified work positions when available.

TABLE 1.   Standard Industrial Classification (SIC) Codes for New Claims for Workers' Compensation at Northwest Kaiser Permanente Clinics, 1994

SIC Description	# Claims	Percentage
Services	3,614	35.0%
Manufacturing	2,035	19.7
Retail trade	1,514	14.7
Transportation and public utilities	1,201	11.6
Construction	550	5.4
Wholesale trade	516	5.0
Public administration	454	4.4
Finance, insurance, real estate	267	2.6
Agriculture, forestry, fishing	133	1.3
Nonclassifiable establishments	21	0.2
Mining	11	0.1
Total	10,316*	100%

*10,316 of 14,257 new claims could be coded with an SIC.

TABLE 2. Summary of Employer/Insurer Report Fields

General Claim Activity	Diagnostic Information	Disability Information
Time period	Frequency distribution of diagnostic categories	Time loss per claim
Number of claims		Modified work per claim
Number of visits	Diagnoses for outlier cases (the two cases with the most prolonged disability in the time period	Time loss per disabling claim
Frequency distribution of clinics where visits occurred		Percent medical only claims

The case-management team is expected to serve as the single-point contact for the employer, to schedule and facilitate site visits, and to communicate the information learned to the occupational health and medical nursing group. Employers are provided with standardized reports on cases treated, the number of visits, visit location, and information pertaining to authorized disability (Table 2). The employer report provides the opportunity to discuss diagnostic frequencies and trends over time. These data, along with industry-specific injury rates, allow for productive discussion among the insurer, the employer, and the health care provider about needed prevention of injury and illness and related costs. These strategies have allowed us to systematize our approach to primary prevention.

Once a work-related injury or illness has occurred, it is critical to provide effective treatment with attention to rapid return to productivity. This is where a managed care plan has complete control and can really make a difference. In addition, an injury or illness often represents a failed or absent preventive strategy and is used to demonstrate the need for prevention. For example, when one of the authors (AF) treated a worker with a near hand amputation due to a faulty dough mixer, she was immediately on the phone with the insurer and patient supervisor to develop an action plan to prevent the injury of others. These steps can be facilitated by using clinical guidelines that are diagnosis-specific and address not only optimal treatment but also suggested length of complete or partial disability. Specific modifications to the workplace should also be described. These may include a review of written job descriptions. Table 3 summarizes clinical guideline content areas. Clinicians will require training on the guidelines, instructions for taking an occupational history, and an adequate case load to provide an opportunity for continuous learning. The case-management process also includes 24-hour callbacks to employers relaying modified work "prescriptions." This begins what can sometimes be an iterative process between the employer and the provider to return the injured worker to modified work (Table 4).

In addition to ensuring appropriate medical care and treatment, it is important for health care providers to understand the major contributors to disability. In studies looking at this, it is very clear that physical examination, biomechanical measures, and medical diagnosis have little predictive value regarding disability. Rather, a host of psychosocial factors appear to be the major contributors in the disabling

TABLE 3. Clinical Protocol Content Areas

ICD 9 code diagnosis	Radiology
Subjective complaints	Physical or occupational therapy visit frequency
Common associated work activities	Specialty referral
Objective findings	Surgical procedures
Laboratory	Expected length of disability

TABLE 4. Summary of Case Management Levels

Level	Usual Initiator	Responsible Party	Responsibilities
1	Patient	Lead clinic nurse supported by primary treating physician	1. Assessment 2. Triage 3. Counseling 4. Education 5. Basic referral coordination; basic case management problem resolution
2	Employer	Assigned regional nurse to employer supported by assigned regional physician to employer	1. 1–4 annual site visits 2. Counseling employer on employer report 3. Identification of recommended preventive intervention 4. Regional resource for knowledge about employer and worker risk 5. More complex case management problem resolution
3	Physician Insurer	Regional nurse case coordinator supported by assistant chief of occupational medicine	1. Reviews regional case management reports 2. Coordinates follow-up 3. Organizes and conducts case management conferences 4. Acts as initial contact for large insurers 5. Tracks highly complex case

process.[4,6] Occupational disability is secondary to a series of factors that include the work environment, the nonoccupational social environment, the medical system, workers' compensation and disability insurance, the legal system, and the economic environment (e.g., social security and welfare).[11] When possible, it is critical to affect the major predictors of disability during the early course of treatment. Many of these predictors are detected by and can be affected by the health care provider. We attempt to intervene in what Krause and Ragland call the "timely" intervention period, 1–7 weeks postinjury.[8]

Data Collection and Feedback

We use a clinical encounter 1032 database called the Industrial Medicine Patient and Claims Tracking (IMPACT) System to enter key epidemiologic and treatment parameters at every visit. The fields include time loss, demographic, diagnostic, and treatment variables. The system facilitates the creation of employer reports and allows us to generate return-to-work information to distribute to our provider group. This is a key component of our quality management system in which specific modified-work and time-loss indicators are used as one measure of quality of care and case management. We provide total disability data to approximately 500 physicians on a monthly basis and complete annual evaluations of results and trends over time on the approximately 80,000 annual workers' compensation visits performed in the Northwest Region of Kaiser Permanente. More specific data are provided to the 22 physicians who focus on occupational health.

Figure 1 shows one example of a reporting strategy. It graphically demonstrates both to the clinician and to management how the group is performing with regard to low back claim disability authorization. Based upon the results, physicians will be

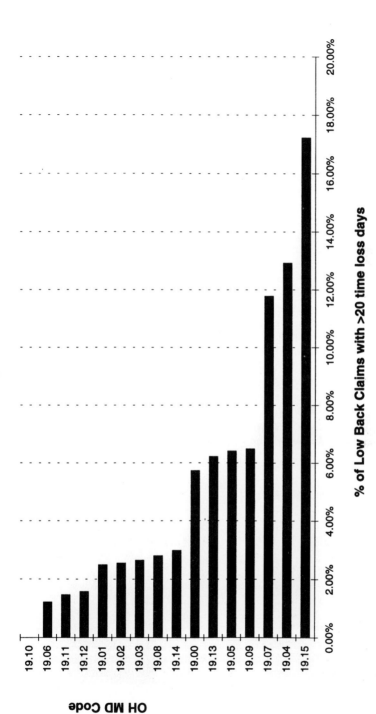

FIGURE 1. Occupational health quality management: in 1995, the percentage of each physician's cases with more than 20 days of authorized total disability. OH = occupational health

counseled on their performance or participate in relevant morbidity and case reviews and continuing education related to disability prevention.

When we developed our outpatient quality management program in 1992, the literature on the use of occupational health disability authorization derived from computerized data sources for work-related injury and illness was scarce. Brewer et al. described a clinic-based surveillance system in which information was collected on more than 14,000 work-related injuries.[3] They were able to give feedback to the employer about diagnosis and disability and to demonstrate the feasibility of an occupational injury surveillance system in a clinic setting. There have been similar reports of such systems by Welch and by Fontus.[5,12] Measures of time authorized away from work, or time on modified work, are thought to be good general indicators of speed of recovery and therefore of quality of medical treatment. Others have recently revealed the shortcomings of return to work as a measure of the effectiveness of health care.[2] However, because indemnity costs are equal to or up to several times the cost of medical care cost in workers' compensation, these costs are a key component of measures of cost effectiveness and quality.[10]

We currently track a combination of diagnostic groups that represent (1) those most commonly seen, such as the low back injury diagnostic group, (2) those associated with severe or prolonged disability, such as the shoulder injury diagnostic group, and (3) those with great diagnostic variability in clinical practice and disability authorization, such as carpal tunnel syndrome. Trends for time lost and modified work per case in the target diagnostic areas are provided for physician and specialty. For example, Figure 2 demonstrates a statistically significant decrease in physician-authorized time-loss averages for low-back cases from 1991–1995. In 1991, an average of 17.8 disability days per case were authorized, compared to 15.0 disability days per case in 1995. Figure 3 compares Kaiser *on-the-job* average total claim costs paid per time-loss claim with those for two preferred provider organization model systems. Results show a statistically significant 33% reduced cost per case for Kaiser compared to the two other systems. The systems are different in many ways, but we are certainly unique in providing feedback on disability. There

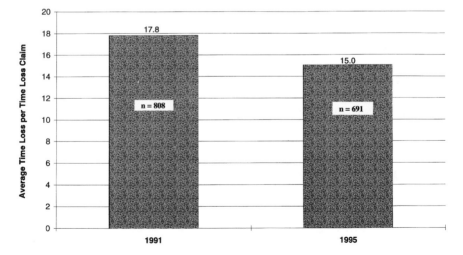

FIGURE 2.   Physician-authorized average time loss per time-loss claim for the low-back diagnostic group.

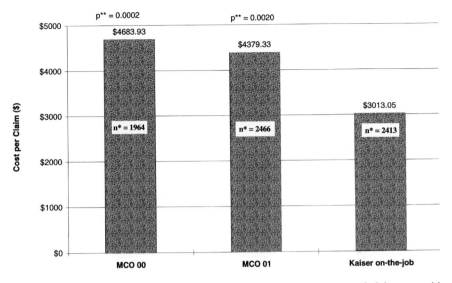

FIGURE 3. Kaiser *on-the-job* State Accident Insurance Fund: average total claim cost paid per time-loss claim, compared to MCO 00 and MCO 01 [two other managed care systems], June 1994–June 1995.

is no reason that similar methods using modified tools would not work within managed care plans organized differently (e.g., network design). When modifying the tools described here for other health care delivery models, special consideration will need to be paid to physician incentives and training and feedback design.

Conclusion

Physicians can successfully understand and manage some of the key contributors to disability. MCOs can make a substantial difference for their customers, i.e., the workers and the employers, by striving to prevent work-related disability. Managed care investment in occupational health is advantageous to all stakeholders.

REFERENCES

1. Accident Facts: 1988 edition. Washington, DC, National Safety Council, 1988.
2. Baldwin ML, Johnson WG, Butler RJ: The error of returns-to-work to measure the outcomes of healthcare. Am J Ind Med 29:632–641, 1996.
3. Brewer RD, Oleske D, Hohn J, et al: A model for occupational injury surveillance by occupational health centers. J Occup Med 32:698–702, 1990.
4. Deyo RA, Diehl AK: Psychosocial predictors of disability in patients with low back pain. J Rheumatol 15:1557–1564, 1988.
5. Fontus HM, Levy BS, Davis LK: Physician-based surveillance of occupational disease. Part II: Experience with a broader range of diagnoses and physicians. J Occup Med 31:929–932, 1989.
6. Gallagher RM, Rauh V, Haugh LD, et al: Determinants of return to work among low back pain patients. Pain 39:55–67, 1989.
7. Himmelstein JS: Worker fitness and risk: Evaluations in content. Occup Med State Art Rev 3:169–178, 1988.
8. Krause N, Ragland DR: Occupational disability due to low back pain: A new interdisciplinary classification based on a phase model of disability. Spine 19:1011–1020, 1994.
9. Miller RH, Luft HS: Managed care plan performance since 1980. A literature analysis. JAMA 271:1512–1519, 1994.
10. Nelson WJ Jr: Workers' compensation: Coverage, benefits and costs. Social Security Bulletin 56(3): 68–74, 1993.

11. Polatin PB: Predictors of low back pain disability. In White AH, Anderson RT (eds): Conservative Care of Back Pain. Baltimore, Williams & Wilkins, 1991, pp 265–273.
12. Welch L: The role of occupational health clinics in surveillance of occupational disease. Am J Public Health 79(suppl):58–60, 1989.
13. Wise D: The promise and peril of managing workers' compensation. HMO Magazine 49–55, January/February 1994.

JENNIFER H. CHRISTIAN, MD, MPH

PHYSICIAN ROLE CHANGE IN MANAGED CARE: A FRONTLINE REPORT

From ManagedComp, Inc.
Waltham, Massachusetts

Reprint requests to:
Jennifer H. Christian, MD, MPH
Vice President, Chief Medical
    Officer
ManagedComp, Inc.
CareManagement Networks
100 5th Avenue
P.O. Box 9146
Waltham, MA 02454-9146

In ManagedComp's new Primary Occupational Provider (POP) program, physicians play an expanded role compared to their traditional role, thereby helping to improve results in workers' compensation cases. The new role links interval-specific managed care technology with an entry point–focused provider network to streamline the initial response to work-related injury and improve outcomes. The change in the physician's role moves more accountability for the result in workers' compensation cases to the front line—to the doctor's office—and thus to one of the parties with the direct power to change what happens. This chapter reviews the results of the program, discusses the evolution in thinking that led to the change in the physician's role, and outlines the broad structure and function of the program.

POPs serve as key entry points in ManagedComp's CareManagement Networks (CMN). The POP program refers to the interaction between the POPs and injured workers, client employers, CMN, and ManagedComp. The program is a dynamic interaction—a system rather than a structure.

The POP program has had good results. Following a small and successful pilot program in Massachusetts in 1996, ManagedComp activated the POP program throughout Florida, Georgia, Texas, Massachusetts, New Hampshire, Rhode Island, and Connecticut in 1997. In the pilot, existing ManagedComp clients with already low average claims costs reduced costs another $1000 if they sent most or all of their injured employees to POPs. The POP program added approximately $60

TABLE 1.   Relative Cost Per Claim Based On the Number of Cases Channeled
To Primary Occupational Physicians (POPs)

Employer Channeling % to POPs	Medical Only	Lost Time	Average All Claims
0–25%	$ X	$ Y	$ Z
75–100%	+$66	–$1,963	–$1,043

to the cost of medical-only injuries but reduced the average cost per lost-time injury by
almost $2000 (Table 1).

A year-end analysis of all ManagedComp 1997 injuries, with POPs active in
seven states, showed that cases treated by POPs were less likely to become lost-time
injury claims: 16% for POPs, 20% for designated initial providers, and 23% for out-
of-network providers (Fig. 1). Cases treated by POPs also had lower total combined
costs per claim (both medical and wage replacement) than those treated by two comparison groups: $800 less than ManagedComp's previous initial care network—the
designated initial providers—and $1200 less than out-of-network providers (Fig. 2).
Most of the savings were caused by lower indemnity rather than lower medical
costs. In all seven states POPs are outperforming the other provider types. Costs per
claim also were analyzed for the 11 most prevalent injuries in the pilot, using ICD-9
codes grouped by body part and injury type. POPs outperformed controls for 9 out
of the 11 and had less variance in cost per claim. Overall, across the 11 injury types,
POP cases cost $600 less than control cases (Table 2).

These results suggest that successful innovations in managed care strategy in
workers' compensation will differ from those used in nonoccupational health care,
and that workers' compensation costs are more heavily driven by disability days
than health care services.

The new relationship ManagedComp has built with physicians has only begun
to produce results. Much of the success to date is likely due to a new emphasis on
selecting providers, setting clear expectations, and spending the time to learn how to
work together. Many of the POPs have not yet qualified for report cards, performance improvement counseling, and incentive payments. The work done so far is

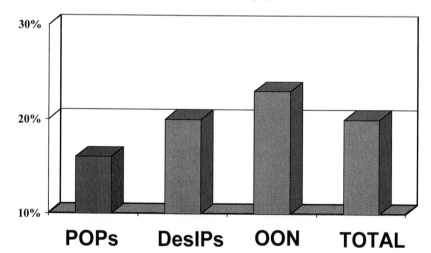
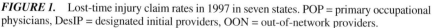

FIGURE 1.   Lost-time injury claim rates in 1997 in seven states. POP = primary occupational
physicians, DesIP = designated initial providers, OON = out-of-network providers.

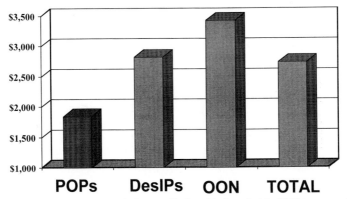

FIGURE 2. Total case costs (including medical and indemnity) in 1997 in seven states. POP = primary occupational physicians, DesIP = designated initial providers, OON = out-of-network providers.

only the first step: installing the foundation of what is expected to become a powerful quality and results improvement mechanism.

THE UNMANAGED STATUS QUO

The unmanaged status quo that created the managed care workers' compensation industry consists of the following features:

TABLE 2. Cost Per Claim During the Primary Occupational Physician (POP) Pilot Program

Injury Type (In Order of Frequency)	Provider Type (Number of Cases)	Mean Cost Per Claim	Median Cost Per Claim
Lumbar sprain	Control (300)	$1792	$350
	POP (70)	$1999	$627
Neck sprain	Control (203)	$5000	$548
	POP (41)	$2626	$562
Lumbago	Control (161)	$3868	$403
	POP (57)	$4732	$400
Lumbosacral sprain	Control (229)	$1960	$344
	POP (57)	$1688	$567
Sacroiliac sprain	Control (96)	$2911	$233
	POP (48)	$1293	$300
Back sprain	Control (186)	$ 584	$232
	POP (52)	$ 323	$300
Shoulder sprain	Control (137)	$1170	$295
	POP (36)	$ 913	$309
Knee sprain	Control (137)	$1416	$300
	POP (36)	$ 658	$333
Wrist sprain	Control (92)	$ 963	$265
	POP (23)	$ 427	$300
Thoracic sprain	Control (82)	$2158	$325
	POP (27)	$ 979	$367
Backache	Control (106)	$2703	$372
	POP (8)	$1980	$449
Weighted average	Control (1671)	$2296	
	POP (431)	$1614	

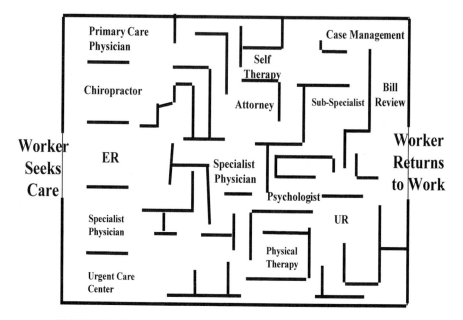

FIGURE 3. The status quo maze in managed care workers' compensation.

    1. Neglected workers lost in the maze of the system with inadequate or excessive medical care, delayed recovery, and vocational disruption (Fig. 3);

    2. Adversarial, untrusting relationships among employers, injured employees, insurers, and medical providers;

    3. Fragmented and poorly coordinated management of claims and injuries and workers' futures;

    4. Weak and ineffective efforts at injury prevention; and

    5. Rapid growth of disability, legal, and medical costs.

The managed care industry will prosper as long as customers perceive it as valuable. Managed care companies have been delivering outcomes to customers that seem as good as or better than the unmanaged status quo but at lower cost to customers. Total employer outlays for group health benefits have been reduced by managed care. Increasingly, the traditional workers' compensation industry—insurance carriers, third party administrators, cost-containment and case management companies, and industrial medicine clinics—has been pressed by its employer customers to give them savings through managed care in workers' compensation like the savings they realized in group health. As a result, managed care has entered workers' compensation in full force and is continuing to evolve.

At the same time, the health care industry is becoming subject to market discipline and is increasingly competitive on multiple dimensions: price, product appearance, customer satisfaction, and perceived quality. The idea of standardizing both process and quality has taken hold, and the mystique of medicine is rapidly disappearing. Patients, and those who buy care on their behalf, increasingly demand evidence-based diagnostic and therapeutic techniques. Big healthcare buyers want big healthcare sellers, and the solo practitioner is giving way to practice consolidation. The term "managed care revolution" is sometimes used to describe this process of industrialization.

THE ORIGINAL MODEL

ManagedComp provides an integrated approach to workers' compensation: obtaining insurance, preventing injuries, managing claims and medical costs, and supervising the health care and recovery processes. The original service model was and continues to be a team approach. Three disciplines—claims adjusters, nurse case managers, and health/safety consultants—work together daily to service an assigned group of client employers. Health and safety consultants evaluate the client's existing performance and develop team action plans. The first review of each injury and illness claim is by a nurse who determines whether case management is needed. Every injury with modified duty days or any time off work is case-managed.

The Role of the Employer

A 1997 Gallup survey of injured workers conducted for Intracorp revealed that only 19% of employers had suggested a doctor to an injured employee. Three quarters of the employees were comfortable with the suggestion, and 90% of them went where they were referred. This survey confirms our impression that most employers have untapped power to improve outcomes in workers' compensation.

ManagedComp customers generally play an active role in the program. To work with ManagedComp, they must demonstrate potential for success. Clients sign a service agreement that lists the five critical success factors for employers:

1. Demonstrating organizational commitment to safety
2. Training supervisors how to respond to and manage injured employees
3. Suggesting/directing where employees should go for injury care
4. Reporting injuries immediately to supervisors and to ManagedComp
5. Providing transitional duty.

Employers first assess their safety and injury management performance and set annual goals and action plans for performance improvement. The client names a coordinator to work with ManagedComp and help coordinate transitional duty assignments.

The Role of the Doctor

Since its inception, ManagedComp's relationship with providers has been oriented toward outcomes rather than discounts. The philosophy has always been to focus on cost per claim rather than negotiate cost per service. In Massachusetts, ManagedComp developed a nondiscounted, contracted, multispecialty provider network. As each employer-client signed on with ManagedComp, a nearby and cooperative "designated initial provider" was recruited into the network and assigned to the client. The initial purpose of the contract was compliance with a law that permitted employer direction of injured employees into a preferred provider arrangement (PPA). That contract became a formal commitment by the provider to a set of service protocols designed to expedite patient care and enhance cooperation with ManagedComp's claims adjusters and case managers. Case managers worked to maintain good relationships with designated initial providers and preferred specialists. When ManagedComp entered additional states without PPA laws, designated initial providers were usually simply recommended for client use rather than formally contracted by ManagedComp. In a few states, ManagedComp was required by managed care regulations and/or business conditions to lease broad-based discount networks. ManagedComp would then find designated initial providers for its client employers, and some of the providers were within those networks.

The Role of the Case Manager

The original ManagedComp model was one of the first to rely heavily on early intervention case management as an effective way to keep costs low. Every case with potential for compensable lost time is case-managed so that small cases are prevented from becoming unnecessarily complicated and higher-risk cases are kept on track from the start. The case management process starts as soon as the claim is reported. ManagedComp works intensively with employers to make sure claims are reported promptly. In 1997, more than 40% of cases were reported within 24 hours and more than 80% within 7 days. The case manager is accountable for both the medical and return to work outcome of the claim.

Case managers in the original model are doing three basic kinds of work:

1. Most of their time is spent on medical management, which is basically rework and thus inherently inefficient. The case manager's goal is to influence patient management decisions being made by treating physicians. First comes poor quality decision-making by physicians; then comes rework by case managers. Because case managers cannot themselves diagnose, treat, or release to work, they offer help, question, negotiate, confront, suggest alternatives, or request intervention by another doctor.

2. Case managers expedite the recovery and return to work process, making sure that events transpire as planned and on schedule to combat the administrative complexity, confusion, inertia, patient passivity, and hidden agendas that frequently delay case resolution.

3. The case manager participates in the multidisciplinary team, extending the physician's capability by providing patient education, addressing psychosocial issues, monitoring clinical progress, and performing other traditional nursing activities.

The Need for Continued Evolution

In 1996, competition began intensifying in the workers' compensation managed care industry. ManagedComp realized that additional innovation was necessary to further lower costs and improve results and to evolve into the next generation of managed care for workers' compensation. The issues to be addressed included:

1. Weak incentive alignment with providers
2. Continued reliance on a reactive rather than an anticipatory injury management approach
3. High administrative effort and cost of centralized managed care
4. Untapped savings potential.

THE REVISED APPROACH TO MANAGED CARE

ManagedComp's approach to managed care is based on the idea that medical care for a population is as manageable as medical care for an individual. Thus, a population's medical care needs can be anticipated; advance plans can be made that provide for an optimal scenario of care; and delivery of care can proceed as an orderly and intentional unfolding of events. If increasing numbers of cases follow a preestablished appropriate path, more cases receive optimal care. Whether for an individual or a group, careful management of health care cannot eliminate all exceptions and outliers, but the medical care process can work with less waste, delay, and inefficiency and thus be less expensive and achieve better results.

A company is not really managing care unless it simultaneously improves quality, outcomes, and cost by eliminating unnecessary services rather than by simply refusing to pay for them. Managed care in workers' compensation can only be considered effective when total medical and indemnity costs are significantly reduced on an overall basis.

Conceptual Underpinnings of ManagedComp's New Approach

ManagedComp increasingly realized that a well-managed workers' compensation care system creates circumstances in which good decisions are made the first time, thus minimizing unnecessary variability and rework. It was determined that the physician, patient, and employer have the most personal power to improve what usually happens in a workers' compensation case. Claims adjusters and case managers can only attempt to influence the behavior of those three, by raising issues, stating opinions, getting others involved, refusing to pay, getting lawyers involved, and taking other actions. Most of these activities are attempts to change poor initial decision-making. When the employee, employer, and doctor are prepared and committed to achieving a good outcome, outside help is rarely needed.

The new strategy became to equip and encourage the too-often passive but potentially powerful parties to play a more active role. Although the original ManagedComp model actively involved the employer, the employee's and physician's roles were still too passive. In addition, it was clear that expediting care from the moment the injured worker seeks care would be even more effective than waiting until notice of the claim reached the insurance company. The goal was to further engage physicians, employers, and employees in working toward the ideal outcome: the patient's successful return to normal life, which usually means a return to work. The POP program was designed to engage the employer more positively and to change expectations for the physician's role.

Moving from Micro-management to Macro-management

Micro-managed care techniques had been highly developed at ManagedComp. Utilization review, bill review, and all the other processes that involve decisions made on an item-by-item basis are examples of micro-managed care. Traditional case management is another excellent example of micro-managed care. Someone other than the treating doctor tracks, monitors, and tries to assure an appropriate outcome one case at a time.

However, macro-management techniques in group health slowed the growth rate of health care costs more dramatically than micro-management techniques. In its purest form, macro-management is a preplanned, decentralized system that runs itself using protocols, procedures, and operating manuals; self-checking, self-balancing, and self-correcting systems; and incentive alignment among all participants. The most revolutionary tool in macro-managed care has been letting doctors earn more money when they use resources wisely. It acknowledges that doctors make many discretionary decisions.

Focusing on Unnecessary Time Off Work

Managed care will be different in occupational versus nonoccupational systems because the two systems vary in the arena in which maximum opportunity for simultaneous outcome improvement and cost savings exists (Fig. 4).

About half of a health maintenance organization's (HMO) money is spent on one item: inpatient care. Group health managed care companies work hard on two questions: (1) Does the patient really need to be admitted to hospital? (2) If so, how soon can we get him or her out of the hospital?

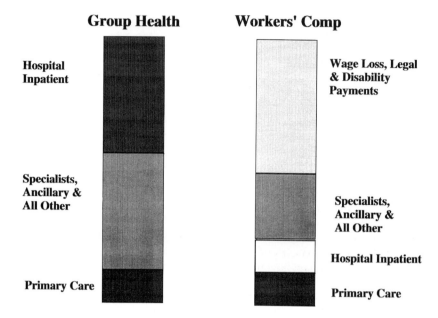

Group Health   **Workers' Comp**

Hospital
Inpatient

Wage Loss, Legal
& Disability
Payments

Specialists,
Ancillary &
All Other

Specialists,
Ancillary &
All Other

Hospital Inpatient

Primary Care

Primary Care

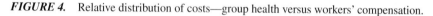

FIGURE 4.   Relative distribution of costs—group health versus workers' compensation.

In workers' compensation and for ManagedComp in particular, only 10% of the costs are in inpatient care but about 50% are for wage replacement. Thus, energy is focused on two different questions: (1) Does the worker really need to be off work tomorrow? (2) If so, how soon can we get him or her back to work safely?

Nationally, in 24% of work-related injuries the worker stays off work long enough to collect wage replacement. The ManagedComp approach has always been to assume that reducing days off reduces costs; the company's lost-time rate has historically been about 20%.

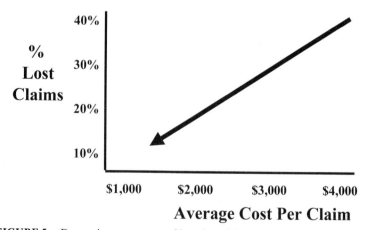

FIGURE 5.   Decreasing percentage of lost-time claims reduces average total cost per claim.

The traditional approach to cost control in workers' compensation has been to reduce cost per lost-time injury. Reducing the lost-time injury rate is a more powerful way (Fig. 5). Nationally, a typical workers' compensation lost-time claim costs more than $19,000, but a typical medical-only claim costs less than $500.

A recent ManagedComp opinion survey of physicians in industrial medicine implied that three quarters of all workers with lost-time injuries are out of work for nonmedical reasons and, thus, that most lost work time is potentially preventable. A total of 90% of the 98 surveyed physicians said that no more than 10% of workers with work-related injuries need to stay off work for more than a few days for strictly medical reasons. In fact, more than half of the doctors indicated that at most 5% of the workers need that much time off. The doctors were asked to make estimates based on their clinical judgment and to assume that employers could provide medically appropriate transitional duty. Interestingly, fewer than 20% of the physicians knew how many injuries actually end up as lost-time claims. That means that most physicians do not know how often nonmedical issues actually create days off work after patients leave the office. Most doctors think they have done all they can or should do by writing a return to work slip. This belief is an iatrogenic cause of unnecessary disability, caused by inattention to the issue.

Seven nonmedical issues were cited by the survey respondents as common nonmedical reasons for unnecessary lost days in their practice or community:

1. A treating doctor is unwilling to force a reluctant patient back to work.

2. A treating doctor is not equipped to determine the correct restrictions and limitations.

3. An employer has a policy against light duty.

4. An employer cannot find a way to temporarily modify a job.

5. A treating doctor feels caught between the employer's and the employee's versions of the situation.

6. A treating doctor has been provided too little information about the physical demands of the job to make an appropriate decision.

7. A conflict exists between the opinions of two physicians.

Becoming More Useful in Workers' Compensation

Workers with work-related injuries need doctors for three reasons: (1) to promptly and accurately diagnose and effectively treat the injury, (2) to answer the medical questions that drive the legal workers' compensation process, and (3) to assist with the life and work disruptions created by the injury.

The work carried out early in a case is some of the most valuable work. During the critical first few days, the case can be adequately or inadequately assessed, the response can be appropriate or inappropriate, and the situation can be set off on the right or the wrong track. Physicians need to be encouraged to reach beyond injury treatment toward a teamwork approach to healing both the patient and the situation. The system needs to be structured to harness the discretionary authority and capability of providers to protect patients and make medical care more useful and economically efficient.

Most workers' compensation companies focus much later in the course of events—finding doctors to provide specialty medical treatment and answer the medical questions in disputed cases. Most doctors and even occupationally trained physicians have not stepped up to meet the practical needs of injured workers and their employers. Almost all physicians are unaware of or reluctant to address the employee's need for help with the life disruption and the employer's need for help with the productivity disruption caused by the injury.

Patient satisfaction can be an important indicator of physician performance in both medical care and customer service. Physicians who overprescribe or skimp on care, who are ineffective healers, or who are inconsiderate, disorganized, or unfair should logically have a larger fraction of dissatisfied patients. In trying to avoid the poor doctor's care, dissatisfied patients will seek costly out-of-network care. Alternatively, physicians who are perceived by patients as delivering high quality medical care and good customer service will help keep patients in network and deliver better overall outcomes.

Likewise, employers are indirect customers of and the ultimate payors for medical care in workers' compensation. They see from a practical point of view how well physicians work with them and with their employees and how effective their care is. Lastly, case managers are medically sophisticated observers of medical care who can compare practices and results among many similar providers. Feedback obtained by systematically listening to patients, employers, and case managers can help guide network operations and coach network physicians.

THE POP PROGRAM

Shifting to macro-management and implementing the initial response to injury system—the POP program—has required significant changes in ManagedComp. The move toward macro-management involved four systemic enhancements: standardizing care, improving value, speeding up processes, and using data to guide change and improvement.

Shifting to Macro-Management

STANDARDIZING CARE

To standardize care, ManagedComp uses guidelines and protocols and shares them explicitly and widely with POPs, clients, and other staff. Clearly stating goals makes them more likely to actually happen.

For medical care, the commercially available guidelines of Milliman and Robertson have been adopted and pricing protocols have been purchased that allow prediction of the cost and mix of services for the injuries of a population. ManagedComp has also developed a set of proprietary service protocols and situation management protocols.

To enhance selectivity and meet the obligation to protect injured workers from grossly incompetent care, internal policies and procedures for provider selection and credentialing have been tightened and made more explicit. ManagedComp had already adopted the credential-verification standards adopted by the National Council on Quality Assurance, which accredits HMOs, and has since expanded, refined, and tightened provider evaluation activities and internal housekeeping procedures.

IMPROVING VALUE

ManagedComp is in business to improve value for its customers, which means lowering overall case costs and improving overall results. Reducing unit costs for medical services may not save money unless it actually reduces overall case costs. Furthermore, low fee schedules are unattractive to successful physicians with full practices, who often choose not to accept workers' compensation patients. Providers who do accept discounts frequently compensate for lost revenue by increasing the number and complexity of services.

The next major opportunity for significant reduction in workers' compensation costs would come from combining three things: (1) incentive alignment with physicians and other health care providers; (2) appropriately focused attention to patient outcomes, including issues such as time off work, patient satisfaction, and lifestyle preservation; and (3) decentralized management of medical care as well as life and work disruption.

These changes have involved backing away from a model that manages care in spite of the doctor and implementing a model that manages the doctor who is managing the care. Under this new design, ManagedComp carefully selects physicians; sets clear expectations; gives them guidance, tools, and incentives to use resources wisely; and then monitors their performance and patient outcomes.

Despite initial concerns about the use of physician incentives, it seemes reasonable to pay more for the services of physicians who are faster and more efficient at getting their patients well and their lives back to normal. Global fees, capitation, and risk-sharing are not the only positive incentives, and they may be too risky for low-volume providers. Bonuses, preferential channeling, information, and feedback are other potential positive incentives. Providers need and value feedback on their performance. Crude report cards may reinforce the wrong behaviors, i.e., evaluation solely on cost may encourage skimping on medical care and lead to worsening of conditions and reinjuries. Multidimensional report cards, on the other hand, can compare provider performance on customer satisfaction, medical quality and utilization, disability management, and other outcomes and can give doctors a solid footing from which to compare themselves with their peers. The availability of training and coaching to improve performance is yet another positive incentive.

SPEEDING UP THE INJURY MANAGEMENT PROCESS

Timelines and targets are used, and the focus is on the interval since injury—rather than the occurrence of particular events—as the preferred trigger for action. The new system begins the task of expediting a case as soon as the injured worker reaches the POP.

USING DATA TO MANAGE CHANGE AND IMPROVEMENT

ManagedComp has started relying more on sophisticated data to operate, understand, and improve its business. It can track internal activities, measure service teams' performance, and analyze the company's overall performance. Specific information is available on channeling rates to POPs, intervals between critical events, POP caseloads and practice patterns, and clinical, functional, and economic outcomes by POP, injury type, employer, service team, and other factors. Ways to track, measure, analyze, and report the performance of the POP have been developed.

Figure 6 depicts the new closed loop injury management strategy. It depicts graphically the new managed care model, which has the following components:

1. Focus on initial response to injury at the workplace and the entry point for care.
2. Find and train the best doctors as POPs.
3. Actively manage channeling so most cases get to POPs.
4. Connect clients with POPs.
5. Have POPs manage routine cases and pay them extra for it.
6. Add centralized case management on high-risk cases.
7. Hold POPs accountable for total results.

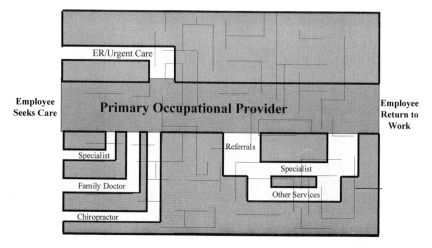

FIGURE 6.   Closed loop delivery system.

Implementing the POP Program

FINDING AND TRAINING POPs

Like most high-quality managed care networks today, the POPs are credentialed and contracted physicians. However, unlike many other networks, the main
selection criteria is not a willingness to accept discounts. ManagedComp seeks
providers who are best prepared for the initial care of occupational injuries.
However, because there is not always a doctor who can meet our standards in a given
geographical area, the credentials, expertise, and commitment of the POPs are somewhat variable. POPs can be based in occupational health clinics, family practice,
urgent care centers, and hospital emergency departments. Therefore, POPs are
trained, educated, evaluated, coached, and monitored to reduce variation among
them.

Physician candidates must share the view that the underlying purpose of health
care is to help the patient recover and resume a normal lifestyle as soon as possible.
Such physicians are more likely to be willing to jump outside their traditional role of
strictly providing medical diagnosis and treatment. POPs must be willing to help
manage the entire life situation created by the injury and to help lower the overall
lost-time rate toward the medically necessary estimate of 5%. To provide good initial injury care, POPs also need to have good clinical skills and bedside manner.
They must know both occupational medicine and the practical realities of the workplace and be located near customers.

The POP networks are generally undiscounted. Moreover, ManagedComp pays
POPs extra money to handle the situation management, including certain nonmedical aspects of the case.

During their first year, POPs meet with ManagedComp network managers and
clinical liaison nurses to become more familiar with protocols and guidelines. Once
a year all the active POPs in a local area are invited to a group meeting for a re-
fresher session and discussion of any changes in ManagedComp's program. Those
who qualify for the incentive program receive their report card and bonus check in a
packet with detailed results and feedback suggestions. POPs having difficulty meeting standards are counseled by ManagedComp staff.

Actively Managing Channeling

The physicians cannot be effective unless the patients get to them. This piece of the POP program was underappreciated at first and has required the most fundamental shift in thinking. Unlike group health PPOs, where patients lose benefits if they leave the network, workers' compensation PPOs are typically "passive" networks of discounted contracts potentially available only if they are "hit." Low network penetration rates are typical, because patients themselves have little or no incentive to use the network.

Aggressively managing a system to actively move each patient into the network has proven to be work-intensive and expensive. The payoff is a steadily dropping lost-time rate and cost per claim.

In ManagedComp's original model, employers were told to channel all injured workers to designated initial providers. Claims data showed that cases in the network did much better than cases out of the network. However, account installers commonly assigned an out-of-network provider because employers wanted to choose their own doctor. Moreover, ManagedComp could not track what percentage of patients sought care from designated providers.

Now, 3 years later, a solid groundwork has been laid for the management of channeling into the POP network. The account installation staff works persuasively until most employers feel comfortable using a POP. All customer communications, from sales presentations to supervisor training materials, talk about channeling. The employer's assigned POP is recorded during the account set-up in the computer. Channeling performance is tracked monthly by service area, service team, and employer. General managers are required to report each week on the reason for each unchanneled case. In early 1998, our documented channeling rate into an intended entry point provider was about 75% and rising. Intended entry point providers are not only POPs but include other designated initial providers such as panel members and assigned emergency rooms. In New England, where the POP network began, the channeling rate to POPs alone is now higher than 65%. Cases channeled to an intended initial provider do much better than cases channeled out of network. Cases channeled to a POP do the best.

The development of a close working connection between the POP and the client is encouraged. Whereas before the case manager worked most closely with the client, the POP is now the primary contact with the client for most injuries. POPs get detailed lists with client names and phone and fax numbers. POPs are encouraged to visit clients. On occasion, the POPs and ManagedComp make joint visits to clients to improve channeling, help straighten out service difficulties, and generally strengthen the relationship among the three parties.

Phase 1: The POP Pilot

The POP pilot program consisted of 15 clinics or outpatient facilities in Massachusetts. The pilot group of POPs was a subset—about 5%—of the control group of all designated initial providers in the existing ManagedComp statewide network of contracted preferred providers. Based on historic claims volumes, the pilot group would receive about 10% of the Massachusetts total.

All 13 New England service teams, especially the case managers, were involved in the pilot. The employers in the test group were all those located around and already assigned to the 15 designated initial providers who were now pilot POPs. This group totaled about 20% of ManagedComp's Massachusetts client base. Employers not assigned to a POP were the control group.

The pilot POPs were specially trained in several sessions during the pilot to manage both the medical and the nonmedical situation created by a work-related injury. At the same time, employers were trained to promptly channel their injured employees to the POP assigned to their workplace, and to work directly with the POP to arrange transitional duty so that injured employees could recover safely on the job.

The pilot test was designed to determine the following:
- Whether POPs would accept the program and cooperate with the new tasks they were being asked to perform,
- Whether the POPs would manage the initial phase of injury as well as ManagedComp,
- Whether employers would be pleased with the POPs' service and whether they would be less happy with ManagedComp's service when the POP replaced ManagedComp's case manager as the employer's primary contact,
- Whether the patients were satisfied with the care they were receiving from the POPs, and
- Whether the POPs helped their patients get better while practicing in a cost-efficient manner.

We evaluated the 3-, 6- and 12-month results of the pilot POP program, each time waiting 90 days for data gathering. The evaluations were qualitative and quantitative and focused on the POPs' performance and the program's effectiveness. The POPs received report cards for the first and second 6-month intervals separately.

Overall, improvements in the outcome of work-related injuries were clearly evident by 3 months, and remained distinct at each measurement interval. Over the pilot period, the cost of a POP caring for a routine injury was about half the cost of care by physicians playing a more traditional role, as discussed in the beginning of this chapter. About 40% of the nurse case managers' previous caseload was handled by the pilot POPs.

All pilot POPs reported to ManagedComp that the program was good or excellent. POPs accepted the report card and were interested in their results.

Customer satisfaction scores in the pilot test were from three sources: patients, employers, and ManagedComp case managers. Patients consisted of employees with work-related injuries that occurred during the pilot period. The test group of patients had been treated by a POP during the pilot period. The control group of patients included patients who either had received treatment by a non-POP initial provider designated by their employer or who had gone to an out-of-network provider. Employers consisted of ManagedComp clients who either did have (the test group) or did not have (the control group) a POP assigned to them during the pilot. Case managers were ManagedComp employees who had observed one or more POPs while working with their client accounts. Case managers were not asked to compare POP performance to that of any other group of providers.

CUSTOMER SATISFACTION

In the pilot, and on an ongoing basis, patients were surveyed by telephone by an outside market research firm using a survey instrument derived from HMO satisfaction surveys but modified for workers' compensation. There were no major differences in patient satisfaction levels whether the treating provider was a POP, another provider designated by the employer, or an out-of-network provider. Patients who were treated by doctors they had selected themselves were slightly more satisfied.

Mean satisfaction scores were 3.8 out of 5 for patients treated by the 15 pilot POPs, 3.9 for patients who saw designated providers, and 4.0 for patients treated by out-of-network providers. Satisfaction scores for several POPs rose from the first to second report card period, and the percentage of patients reporting they were very satisfied rose from 62% to 80%. ManagedComp interprets these results to mean that providers who have been selected by employers must provide more and better customer service to please patients than providers who have been selected by employees.

Case managers show increasing satisfaction with POP performance as POPs become more familiar with their new roles. Most POPs scored better on actual medical care and treatment (typical score 3.5 out of 5) than they did on the situation management tasks such as multiparty communication and effective return to work planning (typical score 3.0 out of 5). Many POPs originally told us they were already doing most of the services called for in the POP protocols. Some discovered that their offices did not have systems in place to assure that the services were actually provided consistently. Moreover, POPs were slow to realize that case managers are customers of a type also and that these relationships are as important to their success as employers and patients. Report card feedback and counseling to POPs resulted in case manager satisfaction, rising through sequential report card cycles.

THE POP REPORT CARD

ManagedComp has developed a provider feedback and evaluation program which includes a report card for POPs. The goal was to create a method of evaluating physician performance in workers' compensation cases in a way that is as objective, valid, and fair as practical with easily available data. The uses of the report card include the following:

1. Giving helpful feedback to physicians and their staffs to improve performance,
2. Guiding provider contracting decisions,
3. Providing a basis for incentive compensation payouts, and
4. Improving overall results.

The Efficient, Effective Provider Information Program (EEPIP) generates a multi-dimensional snapshot of a provider's performance with their ManagedComp caseload and is discussed elsewhere in this volume (see chapter by Ronald Leopold).

Customer Satisfaction.   At intervals, feedback on POPs is requested from patients, employer-clients, and ManagedComp case managers. An independent outside firm is used to collect, tally, and score results for each POP.

Medical Costs.   EEPIP compares actual costs to predicted costs for each case after adjustments are made for case mix and case severity. Highest scores are *not* given to POPs with lowest costs but to POPs with actual costs nearest those predicted.

Preserving Productivity.   Because disability is a major cost-driver for workers' compensation, EEPIP considers both the frequency and duration of disability on a per provider basis. Because medically-appropriate physical activity generally speeds recovery, highest scores go to POPs with lowest disability rates.

Medical Quality and Efficiency.   Survey data and actual utilization rates for certain key services and indicator injuries are compared with rates predicted by nationally recognized clinical practice standards. Highest scores are *not* given to POPs with lowest utilization rates but to POPs whose actual scores come closest to optimal.

Patient Protection.   As many as five sentinel indicators are monitored for quality problems or adverse events.

TABLE 3.   Scoring the Results: A Sample Report Card

	Medical Costs	Preserving Productivity	Medical Quality	Customer Satisfaction	Patient Protection	Total
POP A	3.56	3.37	3.25	3.80	3.50	3.46
POP B	3.08	2.50	3.30	2.33	2.75	2.80
Average POP	3.25	2.76	3.30	2.85	3.00	3.00

POP = Primary occupational physician

GIVING FEEDBACK TO POPs

Most physicians are understandably wary of "report cards." They are particularly concerned that they will be unfairly evaluated and judged. They also will not pay much attention to nonphysicians who attempt to coach them.

ManagedComp's report card was designed and developed by a team consisting of two occupational physicians, a health care actuary, and a data analyst. Not all POPs get report cards. They must have a sufficient number of cases to be evaluated. Qualifying POPs are taught about the report card, its history, development, philosophical and technical underpinnings, and its intended uses. They learn the results for the whole group of POPs and have a chance to ask questions and make comments, usually in a group meeting led by a physician. They are then sent a packet of information that includes their own scores and a summary of the scores for the POP group as a whole (Table 3). Accompanying the scores are interpretative remarks to help put the results in perspective and, also, suggestions on how to improve performance. Lastly, new POPs and POPs with low percentile total scores meet with network managers and a medical director to make sure that they and their staffs comprehend the potentially helpful feedback contained in the report card and that they make a commitment to improve.

Along with the report card, most POPs receive incentive payments. ManagedComp views the incentive payments as a retrospective upgrade of fees to reflect the high value of services received. The philosophy is that the POPs are an "honor class," having been carefully selected and trained, so almost all POPs qualify for incentive payments. The incentive bonus is paid on a sliding scale depending on the POP's overall rank on the report card. Only those in the lower percentiles fail to qualify for any payment. Funds for the incentive bonus come from a portion of the situation management fee that has been withheld and pooled. All withheld fees are paid out.

Phase 2: Multi-State POP Program Implementation

After initial good results in the first 6 months of the pilot, ManagedComp rolled out the program on a state-by-state basis. POPs in seven states have now been active for about a year. POPs are out-performing other providers in each state.

TABLE 4.   POP Performance in Seven States, All Business Lines—1997 Accident Year Valued at 5/31/98

	Average Cost Per Claim (All Claims)	Cost Per Claim with Indemnity Incurred	Cost Per Claim Medical Only	Ratio of Indemnity to All Claims
ManagedComp	$2,607	$15,210	$360	15.1%
POPs	$2,289	$13,215	$488	14.5%
CMN	$3,234	$15,054	$485	18.9%
Out of Network	$4,103	$17,923	$413	21.0%

TABLE 5. "Snapshot" Comparisons of Program Implementation

	Cost Per Claim	Percent Indemnity Claims	Total Claims Per Million Premium $	Indemnity Claims Per Million Premium $
May 97	$1,938	14.9%	224	33
May 98	$1,634	11.9%	203	24

The POPs' 1997 lost-time claim rate of 14.5% compares favorably both to the national average of 24% and to ManagedComp's CMN rate of 18.9%. The CMN is a much larger network comprised of the small POP network plus specialists and ancillary providers, as well as all of the remaining designated initial providers—the previous network model. Even out-of-network cases, handled by ManagedComp's original intensive case management approach, had lost-time rates of only 21%. ManagedComp's overall lost-time claim rate for 1997 was 15.1% (Table 4).

"POP claims" are all injuries treated by a POP within the first 7 days of treatment, whether the patient was subsequently referred to specialists or left the network, and include all medical and indemnity payments and reserves. Average cost per claim of $2289 for POP claims is only 70% of the $3234 cost for injuries treated by other CMN providers, and about 56% of the $4103 cost for claims treated out of network. POP claims for lost-time injuries have average costs of $13,215, compared to $15,054 for claims treated by CMN network providers, or to $17,923 for claims treated by out-of-network providers.

Results are still improving. Preliminary first quarter results for 1997, valued at the end of May of that year, showed ManagedComp's lost-time (indemnity) claim rate in the insurance book of business as 14.9%. This year at the same time, it was 11.9%. Company-wide claims costs have decreased by about 19%, and the number of indemnity claims per million dollars of premium has declined by about 38%. Absolute values for both years will rise as claims mature, but their comparative relationship to one another is a good predictor of real differences in final results (Table 5).

CONCLUSIONS

ManagedComp has drawn several preliminary conclusions from the initial success of the POP program.

1. The selective, undiscounted, entry point–focused, dynamic network system—as opposed to the large, discounted, passive, broad-based network structure—is workable.

2. The POP role, in which physicians become accountable for results and responsible for nonmedical tasks, is acceptable to physicians, and they can satisfactorily perform it. Similarly, minor changes in the role of case managers and claims adjusters, which occur because the POPs have a new role, increase job satisfaction; nurses and adjusters have fewer routine interactions and more time to focus on high-risk cases.

3. Report cards can be structured to be philosophically and technically acceptable to physicians, can provide an ethical basis for incentive payments, and can supply useful information to guide performance improvement by providers and networks.

4. The lost-time claims rate can be reduced by telling physicians that it is their role to work with employers and case managers to promote return to work and reduce unnecessary indemnity claims.

5. The channeling rate can be significantly increased through effective employer education, an accurate and timely method to track performance, and prompt feedback to employers.

6. Decentralization of a significant portion of claim management is possible by delegating responsibility for many routine tasks to provider offices. Workload reductions occur for both case managers and claims adjusters because of reduced variability.

7. The total cost per claim is significantly reduced when cases are immediately channeled to a network provider. It is reduced even more when the provider has been carefully qualified, has agreed to follow medical practice guidelines and service and situation protocols, has been empowered and made accountable, and has been adequately trained and rewarded.

8. POPs need significant case volumes in order to perform situation management optimally. Mastery of their new role requires practice. POPs pay more attention to suggestions for improvement when dozens of cases are at issue rather than a handful.

9. The POPs add independent value. CMN was formed to bring more volume to POPs. Customers who prefer to buy managed care services as components rather than as fully integrated products can now have access to this network of high-quality physicians.

FRANK H. LEONE, MBA, MPH
KAREN J. O'HARA

THE MARKET FOR OCCUPATIONAL MEDICINE MANAGED CARE

From RYAN Associates
and
National Association of
Occupational Health
Professionals
Santa Barbara, California

Reprint requests to:
Frank H. Leone, MBA, MPH
RYAN Associates
1525 State Street, Suite 204
Santa Barbara, CA 93101

Perhaps no two words have had a greater impact on health care delivery in the late 1990s and been so frequently misunderstood as *managed care.*

The precise definition of managed care in occupational medicine can be elusive. The authors tend to think of managed care as a process in which either the care of an individual or a defined population is completely managed by a health care organization. In turn, that organization is compensated in accordance with its ability to generate positive results. Occupational medicine practitioners have long provided this type of care; however, the practice only recently has been labeled *managed*, and it has typically been conducted in the absence of an outcomes-based compensation structure.

The occupational medicine market, in general, is undergoing a metamorphosis. A health care niche that was once reserved for larger corporations has evolved into a service within the grasp of employers of all sizes. Occupational medicine programs and practices are poised to become a driving force—perhaps *the* driving force—in the delivery of managed occupational and personal health care services to Americans.

Providers, managed care organizations (MCOs), and entrepreneurs seeking new business ventures and diversification strategies have inevitably been attracted to the employer market because of its almost limitless potential and comparatively strong reimbursement. Meanwhile, the health care industry has a history of being "recession proof." Historical data indicate that health care expenditures rise as unemployment increases, and provider failures tend to lag well behind failures in other types of industry.

However, employers are finding it increasingly difficult to compete in the global market, and they feel stymied by uncontrollable health care costs. For example, about 25% of the typical company operating budget in the United States is devoted to health care expenditures, but the figure is about 10% in other industrialized nations. Many large employers are eliminating in-house medical personnel and contracting for outside services.

Attempts by companies to remain financially viable have forced a shift in the balance of power in health care from the government to the private sector. As a result, close associations with employers have become a paramount positioning strategy for physicians and institutional providers. Well-conceived occupational medicine programs and delivery systems represent extraordinary opportunities for physicians, clinics, and hospitals able to adjust to the outside forces influencing the delivery of health care services.

WORKERS' COMPENSATION MANAGED CARE

In the 1980s, workers' compensation managed care emerged as another effort to control utilization and discount medical services. Initial efforts to manage workers' compensation focused on state-mandated fee schedules, employer-directed care, and utilization review.

Utilization review typically was retrospective and did not substantially change treatment patterns. In addition, state legislation generally failed to address prevention and risk management, incentives for early return to work, and criteria for physician participation—all important elements of an effective managed workers' compensation cost-containment product.

These initial efforts were followed by the development of managed care plans, medical treatment guidelines, and 24-hour coverage pilot projects. For a time, there was considerable national enthusiasm for blending workers' compensation and group health by using the same resources for both personal and work-related care. The degree of interest in the 24-hour product has since waned, primarily because of fundamental differences in the two systems. However, useful by-products of the 24-hour movement have emerged. For example, experiments with various 24-hour care models have shown that the true cost drivers in workers' compensation are nonmedical factors such as paid absence, lost productivity, and litigation. This indicates that cost-management efforts should be broadened beyond attempts to control medical costs.

MCOs interested in the occupational medicine market have been developing networks of physicians, free-standing clinics, and hospital-affiliated occupational health programs. These network providers are typically expected to accept discount arrangements and agree to comply with certain documentation and customer service requirements, and many provide some degree of clinical coordination to ensure timely feedback to the employer and ongoing case management services.

Meanwhile, states continue to vary in their approach to MCO participation requirements in areas such as regulatory jurisdiction, network licensure and certification, employer and employee opt-out provisions, program components, and dispute resolution procedures.[4] In response, organizations such as the National Council on Quality Assurance and the American Accreditation Healthcare Commission/URAC have attempted to address state-by-state inconsistencies by illustrating to purchasers and consumers that an MCO has structures and processes in place to promote high-quality care and preserve patient rights. There also are indications that recent attempts by states to tighten regulation of MCO-provider contracts will have an impact on the delivery of managed occupational medicine.

A new generation of relatively sophisticated managed care programs has recently evolved to offer services such as extensive medical and utilization management, professional bill review, disability management, return to work coordination, prescription drug management, data collection, and outcome analysis. Alternative "coordinated" or single-source administration and integrated disability management models, the offsprings of 24-hour care, also have emerged. American corporations are interested in developing health management, benefit plan analysis, and worker productivity initiatives that collectively have the potential to cut costs and boost stockholder confidence. The national trend is toward an approach in which all circumstances involving paid absence are taken into consideration. Paid absence may run the gamut from short-term and long-term disability, to cases applicable under the Family and Medical Leave Act or the Americans with Disabilities Act, to those covered under state-specific workers' compensation laws.

Worker productivity, once an issue associated with cost and work process, is now aligned with health and benefits management in the minds of many American business executives. Many believe that the management of worker productivity may be the most effective way for a company to achieve a maximum return on its investment in the health and well being of its workforce.

Given the current environment, occupational medicine programs are finding it expedient to enter into informal and formal relationships with other health care organizations and product vendors to better position themselves for geographic expansion, managed care contracting, insurance product offerings, and service line enhancement. Provider-owned workers' compensation managed care companies also are becoming more prevalent. These companies market their products to self-insured companies, traditionally insured companies, and insurance carriers, in some cases assuming a degree of risk. Another delivery model, hospital exclusive provider organizations, are attracting customers by offering small, tightly managed provider networks, trained staff, and relatively sophisticated reporting.

At this stage in the development of occupational medicine managed care, physicians and provider organizations are finding it necessary to place a greater emphasis on some basic issues:

- Targeted savings for insurers and self-funded employers.
- Intervention at the worksite to provide risk assessment and injury prevention.
- Adherence with clinical and economic credentialing requirements in fields most often needed to provide care for work-related injuries (occupational medicine, emergency medicine, orthopedic surgery, internal medicine, rehabilitative therapies, ophthalmology, plastic and reconstructive surgery).
- Development of clinical protocols for work-related injuries that assess the potential timeframe for return to work and ensure that the course of treatment is in line with standards of medical care.
- Tracking patients throughout the system to curb potential fraud and abuse and flag recurrent injuries and claims.

Occupational medicine providers who position themselves as cost-containment consultants to business and industry must offer a comprehensive health and safety management product that ultimately addresses group health, occupational health, and disability management needs. Providers also are being held accountable for tracking and measuring outcomes based on their own and on employers' perceptions of "best practices." Providers with weak data collection and analysis capabilities are likely to lose business to those who invest time and money in high-quality information management systems and data analysis.

Industry analysts estimate aggregate expenditures related to workers' compensation in the United States at $70 billion to $100 billion per year. Without effective cost-containment measures, workers' compensation claims costs could continue to soar. One might assume that consumer support for managed care in the occupational health arena will increase as financial results are published.

Barriers in Managed Care

Pressure on MCOs and medical providers to enter into alliances, form integrated delivery systems, and diversify product lines comes from many directions on the health care industry compass. Perhaps the greatest pressure is being applied by employers who are facing rising insurance costs. Next to labor costs, per-employee group health insurance coverage represents that largest expenditure in American business.

There are other potential barriers to the ability of MCOs and occupational medicine practitioners to achieve the combined goals of quality care and cost-containment. For example, some states allow employee choice of providers, although this can be circumvented by encouraging voluntary use of specific providers through enhanced services, elimination of claims forms, and guarantees to employees that the work-related nature of their injury will not be disputed if they use a preferred provider. Another potential obstacle to the increased penetration of workers' compensation managed care is the lack of expertise that MCOs have in managing associated wage and disability benefit issues.

In addition, a number of other pressure points exist that affect the role of occupational medicine professionals: consolidation, product diversification, accountability, and affiliation issues. MCOs are consolidating at a fast pace to build their capital base, expand their geographic coverage, and improve their positioning for risk-based contracting. Many health systems and occupational health networks are doing the same. Insurers simultaneously are merging with managed care companies in an effort to stretch the boundaries of traditional indemnity insurance. Despite the risks associated with customer-driven diversification strategies in a transitional marketplace, many organizations are attempting to diversify by adding new lines of business, such as managed workers' compensation and Medicare and Medicaid programs.

While consumers and purchasers are demanding accountability and quality, health care professionals are struggling to define their role within the emerging organizations. Specialists are finding it necessary to assume a greater role in care management to measure their own efficiency and performance.

The Risk-Sharing Product

Consulting services are rapidly overshadowing injury management as the centerpiece of financially viable provider-based programs. Screening programs such as preplacement examinations, drug tests, and annual physicals are common. Individual companies and informal or formal business coalitions are becoming more astute purchasers of health care for their employees. Employers tend to view continuity of care, breadth of services, and care management of injured workers as more important than price in selecting a provider. Employers also seem to be seeking providers with personnel who are well-trained in occupational medicine.

There is no model occupational medicine delivery system because each situation and market is unique. However, the product of most occupational medicine programs that are based outside of industry is relatively consistent. Occupational medicine practitioners typically emphasize the value of using a comprehensive approach to the prevention and management of work-related injuries and illness to reduce health and safety costs for employers. Rather than strictly relying on a fee-for-service, menu-driven list of services, external occupational medicine programs and practices are encouraged to develop a product that can be offered to employers as some form of prepaid package. This type of product generally requires a transition to contractual relationships with employers that assume some degree of risk.

Most states have not explicitly promoted—or prohibited—risk-sharing in workers' compensation managed care legislation as an alternative to discounted fee for service. Early risk-sharing arrangements largely have been designed to align provider and payor incentives to control medical costs rather than focus on long-term reduction of total workers' compensation costs.

The introduction of a new product or concept, such as occupational medicine managed care, should be built around the dynamics of a given marketplace. Factors such as the industrial mix, provider competition, barriers to market entry, the workers' compensation environment, managed care penetration, the organization's cost-competitive position, its reputation, and its potential for obsolescence all are worthy of consideration. In the absence of quality market research, health care organizations tend to go after the wrong audience. For occupational medicine providers, it may be necessary to hire a firm that specializes in health care market research to ensure that appropriate and statistically significant methods are used.

Quality research also is defined as a complementary combination of quantitative and qualitative research. For example, relative to quantitative research, a benchmarking study might be conducted every 9–12 months to measure the impact of marketing efforts. In terms of qualitative research, information might be gathered via focus groups, benefit testing, or "laddering," in which a market researcher conducts in-depth one-on-one interviews.[3]

If employers are the subject of a research project, it is advisable to survey a representative sample of small, medium, and large companies. Subsequently, tools can be developed to help the program's or practice's representative make targeted sales calls. Without that type of market intelligence, an organization may set itself up for failure.

The provider's goals should be to acquire enough capital to assume risk, compile information about outcomes, measure patient satisfaction, and obtain access to contracts that represent the future of their business. An occupational health practice that is poised to assume risk on both the medical and indemnity sides of the equation can then differentiate itself in the context of its ability to help employers reduce or eliminate unnecessary health and safety expenditures. The transition to risk-based contracting invariably involves a focus on lowering incidence rates through proactive health and safety management and on managing injuries and illnesses effectively.

The ultimate managed care product is likely to be some form of workers' compensation capitation, with a performance bonus component based on measurable outcomes such as reductions in injury incidence rates and lost work days and their corresponding effect on a company's costs. For example, an occupational medicine program or practice might capitate a company's workers' compensation medical costs at a fee 10% below previous medical expense levels but be eligible for significant performance bonuses if lost work days and associated costs are reduced.

There is a learning curve associated with risk-sharing, and occupational medicine providers must work to develop the infrastructure, communication skills, and information management systems necessary to sustain it. As a transitional measure, occupational medicine programs are advised to pilot-test risk-bearing health management contracts with a few select employers to focus on enhancing workforce health status, addressing the bottom line, establishing a precedent in workers' compensation managed care contracting, and developing fundamental capabilities in outcomes analysis.

MARKETING OCCUPATIONAL MEDICINE MANAGED CARE

Health care institutions have been slow to acknowledge that a strong sales and marketing effort is essential to continued viability. This situation has proved particularly challenging to occupational medicine programs and practices that wish to pursue an aggressive, targeted approach to sales and marketing, especially in a competitive marketplace.

Because the occupational medicine sales effort should emphasize that the product is the provider's ability to use its considerable resources to reduce costs while attaining optimal health status of the workforce, the sales and marketing effort should take the following specifics into consideration:[2]

1. The goal is to develop a relationship with the buyer that will allow the program to solve the employer's "bottom-line" problems by astutely matching services to problems.

2. The fee-for-service era in medicine is diminishing. Numerous occupational health programs are contracting with selected employers or employer groups for various types of managed care contracting. This practice is likely to expand until risk-based managed care contracting becomes more commmplace.

3. Every aspect of occupational health sales communication (the introductory sales call or letter, written proposals, sales presentations, and associated collateral materials) should focus on the ultimate benefit to the consumer. In occupational medicine, *employer cost savings* are the ultimate benefit, with the understanding that cost savings are invariably correlated with optimal health status of the workforce.

4. Most sales incentives are driven by a formula associated with gross occupational health clinic or program revenues. The managed care era suggests that incentive pay to the occupational health salesperson will more likely be tied to the ability to generate new managed care contracts.

The successful occupational health salesperson, and the physician supporting him or her, should be able to present solutions to an employer's problems in quantifiable terms. Consequently, the sales professional should master the basics of workers' compensation economics. In many respects, these economics are what the buyer views as important. Hence, an overly detailed approach to an occupational medicine return-on-investment analysis is often unnecessary.

The average annual cost per employee for workers' compensation coverage is about $800 and has been growing by at least 10% a year in many markets. The figure includes medical costs (40–50%) and indemnity, or wage replacement, costs (50–60%). This translates to a total cost of about $240,000 for a typical 300-employee company. A company's costs are directly related to illness and injury incidence and lost work time.

The primary challenge is to equate reductions in *both* incidence and lost work time with a quantifiable cost savings for employers or other payors. There are two basic ways to address this issue:

1. The salesperson may ask an employer to estimate the worth of a lost work day, including direct medical costs, lost work time, indemnity insurance costs, wage replacement costs, retraining costs, incremental overtime payments, productivity loss, and the possibility of litigation. Employers are likely to evaluate a lost work day at $1,000 or more. The salesperson may offer a simple return-on-investment equation: Eliminating at least 10 lost work days in a year can—by the employer's own estimate—provide the company with an immediate, tangible return of $10,000.

2. In certain instances, such as larger companies or high-injury incidence employers, a more detailed return-on-investment analysis may be made using the following assumptions:

- There are approximately 8.1 work-related injuries annually per 100 employees across all industries (1996 data).
- About 30% of all reported injuries result in lost work time (1996 data).
- There are 23 lost work days per lost work-time injury.
- Average wage replacement costs are approximately $150 per day per injured worker.
- The average workers' compensation cost per employee is about $800 per year.

For example, a provider-based occupational medicine program provides services to a company with 300 employees and an injury incidence rate of 11.0 per 100:

- 300 employees × 11 injuries per 100 employees = 33 injuries per year
- 30% × 33 injuries = 10 lost work-time injuries per year
- 23 lost work days × 10 lost work-time injuries = 230 lost work days per year

Assume that the occupational medicine program reduces *both* the number of injuries and the duration of injuries by 10%:

- 90% of previous incidence rate × 90% of previous longevity rate = 81%
- 81% of 230 lost work days = 186 lost work days
- 230 lost work days – 186 lost work days = 44 saved lost work days per year.

Wage replacement cost savings: $150 × 44 saved lost work days = $6,600
Workers' compensation premium savings:

- The company pays $240,000 ($800 × 300 employees) per year.
- $168,000 (70% of $240,000) is variable experience-rated.
- The company saves $32,139 ($168,000 × 44/230) in the experienced-rated variable expense side of workers' compensation premiums.

Thus, a modest 10% reduction in both the number of injuries and lost work days would save the company approximately $38,739 ($32,139 + $6,600), not including cost savings associated with retraining, production disruption, potential legal expenses, and other costs.

In presenting and discussing return-on-investment analysis, the occupational medicine professional is advised to ask the prospective client to define *all* assumptions. If a return-on-investment worksheet is used, it is essential to ask the company representative to define such figures as wage replacement costs, experience rating percentage, and average lost work days per lost work-time injury or illness.

The occupational medicine provider should not promise or guarantee a result; rather, the provider should describe what a relatively small (e.g., 10%) reduction would mean to a company. The more readily the program or practice representatives can discuss both health status *and* cost savings in casual conversation, formal sales calls, and written proposals, the more conversant they are likely to be on the topic and the greater their likelihood of success.

The customer's health and safety costs should be the provider's primary focus. The provider must translate this need into the value of the program's services to the company.

The challenge is to move from promise to proof and to recognize that consumers are likely to define quality in terms of their relationship with a physician rather than with a clinic or provider system. Health care organizations should move beyond traditional methods of marketing segmentation, such as zip codes, and focus more on opportunities and trends among target populations. Customer retention is an essential component of health care marketing. Assuming the annual growth rate of companies in the United States is 2.5%, then 5% customer retention triples growth and increases profits by 25%. A 2% increase in retention lowers costs by 10%, and frequent customers spend 2.5 times more than infrequent users. Consequently, it pays to recognize and reward repeat customers.

OCCUPATIONAL MEDICINE AS A PROTOTYPE

As American health care moves to a managed care orientation, occupational medicine programs appear to offer a striking prototype of the larger delivery system. Examples of well-conceived occupational health programs include the following:

1. The American Hospital Association emphasizes the growing influence of **community-based health care delivery**. What better community venue than the workplace to provide services, disseminate information, and instill peer influence in a self-reliant health care delivery system?

2. As the nation's health care delivery system moves from the qualitative to the quantitative, the notion of **population-based medicine** begins to assume center stage. This system rewards its practitioners on their ability to quantify improvements in the health status of populations. Occupational medicine, with its historic emphasis on addressing health status issues of an entire working population, has always been a population-based discipline.

3. The need to reorient toward an **outcome measurement capability** and focus should be apparent to all health care organizations. Occupational health provides a useful starting point to develop such a capability, given that workers' compensation involves measurable parameters such as direct medical costs, injury incidence rates, lost work time, and modified alternative duty days.

4. Tightly **integrated delivery systems** are central to the new health care delivery model. Occupational health provides an excellent prototype for developing integrated networks and systems, both internally and across multiple sites. Occupational health has always involved a multidisciplinary approach to addressing health care challenges.

PREVENTION AND THE NEW MANAGED CARE ERA

The emerging occupational medicine delivery model is not limited to contracting and government mandate. As the nation becomes oriented toward prevention, the workplace becomes an optimal setting for the provision of safety training, health monitoring, and management of acute and chronic conditions. In the absence of a more genuine effort by providers to establish long-term relationships with employers in their market, other physicians or providers are almost certain to fill the void.

All of health care is moving toward a community-based model. The home, workplace, schools, and neighborhood clinics are becoming primary health care service delivery sites. In occupational medicine, the traditional focus on the relationship between the workplace and the employee's health is evolving into one that recognizes work as only one of many factors that contribute to a person's well being.

Millions of American workers are a captive, and probably willing, audience for health care providers who are willing to come to them. According to *Innovations at the Worksite,*[1] a 1992 report by the American Nurses Association on the delivery of nurse-managed primary care services, the cornerstone of nursing's agenda for health care reform is the delivery of primary services to households and individuals in convenient, familiar places. The growing popularity and increased use of mobile medical services, mini-clinics at the worksite, and home health programs are evidence of this trend. The report proposes models for health care delivery at the worksite that emphasize health promotion, prevention of illness and injury, early intervention, case management, recognition of the needs of the changing workforce, and the use of qualified providers.

If health care services are made more accessible to the American workforce, workers and their families probably will seek those same providers when the need arises *outside* the workplace. Occupational medicine programs have the opportunity to introduce these workers to the many health care networks and multiple-site delivery systems that are being formed throughout the United States to achieve vertically integrated services, increased efficiency, and cost savings.

Corporate inattention to employee health and safety can be costly. For every dollar spent on direct costs for workers' compensation care, employers spend an additional $1–2 on indirect costs. The National Safe Workplace Institute in Chicago reports that the United States has a higher injury incidence level than other industrialized nations. It is apparent, therefore, that providers need to adjust their approach to help employers better manage their health care costs by reducing injury incidence rates, lost work days, and disability claims.

In the past, larger companies had their own medical staffs. Now, the term *company doctor* has another meaning: a physician affiliated with a provider-based occupational medicine program who works in a free-standing or hospital-based clinic or in a health center located at the workplace and staffed by the external provider.

A MODEL FOR THE FUTURE

It appears that the successful occupational medicine program of the future will emphasize a preventive approach and the importance of working with, and in the best interests of, all parties. The medical community is now able to identify many of the major risk factors responsible for most of the premature morbidity and mortality in the United States, and there is a scientific foundation upon which to formulate recommendations for improved health.

The authors believe the occupational medicine delivery system of the future will revolve around eight components:

1. Externalized Care: Trends indicate that occupational medicine delivery will increasingly be orchestrated by external providers, provider systems, and regional and national networks. Such externalization of services seems inevitable given the considerable economies of scale associated with a centralized delivery system that emphasizes outcomes analysis and large-scale database management.

2. Consolidation: The sheer number of external providers will diminish as larger firms continue to acquire occupational medicine clinics and practices. We envision perhaps five large national networks emerging, whether they are specifically dedicated to occupational medicine or a subsidiary of a health care conglomerate.

3. Geographic Coverage: Occupational medicine delivery systems will become increasingly decentralized in most delivery areas. The typical occupational medicine delivery system is likely to include a hospital base surrounded by a network of affiliated or owned ambulatory care clinics. Such provider systems will possess both strategic and delivery advantages because of the proximity to more workplaces, economies of scale, and enhanced ability to dominate the local market.

4. Outcomes and Accountability: The occupational medicine program of the future will evolve from fee for service to one in which providers are rewarded on their ability to generate positive, mutually acceptable outcomes, including injury and illness incidence, lost work time, employee health status indices, and reduction in workers' compensation-related expenses.

5. Technologic Innovation: Technologic advances will bring employers and providers even closer together. Many employers and providers already exchange information and gain access to documents through computer networks and modems. Interactive video technology and other advanced communications systems make immediate access to information a necessity for occupational medicine programs.

6. Total Health Management: There will be fewer dedicated occupational medicine clinics and more clinics that offer both occupational medicine and urgent care. Such an arrangement is generally more cost-effective for the provider, more convenient for the worker, and provides a better opportunity for merging some or all aspects of both types of care.

7. Externally Provided Onsite Services: A managed care-oriented occupational medicine delivery system is likely to offer considerably more patient care management and service delivery directly onsite than is currently available.

8. Risk-Based Arrangements: The occupational medicine delivery provider in the managed care environment is likely to be rewarded primarily on the ability to control workers' compensation costs through the prevention of work-related health conditions and associated employer reductions in health and safety costs. Numerous formulas are likely to evolve: a constant of most at-risk models is likely to be some form of medical cost capitation and performance bonuses.

In conclusion, the authors offer the following suggestions to help occupational medicine professionals become better positioned for workers' compensation managed care:

- Be informed. Know what is happening in your state as it relates to the insurance industry and workers' compensation. Are regulations being proposed? Do they address the concerns of providers? What chances do you have of influencing the reforms?
- Develop an integrated organization. Use the strengths of physicians, hospitals, and other health care providers to develop a quality occupational medicine organization that offers coordinated care at reasonable rates.
- Establish relationships with area employers, insured and self-funded, to pilot the program and document clinical outcomes and financial results.
- Explore the potential of your organization to contract with existing managed care networks to determine if a joint venture could be developed for local employers, particularly if the insurance carriers that participate with the networks have a strong presence in your marketplace.
- Establish relationships with insurers handling the workers' compensation business in your area to deliver all of the work-related injury care for specific groups.

• If state laws require open choice, explore the incentives that can legally be placed into the program to encourage use of the network by employees.

Occupational medicine providers are involved in a field that is dynamic, altruistic, and multidisciplinary. Occupational medicine blends management, marketing, and medicine in a way unlike any other aspect of health care. The field is replete with challenges, monetary rewards, and personal satisfaction. Even more encouraging is the fact that, despite a recessionary economy, occupational medicine programs engaged in periodic assessment and reaction to changing demands in their marketplaces appear to progress.

Occupational medicine professionals must maintain a broader perspective as daily demands on their time and attention increase. They must be aware of what they can contribute, strive to stay in a learning mode, ask questions, and think critically and creatively. Occupational medicine professionals must learn to appreciate the consumer's viewpoint and react accordingly. With the right attitude, success becomes a self-fulfilling prophesy.

REFERENCES

1. Burgel BJ: Innovation at the Worksite: Delivery of Nurse-Managed Primary Health Care Services. American Nurses Publishing, 1992.
2. Leone F, Merriman C: A Comprehensive Guide to Occupational Health Sales and Marketing. Santa Barbara, CA, RYAN Associates, 1998.
3. O'Hara K: Giving marketing the attention it deserves. Visions 8(5):1–5, 1998.
4. Tracy G: Legal and regulatory issues in the use of risk-sharing arrangements in the workers' compensation setting. Presented at a meeting of the National Managed Workers' Compensation Institute, September 1997.

INDEX

Entries in **boldface type** indicate complete chapters.

Statement of Ownership, Management and Circulation
(Required by Section 3685, Title 39, United States Code)

1. Title of publication: OCCUPATIONAL MEDICINE: State of the Art Reviews
2. Publication number: 0885-114X
3. Date of filing: September 21, 1998
4. Frequency of issue: Quarterly
5. Number of issues published annually: 4
6. Annual subscription price: $88.00
7. Complete mailing address of known office of publication: Hanley & Belfus, Inc., 210 South 13th Street, Philadelphia, PA 19107
8. Complete mailing address of headquarters of general business office of publisher: Hanley & Belfus, Inc., 210 South 13th Street, Philadelphia, PA 19107
9. Full names and complete mailing addresses of publisher and managing editor: Publisher: Jacqueline Mahon, Hanley & Belfus, Inc., 210 South 13th Street, Philadelphia, PA 19107
    Managing editor: Jacqueline Mahon, Hanley & Belfus, Inc., 210 South 13th Street, Philadelphia, PA 19107
10. Owner: Hanley & Belfus, Inc., 210 S. 13th St., Philadelphia, PA 19107
    Holtzbrinck Publishing Holdings Limited Partnership, 415 Madison Ave., New York, NY 10017
11. Known bondholders, mortgagees, and other security holders owning or holding 1 percent or more of total amount of bonds, mortgages or other securities: None
12. Special rates: N.A.
13. Publication name: OCCUPATIONAL MEDICINE: State of the Art Reviews
14. Issue date for circulation data below: July–September 1998
15. Extent and nature of circulation:

	Average no. of copies ea. issue during preceding 12 months	Actual no. copies of single issue published nearest to filing date
A. Total no. copies (net press run)	2225	2225
B. Paid circulation:		
1. Sales through dealers, carriers, street vendors, and counter sales	–	–
2. Mail subscription	1208	1208
C. Total paid and/or requested circulation	1172	1172
D. Free distribution by mail	6	6
E. Free distribution outside the mail	30	30
F. Total free distribution	36	36
G. Total distribution	1208	1208
H. Copies not distributed		
1. Office use, leftovers, spoiled	1017	1017
2. Return from news agents	–	–
I. Total	2225	2225
Percent paid and/or requested circulation	99%	99%

I certify that all information furnished on this form is true and complete.

Linda C. Belfus, President